Analysis of
Straight-Line Data

Analysis of Straight-Line Data

FORMAN S. ACTON
Associate Professor of Electrical Engineering
Princeton University

DOVER PUBLICATIONS, INC.
NEW YORK

Published in Canada by General Publishing Company, Ltd., 30 Lesmill Road, Don Mills, Toronto,
Ontario.
Published in the United Kingdom by Constable
and Company, Ltd., 10 Orange Street, London WC 2.

This Dover edition, first published in 1966, is an
unabridged republication, with minor corrections,
of the work originally published by John Wiley &
Sons, Inc., in 1959.

Library of Congress Catalog Card Number: 66-29057

Manufactured in the United States of America
Dover Publications, Inc.
180 Varick Street
New York, N.Y. 10014

To D. L. and R. P.

Preface

THIS BOOK WAS WRITTEN FROM THE CONVICTION THAT WE NEED more detailed expositions of classical and modern statistical techniques than are now possible in a general text surveying the entire field. Accordingly, I have selected the topics most pertinent to the engineer or physical scientist when he deals with data containing one or more lines entrapped within his experimental variability. He may seek to reveal the line, or he may desire to remove it in order better to examine the residual fluctuations. In either event, he must encounter the philosophy and arithmetic of the analysis of variance—a philosophy that all too often has been shoved off as a stepchild because its mathematical theory is rather tedious and pedestrian.

In particular, I wanted to set down a strong plea for the use of these analytical techniques by the experimentalist himself, rather than by a professional statistician. The structure of the experiment determines the proper method for analyzing its data, and the experimenter himself knows that structure best. Since his statistical background is apt to be shaky, he needs to be guided—at times in considerable detail—and he usually prefers concrete examples from which general principles may be inferred. I have therefore tried to introduce each subject with data from a real experiment—examining them at first broadly, and then again with an increase in detail that occasionally they do not deserve. When I have felt that they will not mislead, I have sometimes relied on explanations that are heuristic, but in general I have tried to emphasize the essential questions that are posed by the mathematical models our experimenter may choose in analyzing his data. It is with the influence of the model on the nature of the extractable information that I have been chiefly concerned.

A book is a personal thing. This one includes techniques that I have liked or felt to be pertinent and useful to the experimentalist who approaches a statistician to ask help—perhaps inadvisably—in fitting a straight line to some of his data. I have deliberately omitted some of the classical approaches, found mostly in articles on "least squares" dating from the Twenties, because they encourage an unthinking mechanical solution to the problem of straight-line fitting precisely where the experimentalist needs most to think about the structure of his experimental variability. Some of the techniques of Chapter 5 have been included without the comfortable backing afforded by a polished theory set down in a recognized journal. Although they thereby lack the sanctification enjoyed by most of the other material included in the book, I do not for the moment doubt their usefulness. If we waited for all the epsilons and deltas to be supplied before we used techniques that statistical common sense suggests, we would be technical paupers. Mathematical rigor is desirable, but its absence is not a just basis for rejection. To adopt a stricter policy would be to succumb to a different kind of rigor.

I have sought much advice and am grateful for the large amount I have received, but to acknowledge my indebtedness in detail would not only require more space than is warranted here—it would also lay the burden of my sins on many who may not wish to assume them. For I have frequently not taken the advice I sought! I have, for example, persistently refused to attempt a mathematical definition of the term *random variable*. I believe that most experimentalists have an intuitive appreciation of what is meant by these words in the contexts in which I have used them, and that for those who don't, no amount of *mathematical* discussion is going to confer that appreciation upon them. I have likewise omitted a number of results on transformations that are hedged with so many restrictions that they seem to me of little practical value.

Some of the later chapters discuss important problems for which, unfortunately, no adequate answers have been found. When to transform data and how to eliminate outlying observations honestly are questions that plague all experimenters. In the absence of a comprehensive mathematical theory the stubborn presence of data urges upon us procedures that are sanctioned primarily by experience and statistical intuition. These later chapters do little more than raise the necessary questions and summarize the philosophy underlying the all too pragmatic answers they must recommend. They explore, for the most part, single topics rather than ordered sets of procedures. Accordingly, I cast them into essay form—an experiment I undertook from a long-standing conviction that technical expository style should suit the material being set forth. I hope you enjoy the reading of them as much as I did the writing, but if not, please don't blame the editors—for they certainly tried to talk me out of it!

I did not intend this book for classroom use. Rather I wanted it to be a reference book in which the exposition was sufficiently detailed to make it satisfactory for home perusal by the statistically self-educating physical scientist and engineer. I think of the book as following the philosophy of Snedecor's *Statistical Methods* and Brownlee's *Industrial Experimentation*. Throughout the book I have tried to include, in smaller type, additional material which is informative but is not essential to the main arguments of the chapter. On a first reading such material should probably be skipped. As the topics progress in their sophistication, the exposition follows suit—with much more explanation being offered near the beginning. Thus the man who seeks information from Chapter 6 may find the detail of Chapter 2 somewhat excessive—and his friend who reads 2 with profit may expect to work harder when he turns to 6. Although this pattern seems to be a reasonable one, I must confess that a certain loss of enchantment with the later material added expediency to reason in hastening the volume to its conclusion. It is not considered natural to hate our children, but we may perhaps be excused if at times we wish they would go away for a while and play somewhere else.

I originally intended to write a small pamphlet, setting forth for my fellow engineers those statistical techniques that I had found effective in analyzing the commoner forms of linear data which arise in our experimental work. With the passage of time and the acquisition of friendly suggestions the pamphlet has become a book. I hope that the reader will find it useful.

FORMAN S. ACTON

Princeton, New Jersey
February 1959

Acknowledgments

THIS BOOK WAS CONCEIVED WHILE THE AUTHOR WAS EMPLOYED by the National Bureau of Standards at their Institute for Numerical Analysis in Los Angeles. It was encouraged by Dr. John H. Curtiss, at that time Director of the Mathematics Division of NBS, and by other members of Committee E-11 of ASTM, who were concerned with the preparation of a handbook on the statistical treatment of data. During this early period, the Office of Naval Research was supporting the author's mathematical activities, and the opportunity to embark upon this work is due in part to their support.

The bulk of the book was written while the author was Director of the Analytical Research Group of Princeton University, a contract supported in part by the Air Research and Development Command of the U.S. Air Force. In this position the author worked almost continually with Professor John W. Tukey from whose researches came much of the material of Chapter 5. Professor Tukey also contributed heavily to the advancement of the book by his willingness to discuss for many hours the concepts that the author was trying to clarify. It is fair to say that without his help and encouragement, the book would never have been attempted.

Contents

Analysis of
Straight-Line Data

CHAPTER 1

The Choice of a Model

When the experimenter sits down to analyze his data, he wants to know many things. For instance: How accurate are my measurements, as judged from the data themselves? Do my points confirm or deny a structural relation between the variables? If they seem to fit a curve, what equations do I believe to be most nearly correct—in some vague sense? How wild could my equation really be and still give rise to these data? Can I use these data to predict future values, and with what degree of assurance?

It is with the partial answering of these, and similar, questions that this book will be concerned. Whether or not the answers will be satisfactory will depend in considerable measure on whether or not the experimenter has designed his experiment so that the information is in the data, available for extraction. This, in itself, is a large subject. We can only note the more obvious points as they may incidentally occur, leaving any detailed treatment to books on the subject, or to the curiosity of the reader in drawing conclusions about experimental design from the types of analysis which we have proposed.

Any successful analysis of data demands a careful choice of the underlying mathematical model. If we force our data into a model which is too far from reality, we shall get answers that are worthless; if we construct a model sufficiently complicated to correspond exactly with our ideas of the experimental facts, it will be too cumbersome to yield much information. Historically, one model has been used for almost all data that look as if they ought to lie on a line. The independent variable x has been assumed exact, the dependent variable y to have all the error, and we minimize some power of the absolute deviations of the points from the fitted line. Where this model fits the facts it gives simple formulae, convenient interpretation of the variations in the data, and a general sense of security to the user. Where it does not fit, it deludes to the point of causing a general loss of faith in statistical methods. Although this model is well known, we shall devote considerable space to it in the next two chapters, largely because it provides firm, familiar ground on which to display less familiar techniques, and because it contains in the simplest and the least sophisticated form the analyses that can become quite cumbersome where errors are present in both variables.

Before more generalities obscure the facts of experimental life, we shall set forth some concrete examples in which the data might be expected to contain, or conceal, a linear relation, but which require several different mathematical models for their respective analyses.

1. A chemist, anxious to calibrate a new analytical technique, analyzes several solutions containing known concentrations of calcium. Data are milligrams of calcium found by the analytical technique versus the known concentrations.

2. An anthropomorphist measures the length of the forearm on sons and fathers, attempting to find a relationship.

3. A physics student measures the elongation of a copper wire under various applied weights, which are inaccurately labeled.

4. Two counters measure the same random source of photons, both counters having errors of several types.

5. A chemist attempts to pour out x grams of sugar onto a scale; the sugar is then added to an exactly known volume of water whose refractive index is then measured. (He does not really get x grams, but he *records* the weight as x grams.)

6. A more careful experimenter tries to weigh out x grams, fails, but reads more closely and records $x + e$. (He, too, is wrong, as he really got $x + d$.) The y variable is still the refractive index of the diluted solution and contains its own errors.

7. An engineer measures the thickness of a zinc coating on steel sheets. Several readings are taken by two magnigages on each of several samples with different nominal thicknesses. The thickness varies erratically on each specimen from point to point, and the gages are certainly not identical. The engineer would like to measure the variability of the zinc coating, obtain an estimate of the precision of each gage, and find how the readings of the gages are related to each other and to the nominal thickness of the zinc.

A little reflection about these hypothetical experiments will soon convince the most skeptical that it would be sheer folly to apply classical least-squares fitting to most of these data. Except in the first experiment, the conclusions reached would be both fragmentary and wrong. More specifically, these experiments are set forth as roughly representing these mathematical models.

1. x exact, y in error, $Y = \alpha + \beta x$, and $y = Y + \eta$ where η is random. The assumptions about the distributions of η depend on further knowledge from the experimenter.

2. Sampling, whether random or stratified, from a bivariate population, perhaps normal. The correlation between son and father is desired.

3. $Y = \alpha + \beta X$; $x = X + \xi$; $y = Y + \eta$; η, ξ are both random variables which are independent.

4. $X = \alpha + \beta U$; $Y = \gamma + \delta U$; $X + \xi = x$, $U + \eta = y$; various assumptions are possible about ξ, η.

5. $Y = \alpha + \beta X$; $Y + \eta = y$; but what can we say about x?

6. This model is the same as model 3, except that the errors may not be independent because of the errors in surface tension and viscosity which are both functions of concentration.

7. This model is similar to model 4, except that random sampling of the sheets is combined with arbitrary levels of coatings. If the data are taken correctly, more freedom is available in estimating some of these variances than in estimating those of some of the earlier models, but the overall complexity is sufficiently great to preclude any real analysis here. (We shall probably never treat this model, unless someone furnishes us with an interesting set of data.)

Before data from any of these experiments could be treated, we would have to make additional assumptions about the nature of the errors. The additional properties needed, however, are details which, although necessary, are not controlling. Most common physical situations are already encompassed in these models, and in this chapter we merely wish to discuss some of their more global properties.

In all quantitative experiments two variables may exhibit a suspicion of a functional relation for at least two reasons: They may *be* directly dependent one on the other, or they may both depend on a common antecedent variable. In either case the dependence may be only partial; other variables which are unobserved, and perhaps uncontrolled, may contribute greatly to the fluctuations of the measured quantities. If these other variables are small in their effects, and if no attempt is made to control them, their combined results on the observed variables may appear as some sort of random noise or error with a distribution whose parameters can be crudely estimated, either *a priori* or from the data of the experiments themselves.

Consider, for example, the Hooke's law experiment (model 3). The length of the wire is measured inaccurately. Part of the inaccuracy can be ascribed to a faulty measuring rod, part to the careless use of it. Also, the temperature of the wire may not remain constant, and expansion could contribute serious errors.   This last effect is clearly apt to be systematic rather than random and could perhaps be allowed for by recording temperature as well as length.   The errors in the weights and the variations in the acceleration of gravity are two more possible sources of trouble, although the latter is certainly so small as to be lost in the shuffle of the larger effects.   It is possible, by proper use of several experimeters, several measuring rods, copper wires, sets of weights and thermometers, to design an experiment that not only would yield the constants in Hooke's law (which would probably turn out to have an appreciable quadratic component after all!) but would also break up the scatter of the data around this law into *components of variance*, each ascribable to some source of error which we designed our experiment to measure.   Such an experiment could be very informative, but it would be costly—and it would require that we know in advance all the important sources of variability.   When we are limited in knowledge, we guess at the sources, design our experiment to obtain rough estimates, then design a better experiment to sneak up more closely on these effects.   If we do not have enough money, we are unhappy, but we design a less ambitious experiment which attempts to remove or balance out some of the error effects without precisely estimating their magnitudes.   If this leaves us with a smaller experiment, and if it still contains the basic information we are seeking, we may well settle for this streamlined model.   (For example, to separate the effects of the rod and the experimenter, it would be necessary for each man to use several rods; whereas if each man used only his own, these sources of error would be inseparable, although their combined effect is still estimatable.)

In contrast to the Hooke's law model, where the relation sought is quite deterministic and a functional dependence is postulated theoretically, we have the biological measurements on successive generations.   Here there is clearly some loose mechanistic dependence, but it is certainly so vague that few experimenters would be tempted to argue for an equation in the sense of the physicist.   We ask instead for the degree of *information* one generation gives us about the next—the degree of *correlation* between the two variables.   We want to discover whether a measurement on one generation, x, gives us any information about a measurement, y, on the next.   If it does, then we want to find the equation which, among all equations of a certain general type (usually linear), gives the best *prediction* of y from x. This is called the *regression of y on x*.   If we use the data to set up an equation to predict x from y, it is called the regression of x on y.   *These are usually different equations*.   This sort of functional dependence is certainly not the type we think of in physics, but the algebraic manipulations in computing regression lines are frequently similar to those used in fitting

straight (functional dependence) lines to data, and the attendant philo-
sophies tend to get confused thereby.

Still a third general model (3, p. 3) is the one in which errors are
present in both x and y, thereby creating little bivariate populations from
which each datum point is drawn. "Repetition" of a measurement is
equivalent to drawing another sample from the same population. These
separate distributions are strung out along the line we wish to estimate,
and if they are widely separated, they look like isolated mountains of
probability (Figure 1).

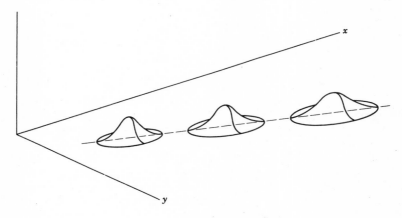

Figure 1

If the points are chosen close together, the distributions lose their indi-
viduality and coalesce into a range (Figure 2) which could also be the
picture for the Hooke's law model in which x has no error. What Figure 2
cannot show, however, is whether or not each datum point is labeled as to

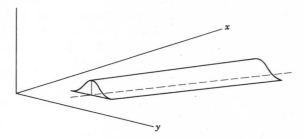

Figure 2

which distribution it came from. The analysis of the data will depend rather strongly on this distinction, as the additional information allows a more nearly complete separation of the components of variability and, hence, the more nearly complete removal of obscuring variation from the underlying physical law.

Finally, the biological model would appear as a single mountain (Figure 3) which is a larger version of the small ones in Figure 1. Note that here we really have a bivariate population from which to take random samples, and if we do so, we generate a mountain of data points quite similar to the sketch.

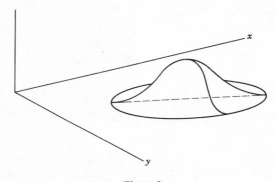

Figure 3

On the other hand, there is no reason compelling us to sample randomly, and so it is perfectly possible to generate sets of data from a bivariate population that resemble Figures 1 and 2 (by measuring ten y values at each of five integer values of x, for instance). Thus, a bivariate population may be forced to yield data that resemble those arising when x is a real independent variable, but having distributions connected with it because of minor, error-like fluctuations. Here the information extractable from the data is less than if random sampling had been used to reveal the full bivariate structure of the situation; and the information that is still extractable is the information about regression lines rather than that of distributions and correlations.

Historically, there has been entirely too great a tendency to stop with the degree of correlation when regression lines were really wanted. Degree of association is a nice thing to know about—it is a preliminary tool in exploring those fields where bivariate populations may reasonably be expected. Once the association has been demonstrated, however, the immediate question is then usually the predictive one, and prediction is most naturally answered by a regression function. Moreover, when no bivariate population can reasonably be hypothesized, the concepts of correlation do not apply and any attempt to force data into that mold can only produce confusion. In the interests of expositional clarity we shall discuss the bivariate case, together with the elementary concepts of correlation and their arithmetic in Chapter 4—largely to remove them from the later discussion.

Our general plan then is to treat first examples where x is assumed to be accurately known, to follow this by a digression on some aspects of bivariate correlation and regression, to return to the major cases of importance where both x and y have errors, and finally to treat miscellaneous aspects such as departures from the normal assumptions and some of the more complicated multivariate problems. Throughout this work we shall frequently recommend quick-but-not-too-dirty techniques whose efficiencies are but crudely known. They are included either because they use less arithmetic than the classic techniques, or because they dispense with the normality assumptions. Whether an experimenter uses these or the classical alternatives will depend largely on the amount of time he feels his data to be worth or on how well he feels the normal assumptions to hold.

One final plea to all experimental men: Take time to design your experiment to answer the important questions. Don't bring data to a statistician *after* the experiment is done and expect him to extract information which isn't there. He can get about 80 per cent of the information without even trying, and by straining a bit can probably increase this to 95 per cent—but if it isn't there to be extracted, no amount of pleading and arguing will increase the yield. The time to consult a statistician, if you are going to consult one at all, is before the experiment is set up, preferably before the plans are more than roughly blocked out. He will annoy you by insisting that you explain quite precisely what it is that you are trying to measure, and you may think him unreasonable when he refuses to accept a vague assurance that your measurements are "really just exploratory," but in the end you will profit by the discussion. It isn't a waste of time. Experiments are expensive, and a quick rule of thumb is to allow 20 per cent of your money to the design of the experiment and analysis of the data; otherwise you can easily waste time and money collecting data which answer very little.

CHAPTER 2

The Classical Model :
x Known without Error ;
Variance of *y* Constant

When an experimental man faces a set of data points which are suspected of lying approximately on a straight line, he usually wants to find the equation of this line. Having obtained an equation, he usually wonders whether perhaps some other line might not be almost as good and asks just how far he can tilt, shove, wiggle, or shift this line before it is clearly not reasonable to expect it to represent these data. Then, if he is a careful experimenter, he is anxious to estimate the amount of scatter in these data around the line he has fitted, as this scatter is a measure of how well his linear theory fits the data. Finally, he frequently wishes to use this theory to make predictions about future values of y for a given value of x, or vice versa. Mathematically this last question is similar to the one about how far the line can be shifted, and it is convenient to treat them together. We have, therefore, divided this chapter roughly into four sections:

1. Classical methods of fitting parameters (lines).
2. Setting of limits on these parameters and future values of y.
3. Variants on classical procedures which are frequently useful.
4. Using replicated data to distinguish between two lines and one.

Our mathematical model in this and the next chapter is the common one in which x is assumed to be accurately known and y is measured with error. In practice this means that x is really known with an error which is much less important than that of y, but we feel we can afford the inaccuracies produced by the neglect of this small error. Models in which x and y suffer from errors of comparable magnitudes are discussed in Chapter 5. Further restrictive assumptions about the type of errors contained in y will have to be made before many of the questions can be answered, or even before some can reasonably be posed, but for the fitting

8

procedures in this chapter we merely assert that the minimization of squared vertical deviations from the fitted line is a useful criterion of fit—the justification for its use resting on computational expediency, analytical convenience, and some theorems by Gauss.   Whether squared deviations or absolute deviations are minimized, or whether some other criterion is chosen, is of less immediate interest than is the influence of the form of the equation to be fitted.

SECTION 1: CLASSICAL FITTING METHODS

A chemical example

Our example is chosen from analytical chemistry. Ten different samples containing known weights, x milligrams, of calcium oxide were analyzed by a standard procedure and were thus labeled as containing y milligrams of CaO. We wish to fit a straight line to these data and to inquire whether its slope may really be equal to one and its intercept zero, since a completely accurate (though naturally imprecise) analytical procedure might be expected to yield such a line. For purposes of this exposition, we are willing to assume that the x values are known much more accurately than the y values and thus they will be considered exact. We shall ask questions about these data which may or may not be realistic for analyses of calcium oxide, but which will involve explaining the basic procedures of hypothesis testing. In Section 4 we shall expand the data by adding a further set of points, and hence raise the more complicated questions of comparisons between two straight lines. For the present, however, we confine ourselves to the data of Table 1.

TABLE 1

CaO Present x	CaO Found y
4.0	3.7
8.0	7.8
12.5	12.1
16.0	15.6
20.0	19.8
25.0	24.5
31.0	30.7
36.0	35.5
40.0	39.4
40.0	39.5
Totals 232.5	228.6

The classical "least squares" procedure is most commonly derived by forming an expression for the sum of the squared vertical deviations from a general line, then demanding that this expression be minimized with respect to the parameters of the line. If our points (x_i, y_i) are compared with a line

$$Y_i = a + bx_i, \tag{1}$$

then the Sum of the Squared Deviations, SSD, is given by

$$\text{SSD} = \sum_{i=1}^{n} (y_i - Y_i)^2 \equiv \sum_{i=1}^{n} (y_i - a - bx_i)^2. \tag{2}$$

We are to choose a and b so that this expression is a minimum, which we accomplish by partially differentiating SSD with respect to a and to b and equating each derivative separately to zero, thereby obtaining the so-called *normal equations* of the system:

$$\begin{aligned} an + b\sum x &= \sum y \\ a\sum x + b\sum x^2 &= \sum xy. \end{aligned} \tag{3}$$

(Summations are over all the data points unless explicitly indicated otherwise; thus $\sum xy$ means $\sum_{i=1}^{n} x_i y_i$, etc.)

Equations (3) are a pair of simultaneous equations for the two fitted parameters, a and b, so it seems as if there might be little else to say about the procedure, except to point out that once a and b have been found the minimal value of SSD may be computed most expediently from the equation

$$\text{SSD} = \sum y^2 - a\sum y - b\sum xy, \tag{4}$$

which follows from (2) and (3) with some algebra. Actually there is quite a bit left to be said, because equations (3) frequently require more computing than some other forms easily obtained from them. Also, equation (1) is not the only interesting version of a straight line, as it is often easier to fit a line in the form

$$y = m + b(x - x.) \tag{5}$$

where $x. = (1/n)\sum x$ is the arithmetic mean of the x's. We shall give the formulae for both versions of the line, since each has sufficient merit to be indispensable. Let us first return to the computational problems of fitting equation (1).

If we solve (3) for b we find that

$$b = \frac{n\sum xy - \sum x \sum y}{n\sum x^2 - (\sum x)^2} \equiv \frac{\sum xy - \frac{\sum x \sum y}{n}}{\sum x^2 - \frac{(\sum x)^2}{n}} \equiv \frac{\sum(x - x.)(y - y.)}{\sum(x - x.)^2} \equiv \frac{Sxy}{Sxx}. \quad (6)$$

The last identity sign is taken as *defining* the symbols Sxy and Sxx, which we note are sums of squares (or cross products) of *deviations from the means* of the variables. In solving (3) for a we get

$$a = \frac{\sum y \sum x^2 - \sum x \sum xy}{n\sum x^2 - (\sum x)^2} \equiv \frac{1}{n}(\sum y - b\sum x) \equiv (y. - bx.). \quad (7)$$

Thus an alternative procedure to solving equations (3) each time would be to compute

$$(a) \begin{cases} Sxx = \sum x^2 - \frac{(\sum x)^2}{n} \\[2mm] Sxy = \sum xy - \frac{\sum x \sum y}{n} \\[2mm] Syy = \sum y^2 - \frac{(\sum y)^2}{n} \\[2mm] x. = \frac{\sum x}{n} \\[2mm] y. = \frac{\sum y}{n} \end{cases} \qquad \begin{cases} 1568.625 \\[2mm] 1557.30 \\[2mm] 1546.144 \\[2mm] 23.25 \\[2mm] 22.86 \end{cases}^{*} \quad (8)$$

$(b) \qquad b = Sxy/Sxx \qquad\qquad\qquad (0.9927803)$

$(c) \qquad a = y. - bx. \qquad\qquad\qquad (-0.2221)$

$(d) \qquad \text{SSD} = Syy - 2bSxy + b^2 Sxx \equiv Syy - \frac{(Sxy)^2}{Sxx}$

$$\equiv Syy - bSxy \quad (0.0872).$$

In general this procedure seems easier than solving the equations (3) in their original form, although the saving in labor is slight. There is a further advantage, however, in that the Sxx, Sxy, Syy are quantities which frequently have physical meaning as measurements of data variability, and in the more complicated models are the starting point for computational procedures which are tractable only in terms of these quantities. Thus,

---

* Throughout this chapter we shall usually juxtapose the various algebraic expressions and the corresponding numerical values from the examples. The particular numbers shown in equation (8) above are computed from the data in Table 1.

since we will need these forms eventually, we are tempted to recommend them from the beginning.

Note that on most desk calculators $\sum x$ and $\sum x^2$ can be formed simultaneously by cumulating x times x, the product dial recording $\sum x^2$ while the multiplier dial records $\sum x$. On $10 \times 10 \times 20$ automatic machines and with only two or three digits in either x or y, it is practical to square ($x00 \ldots 00y$) and cumulate, keeping at least four zeros between the x and y. This gives $\sum x$ and $\sum y$ on the multiplier dial, whereas the product dial records $\sum x^2$, $2\sum xy$, and $\sum y^2$. The only limitation is the separation of x and y by sufficient zeros to avoid confusion on the product dial.

An approximate line removed

Regardless of the method used to fit a and b, computing labor and errors can be saved if an approximate line is fitted to reduce the size of the y variable. If we compute

$$u_i = y_i - (A + Bx_i)$$

for each point, where A and B are picked to be nice round numbers somewhere near the final values, we reduce the problem to fitting u on x instead of y on x. Since the u_i are small numbers, all the $\sum u^2$ and $\sum ux$ remain small,

TABLE 2

$(x - 23)$	u	$(x - 23)^2$	$u(x - 23)$	u^2
-19.0	-0.3	361	5.7	0.09
-15.0	-0.2	225	3.0	0.04
-10.5	-0.4	110.25	4.2	0.16
-7.0	-0.4	49	2.8	0.16
-3.0	-0.2	9	0.6	0.04
2.0	-0.5	4	-1.0	0.25
8.0	-0.3	64	-2.4	0.09
13.0	-0.5	169	-6.5	0.25
17.0	-0.6	289	-10.2	0.36
17.0	-0.5	289	-8.5	0.25
2.5	-3.9	1,569.25	-12.3	1.69
	$-(2.5)^2/10 = -0.625$		$+0.975_a$	-1.521_a
		1,568.625	-11.325	0.169
		Sxx	Sux	Suu

a The 0.975 is $-(2.5)(-3.9)/10$ and -1.521 comes from $-(-3.9)^2/10$. The last number in each quadratic column has its conventional designation appended directly beneath.

thus allowing quicker operations of machines and mental checking with numbers of familiar magnitudes. Without machines this simplification is essential, for it frequently reduces computations to the point where slide rule accuracy will suffice for most of the work, as the subsequent computations are merely corrections to A and B to give a and b. The longhand numerical work for the chemical data is shown in Table 2. Here the computation of u is trivial, for $A = 0$ and $B = 1$ are obvious choices.

We have computed the squared deviations of u and x, as well as their cross product, from their respective means. To fit the line

$$u = a_c + b_c x$$

to these data it is only necessary to form

$$b_c = Sux/Sxx = -11.325/1,568.625 = -0.00722$$

$$a_c = u. - b_c x. = -0.39 - (-0.00722)(23.25) = -0.2221$$

and then to note that the final line is given by

$$y = (A + a_c) + (B + b_c)x = a + bx$$

so that we merely add the *correction* coefficients, a_c and b_c, to the arbitrary approximations A and B. Thus, in our example,

$$y = (0 - 0.2221) + (1 - 0.00722)x = -0.2221 + 0.99278x,$$

and the residual variability is measured by

$$SSD = Syy - bSxy = Suu - b_c Sux$$
$$= 0.169 - (-0.00722)(-11.325) = 0.0872.$$

Even the labor involved in computing Sxx may be reduced if, after noting that $x. = 23.25$, we reduce each x by an approximate $x.$ (here 23.0) and compute Sxx on these reduced x's. Note that Sxx does not depend on the zero point of the x's but merely on their spacing. If it is possible to reduce the numbers to an approximate mean of zero, the reduced numbers will make mental computation easier. If the x's are *uniformly* spaced, a great saving is achieved by reducing them to the integers ... $-2, -1,$ $0, 1, 2, ...$ before carrying out any of these computations, although the fitted line will have to be written in terms of the altered variables. Under these fortunate circumstances, orthogonal polynomials are the efficient medium for fitting. They are discussed in Chapter 7.

The equation $y = m + b(x - x.)$

If we carry out the formation of the normal equations for m and b, we obtain

$$\sum y = \sum m + b\sum(x - x.)$$
$$\sum(y - m)(x - x.) = b\sum(x - x.)^2. \tag{9}$$

Since $\sum(x - x.) = 0$, the first equation simplifies to

$$m = \frac{\sum y}{n} = y., \tag{10}$$

which may be substituted into the second equation, giving

$$b = \frac{\sum(y - y.)(x - x.)}{\sum(x - x.)^2} = \frac{Sxy}{Sxx}. \tag{11}$$

Thus we see that though the formula for b is unchanged from equation (1), the companion formula for m is simpler than that for a and is merely the mean value of y. The different form of the equation gives us parameters which are orthogonal, that is, they can be fitted one at a time because the simultaneous equations (9) break down to separate equations for m and b. Thus for equation (5) the two computational approaches which we had for equation (1) coalesce into a single procedure: Compute

(a) $Sxx = \sum x^2 - \dfrac{(\sum x)^2}{n}$ (1568.625)

  $Sxy = \sum(xy) - \dfrac{\sum x \sum y}{n}$ (1557.30)

  $Syy = \sum y^2 - \dfrac{(\sum y)^2}{n}$ (1546.144)

  $x. = \dfrac{\sum x}{n}$ (23.25)   (12)

  $y. = \dfrac{\sum y}{n}$ (22.86)

(b) $b = \dfrac{Sxy}{Sxx}$ (0.992780)

  $m = y.$ (22.86)

(c) $\text{SSD} = Syy - bSxy \equiv Syy - (Sxy)^2/Sxx$ (0.0872).

Note also that most of the terms of (12) are identical with those of (8). The SSD are also frequently called SSR for Sums of the Squared Residuals. As long as we have only one datum at each value of x these terms are synonymous, and in the rest of this chapter we use them interchangeably.

In Chapter 3, however, a distinction arises, SSD being reserved for the squared deviation of the mean of a group of points, all at the same x, from the line.   We remark that this least-squares two-parameter line must pass through the mass center of the data points, as is seen from $y. = a + bx.$ in (8), or from the fact that $y = m = y., x = x.$ satisfies equation (5). In subsequent chapters we shall frequently use this fact as a criterion for determining a when b is known.   It is not true, however, that the least-squares fit of the one-parameter line $y = bx$ will pass through the mass center of the data, as will be shown.

A graphical least-squares fitting procedure

If our data are *equally spaced in the x dimension*, a rather simple ruler-and-pencil method has been described by Askovitz [2] to locate the line that enjoys the least sum of squared vertical deviations.   We need only start at the leftmost point and move toward the next point to the right until we have traversed two-thirds of the horizontal spacing between them, placing us at A in Figure 4.   We then move toward the next data point 3,

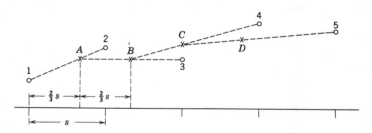

Figure 4

again moving until our horizontal displacement is two-thirds of the (uniform) horizontal separation, s, of our data points.   We continue in this way, always heading toward the next datum, always advancing by two-thirds of the horizontal spacing of our data points, arriving finally at D—which is necessarily two-thirds of the horizontal distance between our first and last data points.   The entire operation, which takes less time to perform than to describe, is then repeated from the other end, leading us to a point D' (D' and D trisect the horizontal distance between our extreme data).   The required least-squares line passes through D and D'.

As a check, the operation may be repeated using one-half the horizontal spacing between points instead of two-thirds, thereby ending at the center of gravity of the system—a point which must also be on the fitted line.

This graphical method has the virtues of speed and simplicity, but it lacks one property essential to all good fitting procedures, a measure of the residual dispersion. Without a simple estimate of σ, the method must remain an interesting geometrical construction rather than a useful analytical tool.

The equation $y = a + x$

Since it might reasonably be hoped that the data of Table 1 have a slope of exactly *one*, we here examine the fitting procedure for the general line of slope *one*, in both of its forms:

$$y = a + x, \qquad y = m + (x - x.). \qquad \text{(13) (14)}$$

We see that

$$
\begin{array}{llll}
a = y. - x. & (-0.39) & m = y. & (22.86) \qquad \text{(15) (16)} \\
\text{SSD} = Syy - 2Sxy + Sxx & & (0.2562) &
\end{array}
$$

and note that the residual variability is a little larger than when we allowed the slope to be fitted.

The equation $y = bx$

It is also plausible that these data might have a zero intercept but a slope different from one, and thus we might desire to fit an equation in the form

$$y = bx. \qquad \text{(17)}$$

Here the calculations become

$$b = \frac{\sum xy}{\sum x^2} = \frac{Sxy + nx.y.}{Sxx + nx.^2} \qquad (0.985361)$$

$$\text{SSD} = \sum y^2 - 2b\sum xy + b^2\sum x^2 \equiv \sum y^2 - b\sum xy \qquad \text{(18)}$$

$$\equiv \sum y^2 - \frac{(\sum xy)^2}{\sum x^2} \qquad (0.2956).$$

Note that these formulae, although analogous to those of the previous cases, are not expressed most concisely in terms of the deviation from the means (Syy, etc.) but rather in terms of deviations from the *origin*. This is not surprising, for this line is forced through the origin by the form of equation (17); hence we might expect that the parameter could be most reasonably expressed in terms of deviation from that point. The line will not, in general, pass through the mass center of the data points, as can be seen by noting that the second form for b is usually *not* equivalent to $y./x.$.

The last two forms of the equations are particular cases of the one-parameter line, which we shall now present in its general forms.

The equation $y = a + Bx$, or $y = m + B(x - x.)$, B known

If we know the slope, B, as a definite number, the fitting procedures for a and m become

$$a = y. - Bx., \qquad m = y. \qquad (19)\ (20)$$
$$SSD = Syy - 2BSxy + B^2Sxx.$$

For a given set of data, the same line will be fitted whichever form of the equation is used. When, in particular, $B=1$, we have the equations (15) and (16), whereas in the common degenerate case of $B=0$ we have

$$y. = a, \qquad y. = m; \qquad (21)\ (22)$$

which give

$$a = m = y.$$

and

$$SSD = Syy.$$

The equation $y = A + b_1x$, or $y = M + b_2(x - x.)$, A or M known

When it is the constant term that is known and the slope is to be fitted, it makes a difference which form of the one-parameter line is used, as they will in general give different estimates for b. The forms are

$$y = A + b_1x, \qquad y = M + b_2(x - x.) \qquad (23)\ (24)$$

where A and M are the known constants. Here we obtain

$$b_1 = \frac{\sum xy - A\sum x}{\sum x^2}, \qquad b_2 = \frac{\sum y(x - x.)}{\sum(x - x.)^2} = \frac{Sxy}{Sxx} \qquad (25)\ (26)$$

$$SSD_1 = Syy - b_1^2\sum x^2 + n(y. - A)^2$$

$$SSD_2 = Syy - 2b_2Sxy + b_2^2Sxx + n(y. - M)^2$$
$$= Syy - b_2Sxy + n(y. - M)^2.$$

The equation $y = y_1 + b(x - x_1)$, x_1 and y_1 known

When a line is known to pass through a definite point (x_1, y_1), its equation may be written as

$$y = y_1 + b(x - x_1) \qquad (31)$$

and the least-squares criterion used to find the parameter b. We see that

$$b = \frac{\sum(x - x_1)(y - y_1)}{\sum(x - x_1)^2} \equiv \frac{Sx_1y_1}{Sx_1x_1} \tag{32}$$

where the double equality defines the symbols Sx_1y_1 and Sx_1x_1 for the squared deviations from the known point. We may also express b in terms of squared deviations from the means of the data as before:

$$b = \frac{Sxy + n(x. - x_1)(y. - y_1)}{Sxx + n(x. - x_1)^2} \equiv \frac{Sx_1y_1}{Sx_1x_1}. \tag{33}$$

The other parameter a is given by

$$a = y_1 - bx_1 \tag{34}$$

and the residuals may be computed from

$$\begin{aligned} \text{SSD} = Sy_1y_1 - 2bSx_1y_1 + b^2Sx_1x_1 &= Sy_1y_1 - bSx_1y_1 \\ &= Sy_1y_1 - (Sx_1y_1)^2/Sx_1x_1. \end{aligned} \tag{35}$$

All these formulae become the standard ones if (x_1, y_1) is the mass center of our data, and they also include the forms already given for a line through the origin.

The equation $y = A + Bx$, A and B known

Finally, for completeness, we note that the degenerate equation

$$y = A + Bx \tag{27}$$

where A and B are known may be considered as the zero-parameter straight line, with a sum of squared residuals equal to

$$\text{SSD} = Syy - 2BSxy + B^2Sxx + n(y. - A - Bx.)^2. \tag{28}$$

If both A and B are known to be zero, we have the equation

$$y = 0$$

$$\text{SSD} = \sum y^2, \tag{29} \tag{30}$$

which is obviously silly for our present data but is a tenable hypothesis in straight-line fitting sufficiently often to warrant mention.

SECTION 2: THE SETTING OF CONFIDENCE LIMITS

The tractable model

The slope of the line which "best" fits the data of Table 1 is 0.993. It seems, however, that the true line might really have a slope of 1.000, and the fact that we obtained 0.993 might merely have been caused by the errors in the values y_i. We should like to know whether the true slope is exactly *one*, but unfortunately no *certain* answer to this problem can be given. Some sort of *probability* answer can be made if we are willing to make further assumptions about the mathematical model we are treating, and the exact statement we make will depend directly on the type of assumption which we consider to be a reasonable approximation to the physical facts.

If we repeat the chemical analyses at precisely the same values of x, we would expect to obtain different values of y. In fact, this is exactly what happened in these data at x equal to 40, where repetitions gave 39.4 and 39.5. Further repetitions would generate a distribution of y values at each x, and a considerable bulk of such data, if available, might be summarized pictorially as in Figure 5. Note that the mean values of these distributions all lie approximately along a straight line, and that the spread of these distributions is different for different x values. (The fact that we have drawn the distributions as bell-shaped curves is *not* intended to imply that they are necessarily normal distributions.)

Figure 5 is proposed as being a reasonable sort of qualitative prediction about the data that would be obtained by repeated analyses of calcium

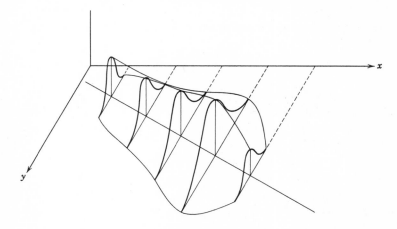

Figure 5

oxide solutions. But this is far too complicated a picture for any expedient treatment of the data, for it would demand detailed knowledge of the various distributions at each value of x. We therefore simplify our model by demanding that, in the "true" model:

1. The distributions are all normal.
2. Their mean values lie exactly on the line $\zeta = \alpha + \beta x$.
3. Their variances, $\sigma_{\eta_i}^2$, about that mean are the same for all x_i.
4. The observations are statistically independent.

The picture now looks like Figure 6.

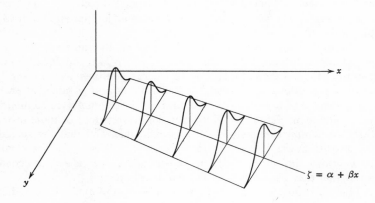

Figure 6

These assumptions may conveniently be summarized by saying that

$$y = \zeta + \eta$$
$$\zeta = \alpha + \beta x$$
$$\eta \Rightarrow N(0; \sigma_\eta^2)$$

where the last line reads "η is a random variable distributed normally with zero mean and variance equal to σ_η^2." A still more concise expression of these conditions is

$$y \Rightarrow N(\alpha + \beta x; \sigma_\eta^2),$$

and we shall use both these forms in this book.

Whether or not this set of assumptions is a reasonable approximation to experimental reality can be decided only by the experimenter—and his decision will usually be based on his prior experience rather than on extensive experiments on the problem at hand. If this model does not fit, others are available, but usually they are less tractable analytically and less pleasant aesthetically. We shall attempt to show what can be done with some of these models at intervals throughout the book, but for this chapter we will stick fairly close to the normal distribution with constant variance, σ^2. It has proved to be a useful realistic model for many physical systems, at least in an approximate sense, and will continue to give satisfactory results, provided the experimenter does not force its analyses onto experiments which he can clearly see violate the basic assumptions.

Confidence limits—the basic concepts

If we are willing to assume the mathematical model just given, we may be tempted to raise such a question as, "What is the chance that for $\beta = 1$ we would have obtained the slope we did (0.993) simply because of the chance fluctuations in y?" A moment's reflection, however, will reveal that the answer to this question is of no use to us, for we do not care whether we obtain exactly 0.993 or 0.996 or any other exact value, but rather we wish to know—for a true β of 1—"What is the chance of obtaining a value *as low or lower than* 0.993?" (The real point here is that a probability statement is useless when concerned with a single value of a continuous variable, as only an interval of values has a non-zero probability of occurring.) This point is most easily appreciated if we consider the frequency function for b, the estimator of β computed from the sample. Graphically, the frequency looks like Figure 7.

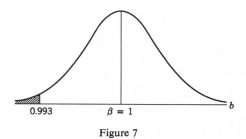

Figure 7

Because of our assumptions, it can be shown that this distribution has a mean value equal to the true slope, β (and in fact it is a normal frequency function, but this point is not essential here). If $\beta = 1$, the probability of obtaining a value from our sample of 0.993 *or less* is the shaded area in Figure 7. If we now ask what is the probability of getting b equal to 0.993 or less for a true β of 1.5, or 3.34, or some higher value, we shall find that this probability decreases with each increase in β. Graphically this is obvious since it corresponds to shifting the frequency function to the right, thereby decreasing the shaded area under the left tail to the left of 0.993. We can get a similar series of decreasing probability statements for a series of β's *smaller* than 0.993, in which we ask if these were the true β's what is the chance of observing a slope of 0.993 *or larger*—and again, if we move β far enough away from 0.993, the probabilities of observing a b larger than 0.993 become so ridiculously small that we feel confident the true β could not have been that far from 0.993.

Rather than construct such a table of hypothetically true β's and the probabilities associated with them, however, we prefer to pick a rather arbitrary level of probability, say 5 per cent, and find those two values of β, one large and one small, which give exactly a 5 per cent chance each of observing a slope worse than 0.993.   These two numbers are called the symmetrical 90 per cent confidence limits on β.   Graphically they are the means, B_1 and B_2, of those two distributions which contain exactly 5 per cent probability in their respective tails, which are cut off by 0.993 (Figure 8).

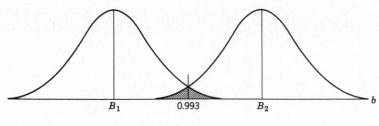

Figure 8

We shall shortly show how to compute such limits, but first let us see what such limits mean.   If we state that B_1 and B_2 are 90 per cent confidence limits on β, we do *not* mean that there is a 90 per cent chance that the true β lies between B_1 and B_2.   This is nonsense, since the true β is either between B_1 and B_2 or it is not, and no probability considerations apply.   What it *does* mean is a much more complicated statement: If we compute 90 per cent confidence limits on β, and if we assert *a priori* that these limits will include the true β, we shall be making a correct statement 90 per cent of the time.   The probability refers to the frequency of *correct statements* in a long conceptual series of statements of this type.   It does not refer to the true value of β, but rather to the *a priori* chance that the limits, when they are finally computed, will contain the true value.

We should also point out that various 90 per cent confidence limits can be constructed.   The ones described above were obtained by finding a

$B_1 < b$ such that an experimental value less than or equal to 0.993 could be expected 5 per cent of the time, and similarly for $B_2 > b$. We could just as easily have asked that B_2 be such that a value $\leqslant 0.993$ could be expected 8 per cent of the time, and that B_1 be such that one $\geqslant 0.993$ could be expected 2 per cent of the time, thus giving a total statement which would be correct 90 per cent of the time. Most confidence intervals are symmetrical ones, or nearly so, since interesting physical questions which they attempt to answer are usually symmetrical. If the cost of a mistake on the lower limit is much greater than the cost of a mistake on the upper, however, non-symmetrical limits are logical; but then they should be reported at the two separate levels, and not have their asymmetry concealed in a lumped probability statement.

The confidence level of 90 per cent is an arbitrary one. If we wish to be more conservative, we could set limits which will include the true value 99 per cent of the time—or we could demand that they be correct only 80 per cent of the time. Our decision about the desirable level of confidence is economic rather than mathematical. It depends directly on the cost of an error, and hence on the frequency with which we can afford to be wrong. High confidence levels lead to wide limits, and if these limits are too wide to be useful, we must reduce the gap between them either by accepting less confidence or by increasing the amount of data, i.e., by increasing the size of our sample. Data are expensive, and mistakes are expensive; the decision is thus one of balancing the cost of gathering more information against the cost of making a wrong move because of insufficient information. Any further discussion requires detailed knowledge of the particular problem—the economic factors, the physical variables, even the personalities of the people involved. This is the realm of the engineer and, having turned the spotlight on the problem, the statistician must dump it, quantitatively, into his lap.

Limits for β

It can be shown that b is distributed $N\left(\beta; \dfrac{\sigma_\eta^2}{\sum(x - x.)^2}\right)$, so that we could easily set limits on β, using the tables of the normal distribution, were it not for the fact that we do not know σ_η^2 but merely have an estimate of it in s_η^2. The way out of this difficulty is the standard trick of resorting to *Student's t distribution*, which is the distribution we obtain if we replace σ_η by its estimate, s_η, in the variate

$$\frac{b - \beta}{\sigma_b} \equiv \frac{(b - \beta)\sqrt{\sum(x - x.)^2}}{\sigma_\eta}.$$

Since

$$s_\eta = \sqrt{\frac{1}{n-2} \Sigma(y_i - Y_i)^2},$$

we find that

$$t_{n-2} = \frac{(b-\beta)\sqrt{n-2}\sqrt{\Sigma(x-x.)^2}}{\sqrt{\Sigma(y-Y)^2}} \equiv \frac{(b-\beta)\sqrt{n-2}\sqrt{Sxx}}{\sqrt{SSR}} \quad (36)$$

is distributed like Student's t with $n-2$ degrees of freedom. If we decide on 90 per cent symmetrical limits, then from our table of Student's distribution (Appendix), $t_8 = 1.86$ and $b - \beta = \pm 0.0049$, which gives 90 per cent confidence limits of 0.988 and 0.998, etc.

More precisely, t_n is the distribution of the ratio of a $N(0; 1)$ variate to the square root of an independent χ_n^2 variate which has been divided by n. [The χ_n^2 variate itself is a sum of n squares of $N(0; 1)$ variates.]

Our $N(0; 1)$ variate is clearly $\dfrac{b-\beta}{\sigma_b}$, whereas it can be shown that $(n-2)s_\eta^2 = \sum\left(\dfrac{y_i - Y_i}{\sigma_\eta}\right)^2$ is distributed as χ_{n-2}^2, so that t_{n-2} becomes

$$t_{n-2} = \frac{\dfrac{b-\beta}{\sigma_b}}{\sqrt{\dfrac{1}{n-2}\dfrac{\Sigma(y_i - Y_i)^2}{\sigma_\eta^2}}}.$$

If we now substitute $\dfrac{\sigma_\eta^2}{\Sigma(x-x.)^2}$ for its symbol σ_b^2, we can eliminate σ_η^2. This simplifies immediately to the expression (36), computable from the data. The $n-2$ degrees of freedom in $\sum\left(\dfrac{y_i - a - bx_i}{\sigma_\eta}\right)^2$ results from the two arbitrary constants which have been fitted—"using up" two of our n data points, to speak very loosely.

Confidence limits for α, μ

Just as b is normally distributed (because it is a weighted sum of variables which themselves are assumed to be normally distributed), so is our estimate of α or μ, and the same type of argument leads to confidence limits for this other parameter. Since a is distributed $N(\alpha; \sigma_a^2)$ where $\sigma_a^2 = \dfrac{\sigma_\eta^2 \Sigma x^2}{n\Sigma(x-x.)^2}$, hence $\dfrac{a-\alpha}{\sigma_a}$ is $N(0; 1)$.

Again we can replace the unknown parameter σ_η by its estimate s_η, thus creating another t_{n-2} variate:

$$t_{n-2} = \frac{(a-\alpha)\sqrt{n-2}\sqrt{n}\sqrt{Sxx}}{\sqrt{SSD}\sqrt{\Sigma x^2}}. \quad (37)$$

Similar arguments lead immediately to a t_{n-2} variate for m which is distributed $N\left(\mu;\frac{\sigma_\eta^2}{n}\right)$, and

$$t_{n-2} = \frac{\dfrac{m - \mu}{\sigma_\eta}\sqrt{n}}{\sqrt{\dfrac{1}{n-2}\sum\left(\dfrac{y_i - Y_i}{\sigma_\eta}\right)^2}} = \frac{(m - \mu)\sqrt{n-2}\sqrt{n}}{\sqrt{\sum(y_i - Y_i)^2}}$$

$$= \frac{(m - \mu)\sqrt{n-2}\sqrt{n}}{\sqrt{\text{SSD}}}. \qquad (38)$$

Equations (37) and (38) may be used to set confidence limits, symmetrical or not, on either α or μ by choosing the t_{n-2} value appropriate to the level of confidence desired. In our example, the 90 per cent symmetrical confidence limits are

$$\begin{array}{llll} \text{on } \beta, & 0.988 & \text{and} & 0.998 \\ \text{on } \alpha, & -0.35 & \text{and} & -0.09 \\ \text{on } \mu, & 22.80 & \text{and} & 22.92. \end{array}$$

Thus the questions asked about β may also be asked about α or μ, and similar limits have been given such that our assertions about the true α or μ being contained within these limits will be correct 90 per cent of the time. From some points of view, however, these limits may be misleading. The limits on α are not independent of the limits on β, and if we are interested in asking questions about what *line* could conceivably have spawned these data (instead of what set of parallel lines, or what line through this particular intercept), it is necessary to compute joint confidence limits on α and β.

If we think of limits on α as a segment of a vertical axis of possible α

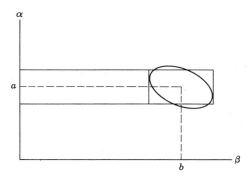

Figure 9

values, and limits on β as a similar segment of values in a horizontal axis, joint confidence limits will be a region, frequently elliptical, in the (β, α) plane and will no longer be a pair of numbers for each parameter. Figure 9 shows an incorrect (rectangular) and a correct (elliptical) joint confidence region for α and β for our data.

Any line whose (β, α) define a point outside the ellipse will be considered to be an improbable parent for the observed data, whereas those inside this ellipse are worthy of consideration, the most probable one being the one we have found, the center of the ellipse.

The orthogonal form

Before computing this (β, α) joint confidence region, we prefer to examine some joint confidence regions for the orthogonal form of the two parameter line, $y = \mu + \beta(x - x.)$, in the hope that more light may be shed on the philosophy underlying such regions and the questions they attempt to answer. The argument just used for confidence limits on β does not depend on which of our two standard forms of the equation we may have used; this should be obvious since b itself is not affected by these forms. The change of the other parameter, however, produces a difference not only in the limits for that parameter but also in the joint region.

We consider the four Sums of the Squared Residuals that we obtain from four lines, ranging from the completely specified line (M, B) through the lines with one parameter specified and the other fitted, (m, B) and (M, b), to the line with both parameters fitted (m, b). Schematically, we show all these possibilities on Figure 10, and also include the amounts by which the SSR are reduced as we pass from the completely specified line to the completely fitted line. The residuals are reduced as we adjust our line to the data, and the amount of a particular reduction is obviously a measure of how inadequately the specified parameter represents our data. We note that the choice of the orthogonal form lends two important simplifications: (1) the fitted m for II and IV is the same number, whereas III and IV share the same value of b, and (2) the reductions on opposite sides of our rhombic diagram are identical.

In actual use we let the specified parameters, M and B, be the hypothesized values of μ and β which we are considering as possible parents for our observed data. If we then find those values of M or B or both which just cause the corresponding reductions in the SSR to be too large to have plausibly arisen from random fluctuations, we obtain confidence limits for our population parameters, μ and β. The quantity with which any reduction must be compared for plausibility is $SSR/(n - 2)$.

Confidence regions are formed by equating the ratio of these reductions

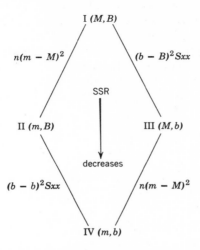

Figure 10. Reductions in SSR as various parameters are fitted

and SSR/$(n - 2)$ to t_{n-2}^2, so observation (2) means that identical limits will be obtained for β and μ, no matter how we gaze at the problem. (Each of these reductions is an independent χ_1^2. Since SSR is χ_{n-2}^2, the ratio of any one reduction to SSR/$(n - 2)$ has a $F_{1,\,n-2}$ distribution, which is identical with t_{n-2}^2.) By invoking each of these reductions separately, we get limits for β and μ separately, limits which bound a rectangular region in the (β, μ) plane. If we choose to consider the sum of the two reductions, itself a χ_2^2, the usual ratio has a $F_{2,\,n-2}$ distribution and we obtain an equation for an ellipse:

$$F_{2,\,n-2} > \dfrac{\dfrac{n(m - M)^2 + (b - B)^2 Sxx}{2\mathrm{SSR}}}{n - 2} \equiv \dfrac{(m - M)^2}{\dfrac{2\mathrm{SSR}}{n(n - 2)}} + \dfrac{(b - B)^2}{\dfrac{2\mathrm{SSR}}{(n - 2)Sxx}},$$

which can easily be plotted since its center is at (m, b) and its semiaxes are parallel to the graphical axes and are $\sqrt{\dfrac{2 \cdot \mathrm{SSR} \cdot F}{n(n - 2)}}$ and $\sqrt{\dfrac{2 \cdot \mathrm{SSR} \cdot F}{(n - 2)Sxx}}$ units long respectively.

A graph of the joint 90 per cent confidence ellipse for (β, μ) is shown in Figure 11 along with the 95 per cent symmetrical limits for β and μ separately. These two regions are not strictly comparable, as the rectangle includes 95 per cent times 95 per cent, i.e., 90.25 per cent probability instead of exactly 90 per cent, but this small difference need not bother us.   It is clear that the rectangle fits the ellipse rather well, and hence the two regions measure somewhat the same thing.   Practically, this is important, as the rectangular limits are more readily computed, and can be summarized by four numbers rather than by an equation of an ellipse. There is a further point that asymmetrical confidence limits can be applied to give other rectangular regions, although it is not clear how to make reasonable distortions of the joint ellipse or, indeed, what hypotheses

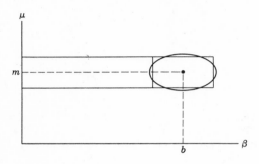

Figure 11

would correspond thereto.   The real difficulty consists of not knowing how to decide whether a line with $(\beta, \mu) = (1.1, 0.3)$ is better as a parent for our data than is a line with $(1.0, 0.5)$ and, if so, by how much.

The non-orthogonal form

If we now return to the non-orthogonal form of our equation, we find that our picture of the reductions in the sum of the squared residuals is now quite complicated.   No longer does the value of α, fitted when B is declared to be known (II), equal the value we get when fitting β as well (IV). Nor are the fitted values for β equivalent irrespective of our treatment of α (III and IV).   Furthermore, the individual reductions differ according to the route traveled, although their sums must agree since the total change from I to IV is not a function of the route, but only of the end points.   As before, we may find a joint elliptical region by equating the total reduction, suitably divided by $2 \cdot \text{SSR}/(n - 2)$, to $F_{2,\,n-2}$.   This time it will be an ellipse tilted in the (β, α) plane, but it is precisely the same ellipse as we had previously in the (β, μ) plane.

To get the analogue of our rectangular region, we consider the individual reductions on the left branch of Figure 12, noting that the second one is identical with its orthogonal counterpart from Figure 10 (and hence so

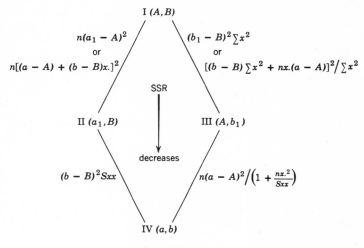

Figure 12

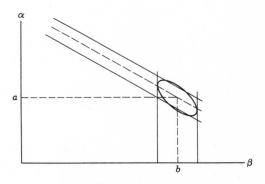

Figure 13

must be the one above it, although the change in variable obscures this). These reductions, being $\chi_1{}^2$ variables, may be treated (Figure 13) so as to give simple limits for β which are parallel to the α axis and inclined lines for the other pair, a parallelogram being the final result. The equations reduce to

$$|b - B| \leqslant \sqrt{\frac{F_{1,\,n-2} \cdot \mathrm{SSR}}{(n-2)Sxx}}$$

and

$$|(a - A) + (b - B)x.| \leqslant \sqrt{\frac{F_{1, n-2}\text{SSR}}{n(n - 2)}},$$

from which we see that the slanting sides have a slope of $-x.$, which is the slope of the locus of midpoints of vertical chords of the ellipse.

The other chain of reductions gives another parallelogram. This time the sides parallel to the coordinate axes are horizontal. The equations are

$$|(b - B)\textstyle\sum x^2 + nx.(a - A)| \leqslant \sqrt{\frac{F_{1, n-2}\text{SSR}\sum x^2}{n - 2}}$$

and

$$|a - A| \leqslant \sqrt{\frac{F_{1, n-2}\text{SSR}}{n(n - 2)} \cdot \left(1 + \frac{nx.^2}{Sxx}\right)},$$

from which we see the sides slope at $\sum x^2/nx.$, which is the slope of the locus of midpoints of the horizontal chords of the ellipse (Figure 14).

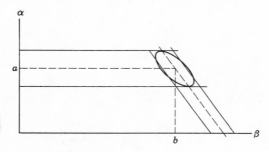

Figure 14

Our previous objections to rectangular limits in the (β, α) plane really boil down to the fact that a rectangle does not fit a tilted ellipse very well. We have removed this objection and secured the virtues and limitations of simple quadrilateral confidence regions in the (β, α) plane by adopting parallelograms. The first of these parallelograms is the region in the (β, α) plane corresponding to our rectangle in the (β, μ) plane, which becomes plausible by noting that

$$y = \mu + \beta(x - x.) = \alpha + \beta x$$

gives

$$\mu = \alpha + \beta x.,$$

and hence a constant value of μ gives a line of slope $-x.$ in the (β, α) plane.

Because the rectangle and the parallelogram are comparatively easy to compute, interpret, and record, we suggest that they are likely to be the most useful forms for joint confidence regions.   On the other hand, if someone proposes a particular pair of parameters, such as (0.5, 1.0), asking if such a line is a reasonable guess for the true line, it is quite easy to substitute these values into the appropriate form for the joint elliptical region, thereby obtaining a number whose significance may be ascertained by looking in a table of the F distribution.   The only cumbersome part of the elliptical region is the plotting of it, and for this present question that is unnecessary.   Since the elliptical regions frequently come closer to answering the questions asked, we do not—in the name of expediency— abandon them entirely, especially for those cases in which expediency is not thereby achieved.

Sketching the joint confidence ellipses

The (β, μ) ellipse may be sketched fairly easily by placing a numerical statement of the (β, μ) equation in the form

$$\frac{(b - \beta)^2}{h^2} + \frac{(m - \mu)^2}{k^2} = 1.$$

In this form h is the length of the semiaxis in the b direction, and k is the other semiaxis.   Thus we merely lay off from the fitted point (b, m) the distances $\pm h$ horizontally and $\pm k$ vertically.   Having the four extreme points on our ellipse, we can then easily sketch in the whole curve.

The (β, α) ellipses are tilted and require somewhat more labor.   The confidence statement is originally in the form

$$n[(a - A) + (b - B)x.]^2 + (b - B)^2 Sxx \leqslant \frac{2\text{SSR}}{n - 2} F_{2, n-2},$$

which may be written as

$$n(r + sx.)^2 + s^2 Sxx \leqslant d,$$

where

$$r = a - A, \qquad s = b - B.$$

If we continue to plot β horizontally, the easily found points on our ellipse (Figure 15) are given by

1. $s = 0$ and $r^2 = d/n$
2. $r = 0$ and $s^2 = d/(nx.^2 + Sxx)$
3. $r + sx. = 0$ and $s^2 = d/Sxx$
4. $r + s(x. + Sxx/nx.) = 0$ and $r^2 = d\left(\frac{1}{n} + \frac{x.^2}{Sxx}\right).$

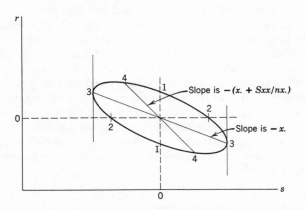

Figure 15

Confidence limits for σ_η^2

In most experimental work, we are interested in finding out the "true" physical law which operates.   The previous discussion answers questions about what line might have been the parent of the data points we observed. But this true line is obscured by the fluctuations about it—fluctuations which our model assumed were normally distributed with the line as a mean value and a variance σ_η^2.   (Graphically, if we slice our mountain range of probability, Figure 2, parallel to the y axis, the cross section is a normal frequency function and σ_η is the horizontal distance from its midpoint to its inflection point.)   This σ_η^2 measures the precision of our observations and hence is important to the experiment in its own right. Strictly speaking, it only measures the variability of the data after the effects of a straight line are removed, and hence part of its size is apparent variability due to the fact that our model was incorrect (the data really fit a quadratic, or the variance is really a function of x, for instance), as well as the inherent random variability of the data which we like to call "error." If we have complicated theories about how the errors in y occur, we are apt to want to break down this σ_η^2 into further *components of variance,* each ascribable to some physical source.   In a set of data the straight line may merely be an obscuring variation to be removed, and our chief interest could be the breakdown of the residual variance into its assignable components.   Such is apt to be our aim while we are attempting to improve the precision of a testing procedure, rather than during its later routine use to give routine measurements on a sample.   The subject is an extensive one, and we shall repeatedly touch on the several phases of it which occur in our straight-line problems.

In the particular problem of this chapter, we have no complicated hypothesis about σ_η^2 except that it is *not* a function of x or y, and we have too few data points to test even that hypothesis effectively. We are therefore confined to estimating the size of σ_η^2 under the assumption that it is constant, and to setting confidence limits on its true value. Fortunately, this is easily done for our simple model. The best unbiased estimator of σ_η^2 has already been mentioned earlier as being

$$s_\eta^2 = \frac{1}{n-2} \Sigma[y - m - b(x - x.)]^2 \equiv \frac{1}{n-2} \Sigma(y - a - bx)^2$$

$$\equiv \frac{1}{n-2} \text{SSR}, \qquad (39)$$

$$s_\eta^2 = \frac{1}{n-2} \left[Syy - \frac{(Sxy)^2}{Sxx} \right] \qquad (0.0109)$$

where the divisor $n - 2$ is needed to avoid too small an estimate—a danger produced by our fitting procedure's search for a *minimum* value of the SSR. (The fact that the divisor is $n - 2$ rather than $n - 1$ or $n - 4.56$ is not explained by this plausibility argument; we only point out that the correction is in the right direction.)

The confidence limits are easily found from the fact that SSR/σ_η^2 is distributed like χ_{n-2}^2. Suppose we assert that 0.04 is the true value of σ_η^2; then the ratio of SSR/0.04 is 2.18. If we assert that the true value is 0.01, the ratio is increased to 8.72. If we ask for the probability that we will observe a χ^2 for 8 degrees of freedom *as large as* 8.7 *or larger*, the tables (Appendix) show that this chance is about 35 per cent. Thus, as with limits on β, we can choose values of σ_η^2 and ask for the probability that this large ratio or a larger one will be observed—which means that the true value of σ_η^2 must be this small or smaller. But again, remembering our discussion of β, we prefer to find those two values of σ_η^2 which give rise to two symmetric probabilities, one of 5 per cent that the true value of σ_η^2 is this small or smaller, and the other of 5 per cent that the true value of σ_η^2 is this large or larger. In our problem, then, we must solve the two equations:

$$\frac{\text{SSR}}{\sigma_\eta^2} = (\chi_8^2)_{0.05} \qquad \text{and} \qquad \frac{\text{SSR}}{\sigma_\eta^2} = (\chi_8^2)_{0.95}.$$

These give limits of

$$0.0056 \leqslant \sigma_\eta^2 \leqslant 0.0319.$$

(The expression $(\chi_8^2)_{0\cdot95}$ means "that value of χ^2 for 8 degrees of freedom which will be *exceeded* 95 per cent of the time"—which is another way of saying that it will *not* be exceeded 5 per cent of the time.) The limits on σ_η are then obtained by taking square roots so that 90 per cent confidence limits are

$$0.075 \leqslant \sigma_\eta \leqslant 0.179.$$

Note that although the probabilities were chosen symmetrically, the corresponding limits are not symmetrical. This happens because the χ^2 frequency function, unlike those for the normal or t, is not symmetrical.

We emphasize at this point that the user of tables of χ^2, F, and t should check carefully the probability he is getting, for χ^2 and F are usually *one-tailed* listings (i.e., their argument is the chance that the random variable will exceed the tabular value), whereas t and the normal variate are usually given as *two-tailed* listings (i.e., their argument is the chance that the *absolute value* of the random variable will exceed the tabular value). These presentations are the ones most often needed, but by no means exclusively, and so thought should be taken. It is advisable to check the particular tables for self-consistency by noting that the one-tailed $F_{1,n}$ equals the (two-tailed) value of t_n^2, that $F_{m,\infty}$ is χ_m^2/m (both one-tailed), and finally that t_∞ is the *normal* abscissa for the same two-tailed probability.

Confidence limits on the true y for a specific x_0

The next more complicated question likely to arise is "What numbers Y_1, Y_2 shall I assign to make an assertion that 'for $x_0 = 3.52$ the true y is contained between Y_1 and Y_2,' such that this assertion shall be correct 90 per cent of the times I make it?" Any estimate, ζ, of the true y will wobble around because the line we computed has two parameters, both of which are in error. The limits we obtain are independent of the form of the equation used for the line, so it is simpler to consider the form in which the parameters are orthogonal, i.e., their covariances are zero. Since

$$y = m + b(x - x.),$$

then, for one particular x_0,

$$\sigma_{y_0}^2 = \sigma_m^2 + (x_0 - x.)^2 \sigma_b^2.$$

Now we know the values of σ_m^2 and σ_b^2 in terms of σ_η^2, which variance is unknown but is estimated by s_η^2. Thus

$$\sigma_{y_0}^2 = \sigma_\eta^2 \left[\frac{1}{n} + \frac{(x_0 - x.)^2}{Sxx} \right].$$

Since y_0 is normally distributed with mean

$$\zeta_0 = \mu + \beta(x_0 - x.),$$

then

$$\frac{y - \zeta}{\sigma_y} \Rightarrow N(0; 1),$$

and hence

$$t_{n-2} = \frac{y - \zeta}{s_\eta \sqrt{\dfrac{1}{n} + \dfrac{(x - x.)^2}{Sxx}}} \equiv \frac{(y - \zeta)\sqrt{n}\sqrt{n - 2}\sqrt{Sxx}}{\sqrt{SSR}\sqrt{Sxx + n(x - x.)^2}}.$$

If we substitute the numerical value t_{n-2} for the confidence level we are using (1.86 for 90 per cent on 8 degrees of freedom), we obtain an equation in x and y describing two hyperbolas which cut off a confidence region around the line (Figure 16).

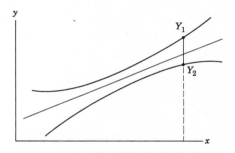

Figure 16

For a particular x we have two numbers, Y_1 and Y_2, at equal vertical distances above and below the line, and these are the confidence limits on the true y which we seek.

Prediction of an additional y_0 from an additional x_0

If we are not so much interested in where the true value of y might lie for a particular x, but rather in where another observation y_0 might reasonably be expected to fall, given its corresponding x_0, the limits will be similar to those of the preceding section. They will, however, be somewhat wider, as this statistic admits a further source of error—the sampling fluctuations of y_0 about ζ. Our best estimate of the new value of y is y_0 of the fitted line for the particular x_0. Hence it is only necessary to find confidence limits around this value.

The deviation of a variate y measured at x_0 from the fitted line may be expressed as

$$d_0 = y - y_0 = y - m - b(x_0 - x.).\tag{40}$$

This is the sum of normally distributed variates and is seen to have a mean value of zero.   In order to establish confidence limits for d_0, we must estimate its variance, which can be shown to be

$$\sigma_{d_0}{}^2 = \sigma_\eta{}^2\left[1 + \frac{1}{n} + \frac{(x_0 - x.)^2}{Sxx}\right].\tag{41}$$

This variance is plausible, as it is merely the sum of variance of the true ordinate ζ_0 and the sampling variance of y from the true value.   Then

$$\frac{d_0}{\sigma_\eta}\left[1 + \frac{1}{n} + \frac{(x_0 - x.)^2}{Sxx}\right]^{-\frac{1}{2}} \Rightarrow N(0; 1),\tag{42}$$

but σ_η is unknown.   If we replace the unknown σ_η by its estimator s_η, the distribution of (42) becomes t_{n-2}, so that

$$d_0 = \pm t_{n-2}s_\eta\sqrt{1 + \frac{1}{n} + \frac{(x_0 - x.)^2}{Sxx}}.\tag{43}$$

By substituting the numerical value of t_{n-2} for the confidence level desired, we obtain values for $\pm d_0$, which distances are to be laid off above and below the y_0 of the line.   For 90 per cent limits and $x_0 = 3.52$ we obtain

$$3.047 \leqslant y_0 \leqslant 3.499.$$

Note that these limits $\pm d_0$ are functions of x_0; in fact they are quadratic functions, and hence they describe hyperbolas on either side of the regression line—delimiting a confidence region which is symmetrical with respect to vertical deviations from the line and wider than those of the last sections.   We should also quickly point out that if we try to use these limits for several values of x_0 by asserting that the limits given by these curves contain the corresponding true values y_0, we shall be wrong with a probability *different* from the 10 per cent error rate we used to calculate these curves—as anyone can verify by trying the experiment.

Perhaps the sort of difficulties involved can be illustrated by considering the case of *two* samples at the same x_0, which itself is near the *end* of the fitted line.   Let ζ_1 and ζ_2 be the expected values of the first and second sample at x_0.   They are both equal to y_0, the ordinate of the fitted line at x_0.   If the *same* confidence limits are applied to both ζ_1 and ζ_2, the joint confidence region for the two will be a small area (rectangle, ellipse, or circle) around the point (y_0, y_0) in the (ζ_1, ζ_2) plane.

When we consider the possible lines that might have given birth to our data, however, we see that, had we chosen another one, we would have shifted ζ_1 *and* ζ_2 about the same amount, so that although they are now both different from their previous values, they are still nearly equal to each other. Thus, if our line is rather inaccurately determined (large variances for $\sigma_a{}^2$ and $\sigma_b{}^2$), we should get joint confidence regions for ζ_1 and ζ_2 that allow large variation in each separately but keep the values of the two together; in other words, the joint region is nearly a segment of the 45° line in the (ζ_1, ζ_2) plane—a long thin ellipse—and not the shaded

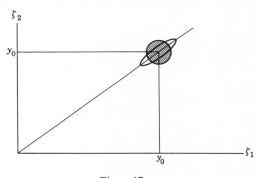

Figure 17

area of Figure 17 to which our first impulse led. To establish joint confidence limits for several additional values is, then, a rather complicated task. Fortunately, we are rarely interested in precisely this problem. We are more apt to be worried about how large or small would be the *mean* of m additional values $y_i'(i = 1, ..., m)$ all taken at x_0. This is a single statistic and has simple confidence limits which are given later.

The use of these limits may seem a trifle complicated, especially since hyperbolas are not the sort of curve we feel able to draw instinctively. Fortunately, we seldom want the entire curve, as these limits have been for single additional values or for the value of the true ordinate at a particular point, so that usually a single pair of limits, $y_0 \pm d$, will suffice. The constant reference to hyperbolas in this chapter is aimed at giving a general picture rather than suggesting a routine procedure. If it should become necessary to sketch the hyperbola, however, it is not too difficult. Consider the limits for ζ_0, the true ordinate at x_0. The equation for d, the displacement of the limits from the line, is

$$t_{n-2}^2 = \frac{d^2(n-2)Sxx}{SSR\left[\dfrac{Sxx}{n} + (x - x.)^2\right]},$$

so that

$$\frac{d^2}{\left[\dfrac{(SSR)(t^2)}{(n-2)(n)}\right]} - \frac{(x-x.)^2}{\left[\dfrac{Sxx}{n}\right]} = 1.$$

If we let $h^2 = \dfrac{Sxx}{n}$ and $k^2 = t^2 \dfrac{SSR}{n(n-2)}$, we can lay off the two asymptotes to the hyperbola easily, as shown in Figure 18.

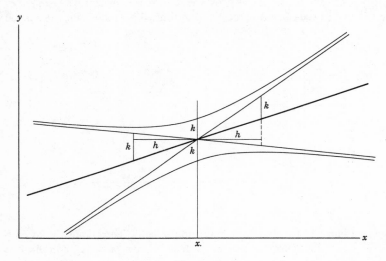

Figure 18

Note that h is laid off horizontally *from the line* at $x = x.$ and k is laid off vertically *from the line* at $x. + h$. The point of closest approach to the curve (at $x = x.$) is given simply by $\pm k$ at that point. At this point the hyperbola is parallel to the fitted line, so it is comparatively easy to sketch.

Predicting the mean of m additional readings at x_0

In order to predict $\bar{y}_0$, the mean of m further readings all taken at the same x_0, we can use the formulae just given for one additional reading if, in the expressions for $\sigma_d{}^2$, we replace the variance of the one reading, $\sigma_\eta{}^2$, by the variance of the mean of m readings, $\sigma_\eta{}^2/m$. This gives us

$$t_{n-2} = \frac{d_m}{\sqrt{\dfrac{SSR}{n-2}}\sqrt{\dfrac{1}{m} + \dfrac{1}{n} + \dfrac{(x_0-x.)^2}{Sxx}}}$$

$$\equiv \frac{d_m\sqrt{n-2}\sqrt{mn}\sqrt{Sxx}}{\sqrt{SSR}\sqrt{(m+n)Sxx + mn(x_0-x.)^2}}.$$

The $\pm d_m$ are the limits to be applied to the best estimate, y_0. Again we have hyperbolas, but they fall between those for a sample of one and those for the true value (which corresponds to the mean of an infinite sample).

Thus far we have given confidence regions for three different probability statements, the first referring to ζ_0 (the true ordinate for an arbitrary x_0), the second to the ordinate of an additional experimental reading, y_0, at an arbitrary x_0, and the third to the ordinate of the mean of m additional readings at x_0. These statements do not by any means exhaust the possibilities. The questions that can be answered either approximately or exactly are legion and, at the risk of beating a dead horse, we are going to describe several further confidence regions, answering questions which sound similar to the previous ones but which are in fact not the same. We are here deliberately giving space far beyond that justified by the intrinsic importance of these questions, in order to emphasize the influence of the form of the question itself on the answer and, by implication, to emphasize the necessity for careful framing of the important questions by the experimenter *before the experiment is carried out*, lest he find himself with confidence limits that are far too wide to be useful—all because the experiment was carefully designed to answer the wrong questions.

Confidence limits on another experimenter's fitted y_0 values

Instead of the confidence questions already posed, we might rather ask what value, y'_0, another experimenter might reasonably be expected to obtain if he were to repeat our experiment and use *his* fitted line to estimate ζ at x_0. This ambiguous question can be made more precise if by a strict repetition of the experiment we mean that a new set of y_i's are obtained at the *same* values x_i which were used in the first experiment and if we presume the population from which we are sampling to be unchanged —a presumption that is frequently false (and unfortunately a discussion of the conditions under which it may be expected to be true is beyond the scope of the present chapter).

Since our fitted line is
$$y = m + b(x - x.)$$
and the line from the second (duplicate) experiment is
$$y' = m' + b'(x - x.),$$
we see that the difference
$$d = y - y' = (m - m') + (x - x.)(b - b')$$
has a zero mean and a variance
$$\sigma_d^2 = \sigma_m^2 + \sigma_{m'}^2 + (x - x.)^2(\sigma_b^2 + \sigma_{b'}^2).$$

We know, however, that $\sigma_m{}^2 = \sigma_{m'}{}^2 = \sigma_\eta{}^2/n$ and $\sigma_b{}^2 = \sigma_{b'}{}^2 = \sigma_\eta{}^2/Sxx$ so that we can substitute in the expression

$$\frac{d}{\sigma_d} \Rightarrow N(0;1)$$

to obtain another t_{n-2} distribution which differs from the t_{n-2} for the true variate only by a factor of $\sqrt{2}$. These limits are also hyperbolas about the regression line we obtained, the vertical deviations, d, from this line being given by

$$t_{n-2} = \frac{\pm d\sqrt{n-2}}{\sqrt{SSR}\sqrt{\dfrac{1}{n} + \dfrac{(x-x_.)^2}{Sxx}}\,\sqrt{2}} = \frac{\pm d}{s_\eta\sqrt{2}\sqrt{\dfrac{1}{n} + \dfrac{(x-x_.)^2}{Sxx}}}.$$

This confidence region, like the one for ζ_0, refers to a point on a line. The statements that these points on our line lie between the calculated limits will be true 90 per cent of the time—and they will be true under two distinguishable configurations:

1. The line of points about whose location we are conjecturing actually does lie wholly between the hyperbolas we draw, Figure 19, line 1.

2. Only part of this line of points lies between the hyperbolas, Figure 19, line 2.

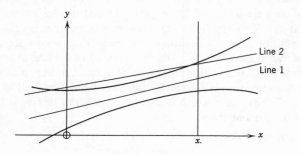

Figure 19

Thus if the question is proposed for the particular x_0 shown in the figure, the statement would be true for either configuration of the true line, whereas if the questions were posed for $x = 0$, it would be true only for line 1. In either case, the 90 per cent confidence of a correct statement might not be violated, provided the segment of line 2 which is above the upper hyperbola is sufficiently small.

Confidence limits for the entire true line

We may prefer, however, to set forth confidence regions which contain—we may assert with 90 per cent confidence—the *entire* true line, or the *entire* fitted line obtained by repeating the experiment.   These are stronger demands, and we would expect to get slightly wider limits than before. Qualitatively we can get the limits for the true line by looking at the joint 90 per cent confidence region for (β, μ) and seeing what the envelope of all these possible lines in the the (x, y) plane might be.   Actually it turns out to be another pair of hyperbolas, in fact the *same* hyperbolas obtained when we only demanded that a particular point be included, except that t_{n-2}^2 has been replaced by $2F_{2, n-2}$; thus

$$2F_{2, n-2} = \frac{d^2(n-2)}{SSR\left[\dfrac{1}{n} + \dfrac{(x - x.)^2}{Sxx}\right]} \cdot$$

We may also find the envelope of all probable lines from a duplicate experiment, and it turns out to give

$$F_{2, n-2} = \frac{d^2(n-2)}{4SSR\left[\dfrac{1}{n} + \dfrac{(x - x.)^2}{Sxx}\right]} \cdot$$

In both these envelope problems a simpler and probably preferable technique is open to us.   We used the elliptical joint regions to get the hyperbolic limits; if we use rectangular joint limits, we shall obtain straight-line limits.   The probabilities are identical and the plotting is easier, even if there are slight differences in interpretation.   We illustrate for the true line by showing the two joint regions and their envelopes in Figures 20 and 21.

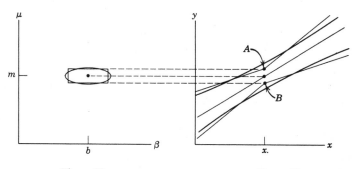

Figure 20   Figure 21

Note that the straight-line limits are merely those lines given by the four corners of the rectangular region in the (β, μ) plane and hence are easily found, for μ is the ordinate at the mass center x. and β is the slope. We thus locate points A and B such that their ordinates are equal to the high and low values for μ and their abscissa is x. . The two slopes are the extreme values of β, i.e., the confidence limits on β.

Our confidence limits for Joe's variance estimate

If a second experimenter, familiarly known as Joe, should repeat our experiment in the narrow sense of taking n new observations at precisely the same set of x values and then compute his estimate, $s_n'^2$, of the residual variance of these data about the true but unknown line, we might legitimately wonder just how far his estimate might wander. When we compared our own estimate with the true value, σ_η^2, we observed that a χ_{n-2}^2 variate was produced. Now we wish to compare two such χ^2 variates—and so we examine the ratio of their mean squares, which is an F variate. Here, if primes signify Joe's statistics, we have

$$\frac{s'^2}{s^2} \equiv \frac{\text{SSR}'/(n-2)}{\text{SSR}/(n-2)} \equiv \frac{\text{SSR}'}{\text{SSR}} \Rightarrow F_{n-2,\,n-2}$$

when SSR' is assumed to be larger than SSR. The inverse ratio allows the other confidence limit to be constructed as easily. (If Joe's experiment had a *different* number of data from ours, the mean squares must be used directly, and the two equations would be $s'^2/s^2 = F_{m-2,\,n-2}$ and $s^2/s'^2 = F_{n-2,\,m-2}$.)

By taking square roots, we get confidence limits for Joe's standard deviation estimate, should we prefer that form.

Our confidence limits for Joe's limits on the population variance

At the risk of carrying the old shell game too far we finally point out that not only can we place our own limits on the unknown population variance but we can also put limits on *Joe*'s confidence limits for this same statistic. This is possible simply because Joe's limits, S_e^2 and S_u^2, come from his equations

$$S_e^2 = \frac{\text{SSR}'}{\chi_{n-2}^2(0.95)} \qquad \text{and} \qquad S_u^2 = \frac{\text{SSR}'}{\chi_{n-2}^2(0.05)},$$

whereas to us SSR'/SSR is an $F_{n-2,\,n-2}$ variate which allows the use of our own estimate. Thus we assert that Joe's limits will lie bounded by

$$\frac{\text{SSR}}{\chi^2_{n-2}(0.95)F_{n-2,\,n-2}} \leqslant S^2_e \leqslant \frac{\text{SSR} \cdot F_{n-2,\,n-2}}{\chi^2_{n-2}(0.95)}$$

$$\frac{\text{SSR}}{\chi^2_{n-2}(0.05)F_{n-2,\,n-2}} \leqslant S^2_n \leqslant \frac{\text{SSR} \cdot F_{n-2,\,n-2}}{\chi^2_{n-2}(0.05)}$$

where we can allow for not only our own level of F skepticism but also that of mysterious Joe. Farther than this we dare not go.

A similar experiment

Still further questions can easily be raised, if not so easily answered. Suppose another experimenter repeats the experiment in the sense that he samples from the same population, but at a known but different set of x values, so that his y_i are not directly comparable to ours? Suppose he uses a different number of points, as well as different locations—how may we then expect his estimated line to differ from ours?

Answer:

$$t_{n-2} = \frac{d\sqrt{n-2}}{\sqrt{\text{SSR}}\sqrt{\left(\frac{1}{n_1} + \frac{1}{n_2}\right) + \left(\frac{(x - x_1.)^2}{Sx_1x_1} + \frac{(x - x_2.)^2}{Sx_2x_2}\right)}} \, .$$

Predicting x when an additional y is known

We have already discussed the problem of setting confidence limits within which an additional y observation might reasonably be expected to lie. Very frequently, however, we wish to use our line and data to answer the other problem, i.e., predicting where the x would be found when all we know is a probably erroneous y value associated with it. Since we are still discussing the classical model in which x values are assumed to be accurately known whenever they are measured and the only error distribution is that on y, it seems injudicious to refer to confidence limits for x lest the term imply that x itself possesses an error distribution—which, of course, it cannot have. But confidence limits they are, so this risk of confusion will have to be taken.

Elaborations of this problem arise with chemical calibration curves. A quicker but less reliable analytical chemical technique is calibrated against the laborious but accurate standard method by analyzing several different concentrations of the "unknown" by each method. The standard analyses frequently may be regarded as without error, placing all blame for deviations on the newcomer. We fit a line in the usual way and reduce all subsequent experimental y values to their *corresponding x values* by reading off an x for each y from the calibration curve. Since the observed y contains an error component (drawn from an error distribution whose variance we have estimated), it almost certainly does not go with an x which would give a point *on* the calibration curve or, indeed, on the unknown true line (our calibration curve, after all, is also erroneous).   If we knew the x coordinate *instead* of the y coordinate, we would have our original confidence interval problem: We would want to know where an additional point, at this x_0, might be asserted to lie so that the assertion would be correct 90 per cent of the time.   If we look at Figure 22, we see

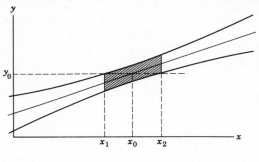

Figure 22

the two hyperbolas defined by this assertion bracketing the fitted line. Returning to our inverse problem, we actually have at hand a y_0 from an additional observation whose x we may assume to have been unrecorded or lost.   We are therefore going to assert that its x lies between x_1 and x_2 (see Figure 22), the best guess being x_0.

Recapitulating, if we were going to take an additional observation with its x value between x_1 and x_2, our assertion that the point would be found in the shaded area would be correct 90 per cent of the time, for that is the way the area is constructed.   Therefore, when we actually get an observation with the value y_0 we assert that, unless this is one of our unlucky 1-in-10 shots, the correct x_0 must lie between x_1 and x_2.   The moral to note here is that although we know y and are predicting x, nevertheless the answer to our problem is obtained from the other point of view, that of knowing x and asking about y—and then using our picture in a backward fashion to get appropriate limits on x.   Our fitting procedure, as well as our confidence region, is based on sure x's and erroneous y's. This is our model and we must use it realistically.   If the questions asked seem to imply that y is known and therefore x is erroneous, we must not yield to the temptation to interchange x and y and to reduce the problem to one already solved—because a little reflection will reveal that y, although known, is measured with error, and x, although unknown, is a sure value. Thus the model used is the natural approach, however foreign it may seem to the casual observer.

We said that the chemist's calibration problem is an *elaboration* of the one already described because he is rarely satisfied with *one* additional value. He wants ten, a hundred, perhaps even a thousand future values to be referred to his calibration curve. Unfortunately, as we pointed out while first discussing these confidence limits, the limits for one additional observation are not adequate for several. The 90 per cent correctness refers to a person who makes the *combined* operation of taking n points, fitting the line, drawing the appropriate region, and asserting that *one* additional observation will lie therein. The chemist clearly is interested in finding a region only once and then asserting that of the next 50 observations, at least (say) 47 will be inside his shaded area, and that— in the long run—this statement will be correct 90 per cent of the time. To demand that all 50 be inside would widen the limits to the point where they are no longer very attractive. Of course some other smaller percentage of the future observations will give still narrower limits and may still be acceptable. The specific problem will determine such questions, which depend on the economic cost of a mistake. If the calibration is to be used for many more than 50 future observations, probably the easiest solution is to construct the region that will include at least (say) 95 per cent of the entire infinite population of points with 90 per cent confidence. (These are the *tolerance limits* of Wilks [41], who treated them non-parametrically. Wald and Wolfowitz [37] applied them to the normal distribution from whence our subsequent material was analogously derived.)

We have here a whole sequence of confidence regions, each of which may be used to answer either the direct question from which it was constructed or the inverse question in which the laboratory technician is more frequently interested. We shall now set out some of the more important and possibly more realistic questions that might lead to useful regions. These are all confidence statements, so the correct regions will be such that the corresponding statement will be true 90 per cent of the time the entire combined operation is carried out, i.e., fitting the line, drawing the region, and making the assertion. These assertions are:

1. One additional observation will lie within this region.
2. The mean of m additional observations, all taken at the same x_0 (even if it be unknown), will lie within this region.
3. The population mean (at a fixed, though perhaps unknown, x_0) will lie within this region.
4. All m additional observations at a fixed x_0 will lie within this region.

5. At least r of m additional observations at a fixed x_0 will lie within this region.

6. At least α per cent of all future observations will lie within this region.

Note that assertions 1 and 3 are limiting cases of 2 as m tends to 1 and ∞ respectively. Likewise assertion 6 is the limit reached by 5 as r and m grow large but preserve the fixed ratio $\alpha/100$.

Of these statements, 3 has no realizable inverse: We cannot observe the population mean, so we cannot usefully ask what x probably went with our observation. (Conceptually, assertion 3 is approached by 2 as we take larger and larger numbers of y observations at the same unknown x and consider the mean of these observations. We are, however, quite dubious about the ability of any experimental man to make small numbers of y observations "at the same x," let alone large numbers of them. Among the myriad of experimental conditions, some are almost certain to change in such a way that the x's are no longer identical, even if they once had been—a further point about which we have serious mental reservations.) Statements 4, 5, and 6 also suffer from the experimental difficulty of taking several measurements at the same x_0. If, however, the experimenter feels that he has, in fact, taken his several y readings on a system in which x remained fixed, then he can use the inverse of these statements to find limits on the unknown x.

Probably the most useful statement is 6. It asserts that at least 95 per cent of all future observations will lie within the region, although the assertion will be wrong 10 per cent of the time. That 10 per cent chance of error occurs because we have drawn a region from imprecise data. As a result, it may not cover the true location of the population as well as it might. If we make further repeated observations of both y and x and refer them to this one specific region, they will fall in or out for two reasons:

1. They may be rare drawings from the extreme tails of our normal population which would not even be covered by a region perfectly placed with respect to the population. This is the 5 per cent of the population (or less) we do not expect to include.

2. They may be perfectly respectable drawings from near the mean of the population, but the region with which we are stuck just happens to be a bad fit and does not cover some of the more likely sections of our population. This is the 10 per cent chance of error allowed by our 90 per cent confidence statement.

Clearly, if we are unfortunate enough to have this second situation on our hands, (too) large percentages of our future observations will be beyond the pale. In an extreme case, if the first additional observation is out, most of the rest will be also. We say that we have obtained one of those bad calibration curves and shrug our shoulders if we finally find it out when some trouble arises through an incorrect analysis. Thus we make mistakes and they cost us money, but presumably we are willing to make them this often, since that is how we set these confidence requirements in the first place.

Our procedure for assertion 6, then, is to refer each new y reading to our calibration curve, and from the intercepts with the limit curves we get two values of x between which, we assert, lies the true x. Because we will occasionally obtain a wild observation, a *good* calibration curve will give us wrong limits one time in twenty or more, and—what is probably much worse—about one in ten calibration curves will not be good, i.e., they will give wrong limits more times than one in twenty. Thus these two percentages may not be the useful ones. The chance that any particular pair (x_1, x_2) will include the unknown true x will be at least as great as the product of these two chances of being correct, i.e., in our example the statement will have at least a 0.90×0.95 or 0.855 chance of being right. (The chance is better than 0.855, but probably not much better, because a bad calibration region can include a wild observation, thereby making the confidence statement correct, whereas a good region would have excluded the observation and thus made the statement false. The probability of such compensating errors is, however, not very important.)

Population tolerance limits

In setting confidence limits we have always dealt with limits for a single statistic—be it one additional observation, the mean of m additional data taken at a single x_0, the true ordinate at x_0, etc. We have emphasized that one set of limits is not to be used for two or more additional readings because of correlations in the joint confidence region. This correlation is caused by the fact that these data are from a regression problem, i.e., they lie on a line.

There is, however, another source of difficulty with setting limits for several values of the ordinate, even at one value of x_0, which has nothing to do with the fact that a regression line is involved. The trouble is perhaps better illustrated by removing the confusion of the line and writing down explicit statements of the analogous one-dimensional problems; hence for the moment let us merely sample from a normal population of unknown parameters.

The old problem says "I shall draw a sample of n, compute y. and s, and set confidence limits such that if I assert that one additional datum,

y_0, will be contained within these limits, I shall be correct 90 per cent of the times I perform *this entire experiment.*"

The new problem says "I shall draw a sample of n, compute y. and s, and set tolerance limits such that if I assert that at least 95 per cent of the unknown normal population is contained within these limits, I shall be correct 90 per cent of the times I perform *this entire experiment.*"

Note that both these statements contain the phrase "this entire experiment" but that the experiment referred to is quite different. The old problem conceives of setting a pair of confidence limits on *one* additional statistic, and if I want my statement to be correct the proper percentage of the times it is made, I must set new confidence limits from a new sample of n by this method each time I consider a new additional statistic. The second statement, however, refers to tolerance limits on the percentage of the population contained within my limits, and hence we see that this experiment gives one set of limits which shall include at least 95 per cent of *all future* drawings we may make from this population. This is a model in which we are often interested, and it is important that we do not confuse it with its mathematically simpler brother.

The confidence limits for one additional datum come from a simple t test, whereas approximate tolerance limits may be found from a more complicated procedure involving inverse interpolation in normal tables.

Tables giving the approximate tolerance limits appear in *Techniques of Statistical Analysis* by the Columbia Statistical Research Group. They were computed by the method now set out, which is slightly tedious because of the inverse interpolation involved.

To compute approximate tolerance limits:

1. Find r from the equation

$$\frac{1}{\sqrt{2\pi}} \int_{(1/\sqrt{n})-r}^{(1/\sqrt{n})+r} \exp \frac{-t^2}{2}\, dt = 0.95$$

(or whatever other value for the tolerance interval we desire) by inverse interpolation in a table of the normal distribution.

2. Compute

$$\lambda = r \left[\frac{n-1}{\chi_{n-1}^2(0.90)} \right]^{\frac{1}{2}}$$

where $\chi_{n-1}^2(0.90)$ is that value of χ^2 with $n-1$ degrees of freedom which will be exceeded by chance 90 per cent of the time. This number may be read directly from the usual tables of percentage points of the chi-squared distribution, and Hald [18] even tables $\chi_{n-1}^2/(n-1)$ directly for some percentage points. It is also $F_{n-1, \infty}$.

3. The approximate tolerance limits are

$$y. \pm \lambda s .$$

The straight-line tolerance problem

If we could take an infinitely large sample of points from our straight-line population, we would then know precisely where our population lay. We would know the position of the straight line which is the mean value of y for every x, and we would also know the amount of variability about that line. Since we can take only a small sample, however, we have only an estimate of the true line and the variance about it. The limits we set on the basis of this necessarily inaccurate information may include most of the unknown true population, or they may not. They cannot, because of the infinite range of the normal distribution, enclose *all* the true population, so the only meaningful assertion will be that they enclose at least α per cent (say 95 per cent) of it. This assertion will be either right or wrong for any particular set of limits (and we cannot know which unless we sample many more points), but we wish to set forth procedures to give limits for which the assertion will be true about β per cent (say 90 per cent) of the times we follow these procedures.

Although this formulation of our problem may sound quite definite, we still have some ambiguities to resolve. Suppose our true population and the particular limits we happened to fit by some procedure lay as shown in Figure 23.

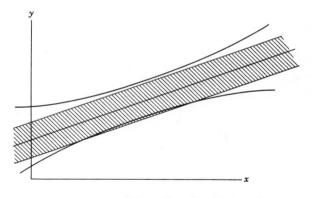

Figure 23

Here we may suppose that the shaded area represents the central 95 per cent of our true population of points. The particular limits enclose most of this area, but not all of it. At most values of the abscissa our limits *do* enclose at least 95 per cent of the possible y values, but for a small region they do not. If this region is small enough, it may still be explained by our 10 per cent failure to set correct tolerance limits; in other words, if such regions do not occur too often, we still may be correct the proper percentage of times we try the experiment.

The following procedure yields approximate population tolerance limits for points on the true line analogous to those given earlier for points from a normal distribution. To compute these limits at a specific point x_0:

1. Find $r(x, 0.95)$ from the equation

$$\frac{1}{\sqrt{2\pi}} \int_{\sqrt{\frac{1}{n} + \frac{(x_0 - x)^2}{Sxx}} - r}^{\sqrt{\frac{1}{n} + \frac{(x_0 - x)^2}{Sxx}} + r} \exp - \frac{t^2}{2} \, dt = 0.95$$

(or for whatever other value we desire for the tolerance interval) by inverse interpolation in a table of the normal distribution or direct interpolation in Table 3.

2. Compute

$$\lambda = r \left[\frac{n - 2}{\chi^2_{n-2}(0.90)} \right]^{1/2}$$

where $\chi^2_{n-2}(0.90)$ is that value of χ^2 with $n - 2$ degrees of freedom which will be exceeded by chance 90 per cent of the time. This number may be read either from a chi-squared table or as $F_{n-2, \infty}$.

3. The approximate limits are

$$y_0 \pm \lambda s,$$

where y_0 is the point on the fitted line corresponding to x_0.

Note that if a region about the line is wanted, it will be necessary to compute the limits at several points and then supply the curve by eye interpolation. The solution of the first step is somewhat simplified by using tables of the abscissa of the normal curve as a function of the total area. (Chamber's *Six Figure Mathematical Tables*, Vol. II, has an excellent one.)

Another approach would be to demand tolerance limits that contain 95 per cent or more of the population of y values *at every value of x* and then develop a procedure that would satisfy this demand 90 per cent of the times it was applied. Although it is easy to formulate this problem, the necessary numerical integration seems laborious, and a useful approximation in terms of existing functions is as yet unknown.

Preset independent variables—the Berksonian line

Suppose that a chemist desires to calibrate a polarimeter by measuring the degrees of rotation produced by several sugar solutions of known strength. He may very well intend to weigh out several different predetermined amounts of sugar, add these to some standard quantity of

TABLE 3

r versus A for Various γ from the Equation

$$\frac{1}{\sqrt{2\pi}} \int_{A-r}^{A+r} \exp -\frac{t^2}{2} \, dt = \gamma$$

A	$\gamma = 0.8$	$\gamma = 0.9$	$\gamma = 0.95$	$\gamma = 0.990$
0	1.28155	1.64485	1.95996	2.57583
0.1	1.28796	1.65306	1.96973	2.58860
0.2	1.30715	1.67748	1.99855	2.62564
0.3	1.33903	1.71745	2.04505	2.68347
0.4	1.38330	1.77179	2.10699	2.75731
0.5	1.43937	1.83875	2.18148	2.84223
0.6	1.50623	1.91611	2.26539	2.93409
0.7	1.58244	2.00147	2.35583	3.02996
0.8	1.66626	2.09251	2.45046	3.12796
0.9	1.75584	2.18733	2.54760	3.22704
1.0	1.84947	2.28447	2.64615	3.32663

water, and then make his observations. He will plot the degrees of rotation, y, against the weight of sugar, x, that he thinks he has measured out, and the slope of the straight line is the number he wishes to know.

Without going into the merits of such an analytical procedure, we would like to raise some questions about the independent variable x. Was it measured with or without error? Was it, perhaps, not measured at all? So much confusion has been created by this point that it seems worthwhile elaborating. Our chemist could have poured a small pile of sugar onto a weighing pan and then weighed it objectively, recording it as 0.9427 grams. About such a number we have little to say, either it represents the weight with so much more precision than we will ever get for y that we choose to regard it as having no error at all, or else the precisions are roughly equal and we must treat both variables as measured erroneously, using the methods of Chapter 5.

But this is not what the chemist did. He decided in advance that he was going to prepare samples of sugar weighing 0.2, 0.4, 0.6, and 0.8 grams. Then, having balanced his empty weighing pan, he added 0.8 grams of weight to his balance and poured in sugar until he was satisfied that he had the right amount on the pan. The number he recorded in his notebook was 0.8000 grams. It is quite clear that this number arose from our chemist's mind and not at all from any objective measurement. The amount of sugar obtained almost certainly would not come to 0.8000 grams if given to a student to be weighed.   The chemist performed an act which looked very much like the formal operation of weighing, but the number that was recorded did not arise from any objective reading of an instrumental scale.   It was a convenient constant picked in advance by the chemist to which he attempted to adjust the physical amount of sugar in his experiment.   In so far as his experimental technique was poor, the chemist certainly introduced error into the experiment by actually providing an amount of sugar different from the weight recorded.   *But this error, although present in the sugar, is not present in the recorded number.*   If anyone doubt this assertion, let him consider a whole sequence of sugar samples prepared by our chemist.   They will, in fact, exhibit a variety of weights fluctuating about the intended weight, but our chemist's notebook monotonously records the values 0.8 grams, 0.8 grams, 0.8 grams, ... — which data clearly have no error information in them.

We can now see that our first approach to this straight-line problem was irrelevant.   It is not sensible to ask whether the weight of the sugar should be treated as being measured with or without error since we have never recorded the weight of the sugar at all.   We have only recorded the *intended weight* of the sugar, and the only straight line that our experiment can possibly produce is a line connecting the observed degree of polarization, y, with the *intended weight*, X.   Once we realize that these are the only variables involved, it is quite clear that this straight line must be fitted by techniques that ascribe all the error to y and take X as accurately known, as indeed it is.   If we wish, we may ask all the confidence questions of this chapter about these two variables, although some of them may not be particularly interesting.   If our laboratory intends to use these analytical techniques, this type of calibration is essential and our confidence statements all involve the dependent variable at several levels of the *intended weight*, X.   Some logical restraint is necessary when interpreting confidence statements lest conclusions be drawn erroneously about the actual weight of sugar used, no information about that physical variable being available in the data.

Whether or not such experimental measuring techniques make sense is a matter for the chemist to decide.   To measure the amount of sugar poured out rather than to attempt to pour out a predetermined amount of sugar seems to involve about the same amount of work at the analytical balance.   The latter technique, however, deliberately discards any information about the precision of the analytical weighings in order to gain efficiency in subsequent calculations by providing nice simple numbers.   If some feel the price worth paying, then we can scarce say nay.

Many laboratory experiments fit into this mathematical framework.

Much automatic testing equipment records the values of the dependent variable when the independent variable reaches one of several predetermined values. Thus we may warm up a rod of standard length until it expands enough to close a contact, or record the temperature of a distillation column bottom when a predetermined weight of distillate has been collected, or measure the light intensity at each of several wavelength settings on a spectrophotometer. In all such experiments, the independent variable is not measured, it is preset; we merely record a hypothetical numerical value which we hope corresponds rather closely to the value actually produced.

This mathematical model of an experiment in which the independent variable is preassigned rather than measured prevails throughout all chemical control laboratories, where routine measurements predominate. The fact that it differs from our other (x, y) models was brought forcibly to the attention of the statistical world in 1951 by Joseph Berkson, M.D., in a voluminous correspondence which culminated in his paper "Are There Two Regressions?" [4]. The tenacity, to use no stronger term, with which he beat down a sizable group of statistical friends and finally made them see that this model was both important and unique has more than justified our reference to the *Berksonian line.*

SECTION 3: MODIFIED MODELS FOR ONE DEPENDENT VARIABLE

Most of the useful results presented thus far were derived from a mathematical model assuming the existence of an unknown line which represents a true functional relationship between x and y. We further assume that the observed points deviate from this line because each y observation contains errors which are *added* on to its true value and which are themselves random normally distributed variates with zero mean and a constant, if unknown, variance. These are stringent assumptions, and although much information may be extracted from our data when they are realistic, nevertheless they are frequently not realistic, and if we force our experiment into an unsympathetic mold, the answers we get may not be good. Then, too, the squaring and summing, basic in the least-squares technique, are fairly slow arithmetical procedures and ones that deal in quantities dimensionally incompatible with our imagination. We would prefer methods requiring less work and using measures of dispersion in the same units as the raw data—provided, of course, we suffer no great loss of information by adopting these more attractive techniques.

In the search for more general models, one of the first changes to tempt us is to allow the errors to be random variables from a *finite* population of

N numbers with a zero mean and unknown variance, σ^2. Much of the algebraic analysis and arithmetic is unchanged. Exact tests for significance are either complicated or unavailable, but the normal ones can be used for good approximate answers, as the assumption of normality does not enter very critically into these tests, and almost any reasonable finite population may be invoked without vitiating the analyses given for the standard assumption. By the same token, no simplification is achieved with this model, just possibly a closer degree of conformity between the model and reality. We shall discuss an example with this model later.

The use of variance as a measure of dispersion, especially distasteful to the neophyte, may be avoided by substituting a function of the *range*. These techniques extract less information from a given amount of data, but the savings in time and convenience which they often effect may justify their use, especially if the data are cheap, and hence a greater number may be used to compensate for the loss in extraction efficiency. The tests for significance again have an underlying assumption of normality. We presently give an example using the Nair and Shrivastava method for fitting lines.

The assumption of normality may be banished entirely by non-parametric tests, or it may be replaced by other common distributions like the binomial, Poisson, or rectangular. Most of the useful non-parametric tests developed thus far are based on rank order of data, i.e., whether a datum is larger or smaller than another, rather than by how much. Naturally some information is lost, but the restriction of a normal underlying population is also banished, and the price may be worth paying, especially if there is strong evidence that the experimental data could not have sprung from a normal parent. The Kendall-slope method exhibited in this chapter is an example of this type of analysis.

The Nair and Shrivastava method

In contrast to the rather elaborate and somewhat formal techniques used earlier, we now wish to propose several quick-but-not-too-dirty schemes for fitting a straight line and for estimating, at least roughly, about how far this line should be pushed or shoved before it can no longer be credibly believed to be the line from whence sprang the data at hand. Perhaps some other exposition might more logically occupy this place, but we feel that the extreme contrast deserves the juxtaposition. Our method for fitting consists of four rules:

1. Divide the data points into three equal groups (in order of increasing x).

2. Find the mass center (centroid) of each of the two end groups, as well as the mass center of *all* the points.

3. Find the slope of the line connecting the mass centers of the two end groups. This will be the *slope* of the final fitted line.

4. Pass the line through the mass center $(x., y.)$ of all the data points, parallel to the line connecting the mass centers of the two end groups.

Most methods require that the line of best fit go through the center of gravity of the data points, as evidenced by the equation $y. = a + bx.$ in the standard procedure. This criterion is simple and logical, and it is difficult to envision a simpler one to replace it. The determination of the slope of the best line is another problem, and it is here that the various methods differ. If the experimenter *knows* his lines are straight, and if he is not interested in additional information which intermediate points would give him, the optimum procedure for determining a line is to take half the observations at the smallest possible value of x and the other half at the largest (assuming still that the errors made are independent of x or y). Usually, however, the data are not taken in this way, either because the experimenter is not really convinced of the linearity of his system (and rightly so!), or because some information about the dispersion of the data around the line as a function of x or y is desired. Whatever the reason, the man who computes is usually faced with a set of data which are stretched out along what is fondly hoped will be a straight line. To determine a slope from these data, a simple division into groups, each containing half the points, will clearly give two mass centers, and the slope of the line connecting these centers bears a close resemblance to the slope of the parental line. Also these centers are located as precisely as is possible in the sense that as many data points were used for each as could reasonably be used.

Why, then, does not our process simply divide the points into two equal groups; why do we "throw away" the middle third? If we ignore the middle third, we lose on the precision with which our two mass centers are located, but we gain in that these centers are pushed farther apart, so their loss in precision of location is compensated for by having a greater moment, by being out farther where a deviation has less effect on the slope. Carried to extremes, we could determine a slope by the two end data points. Here we achieve the maximum separation but also the maximum instability of our mass centers (which are merely the two points themselves). Nair and Shrivastava [27] showed that the optimum balance of these two opposing criteria for a best determination of the slope is achieved by the division of the points into three equal groups. If the standard model of normally distributed errors in y is assumed, Nair and Shrivastava showed that the sampling variance of the slope determined by this method is only a little larger (i.e., less precise) than that of the slope determined by least squares.*

Two minor difficulties may arise in applying this procedure: First, the total number of points may not be divisible by three, in which case we round the fraction $n/3$ to the nearest integer and count in from each end by that number.   Secondly, there may be several data points at one value of x and the division between groups may fall on that value, demanding that some of the points be classed as belonging to the end group and the rest to the center one. Obviously we must either deviate from our optimum division of $n/3$ by putting all the values in one group or the other (safe when n is large, as the efficiency of this procedure is a fairly flat function of p, the size of the end group, near its maximum), or we must assign the proper number of points to each group by some random procedure.   For small values of n we prefer assignation.   One simple way would be to imagine, temporarily, that we alter the identical x coordinates of these points by adding small random increments, $\Delta x = RD/10^9$, RD being random digits between 0 and 99 chosen from a table of random numbers, thereby ordering these points in their x dimension.   We may then count in from the end until our proper integral value p is reached and thus the division of the points has been effected.   When we compute the mass centers and any further statistics, we, of course, use the true x coordinates and not the temporarily fudged ones that allowed the separation.

For the example of Chapter 2, breaking the data points into groups of size 3, 4, and 3 gives a slope estimate (for the data with a rough line already removed) of

$$b_c = -\frac{0.233}{30.50} = -0.0076$$

so that

$$b = 0.9924.$$

The value of the mean, μ, by this procedure is identical with the least-squares fit—they both give y. as the best estimate (22.86), or *zero* on the reduced plot.

If we fit a line by this method and then desire an estimate of the residual variance about that line, we can get it:

---

* The conventional way of expressing this comparison is to give the ratio of the sampling variance of the normal statistic to the one being examined, this ratio being called the *efficiency* of the estimate.   If the underlying distribution is normal and the n data points are equally spaced in x, the efficiency equals $\dfrac{\sigma_b^2 \text{ (normal)}}{\sigma_b^2 \text{ (Nair)}} = \dfrac{8}{9} \cdot \dfrac{n^2}{n^2 - 1}$, and is thus at least 89 per cent.

1. By dividing the sum of the squared residuals of all the n points from the line by $(n - 11/8 - 9/8n^2)$, which is nearly $n - 11/8$ for any practical problem.

2. By dividing the sum of the squared residuals of the points in the two groups used to determine the slope by $(p - 1)[2 + (p + 1)/(12p^2)]$ which is nearly $2(n/3 - 1) + 1/12$ if p is approximately equal to $n/3$; p is the number of points in each of the extreme groups.

3. By removing the line, randomly dividing the points into m groups of n points, adding up the *ranges* of the m groups, and dividing this total range, W, by the constants m and d_n [the expected value of the range in a sample sized n from a $N(0; 1)$ population]. The estimate is of the standard deviation.

Note that these first two procedures lose the no-squares advantage, which the method otherwise possesses, and constitute a heavy mark against the technique whenever the residual variance is computed—and it usually is, or should be, wanted. The third procedure has the operational virtue of being easy to do graphically—vertical residuals from the fitted line being directly involved (rather than their squares)—but its exact statistical properties are not completely understood and it cannot be recommended as orthodox. It is merely offered as a fairly obvious rangized stop-gap procedure which will hopefully soon be replaced by a more exact one. Tables of d_n are available (Appendix Table 14), and a general discussion of the efficient division of N data into m groups of n for standard deviation estimation has been given by Noether [28]. He recommends $6 \leqslant n \leqslant 10$, with 8 being optimal unless it would cause too many data to be discarded.

Confidence Limits

We now ask about how far the line can be tilted before becoming so steep (or flat) that it is unlikely to have been the line from which the observed data arose. We may also inquire about how far the line may be shoved away from the mass center of all the data before it again becomes incredible. In other words, we are inquiring about confidence limits on β and μ in the equation

$$y = \mu + \beta(x - x.).$$

We shall not attempt to give any exhaustive treatment involving joint confidence regions for these two parameters but will merely discuss the setting of limits on each individually.

First let us consider the mean, μ. If we subtract the fitted line from the data points, we have left a plot of residuals; the points are now scattered about the x axis instead of about the line (Figure 24).   If we further project all the points on to the y axis, we have a group of points in a vertical line, with a mean value at the origin.   This same configuration could be achieved by projecting all the points onto the y axis by lines parallel to the fitted line.   The points are now all estimates of the origin, that is, the place all the points would be were it not that they all possess errors.   The question of how far the line may be shoved away from the mass center then becomes another question: How far from the origin could a point on

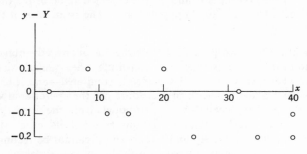

Figure 24

the y axis be and still be a plausible true value giving rise to these observed (projected) points?   The classical answer is given in terms of the mean value (here zero) and the Studentized estimates of the deviation of that mean (the t test), but we wish to avoid squared numbers and hence will apply techniques using the *range* of the sample, or even just a count of the points above or below the origin.

If the data scatter rather widely, a graphical projection scheme works well enough.   If, however, the data cling closely to a line, all the techniques, graphical and numerical, classical or modified, are made easier by the removal of an approximate line—reducing the data to cluster approximately around the x axis.   If we do this and then plot the residuals, we may expand the vertical scale until graphical techniques give rather nice precision, and in the numerical procedures the size of the numbers which must subsequently be dealt with is materially reduced, usually to the point where a slide rule will suffice.   If we remove $Y_i = A + Bx_i$ from the data, choosing A and B as compromises between good estimates and numbers which are easy to handle—thereby avoiding heavy arithmetic— we get data $(x, y - Y)$ for which a fitted line should have nearly zero slope and zero mean.   Furthermore, when we fit either graphically or numerically to find the small slope and mean, these numbers merely add on as correction terms to the values of A and B we used in our approximate line, although we must remember either to correct our approximate line to the form $y = M + B(x - x.)$ before combining or, conversely, to convert our fitted increments to the form $y - Y = a + bx$. [Note that removing a line is *not* equivalent to rotating the (x, y) data until they lie nearly along the x axis.]

Confidence limits on β are set by analogous but more complicated techniques. Roughly stated, we remove a line we feel to be plausible, thereby reducing the two end groups of points to two groups clustering near the x axis. We then project these two groups onto a common vertical line and ask whether one group mean is significantly higher than the other. If the answer is "just significant at the 5 per cent level," we have found the critical value of the slope in that direction. The other limit is found analogously by allowing the group that was just significantly higher to become just significantly lower. This is a way of describing the basic ideas, but it is not the way to carry them out.

No-squares: The use of ranges

The classical confidence limits all invoke a sample standard deviation, s, which is not only an estimate of the underlying population standard deviation, σ, but also a yardstick against which various contemplated values for the parameters μ and β are to be measured for plausibility. But s is not the only useful estimate of σ—indeed, because of the arithmetic involved, in some circles it enjoys psychological disadvantages.

The simplest estimator of the population standard deviation is the *range* of the sample divided by d_N, the expected value of the range in a sample of size N from a normal population with unit variance. Since this estimator becomes inefficient for large samples because of the instability of the range when about 15 or more observations are involved, a slightly modified procedure is usually recommended. The large sample, sized N, is broken up *randomly* into m subgroups of size n, where n is usually from 6 to 10 and is chosen so that as few observations, l, as possible are omitted (N being equal to $nm + l$). The ranges of the m subgroups are then added to give a statistic, W, which can be divided by $m\,d_n$ for an estimate of σ. (Still more efficient estimators have been proposed by Cox* which use the mean of subgroup ranges—but they are considerably more complex and approach the standard deviation in computational labor, as well as in statistical efficiency.)

Most confidence limit procedures that use s have a rangized version

* D. R. Cox, "The Use of the Range in Sequential Analysis," *J. Royal Stat. Soc.*, **B11** (1949), 101–114.

involving W—with the difference that the stability of W depends strictly on two parameters, m and n, and that of s depends only on the sample size, N.   Lord [23] tables the essential statistics for the commoner rangized tests, and Wallace, Kurtz, Noether, and others have recast his tables for more expedient use.   Noether, in particular, reduced the tables, with a slight loss in accuracy, to a single parameter, ν, equal to $m(n - 1)$ in an analogue to the familiar degrees of freedom of s.   In the following paragraphs we set forth our preferred form for obtaining confidence limits using W, the requisite tables appearing in the Appendix.

Confidence limits for means or sums via ranges

If a group of points are arranged in order on a scale, we may test an arbitrary guess for the mean of the normal population from which they may have been derived by a statistic, $u(1, n)$, which is the rangized analogue of the t test.   Here

$$u(1, n) = \frac{|x. - M| d_n \sqrt{n}}{W(1, n)};$$

$x.$ is the sample mean and $W(1, n)$ is the range of our sample of n numbers, whereas d_n is the expected value of the range of a sample of n from a normal population with unit variance.   (The symbol $W(m, n)$ stands for the mean value of m ranges each referring to a subsample of size n.   If m is one, then W is the range of the entire sample, and the symbolism becomes redundant.   We shall shortly have occasion for other values of m, however, and hence we introduce a systematic notation here.)   Lord [23] has tabled percentage points of $u_\epsilon(m, n)$.   If our computed value of u is larger than u_ϵ, we can expect that our assertion that M is a possible value for μ will be right less than ϵ per cent of the time.   For greater calculational convenience, we employ a companion statistic

$$\frac{|x. - M|}{W(1, n)} \geqslant \frac{u_\epsilon(1, n)}{d_n \sqrt{n}} = \tau_\epsilon. \tag{44}$$

A table of $\tau_\epsilon(n)$ is given in the Appendix (Table 4).   Our problem, then, is to shove our line up or down until we move the projection of the residuals just far enough so that our already determined best estimate of μ is no longer plausible as a population mean from which the shifted points could have arisen by random sampling.   (In our example μ is nearly zero since we have removed an approximate line.)   The table gives 0.186 as a value of $\tau_{10}(10)$ and $W(1, 10)$ is 0.260, so that equation (44) gives

$$|x. - M| = \tau_{10}(10) \cdot W(1, 10) = 0.048.$$

Thus we may move the group of points by ± 0.05, since this moving of the line parallel to itself cannot change the range of the sample of residual projections.

If the number of points is larger than 12 or 15, we should use a test involving $W(m, n)$ rather than $W(1, n)$ such as

$$u(m, n) = \frac{|x. - M|d_n\sqrt{mn}}{W(m, n)} m.$$

Here the useful table contains the right-hand part of the rearranged statistic

$$\frac{|x. - M|}{W(m, n)} \geqslant \frac{u_\epsilon(m, n)}{d_n\sqrt{mnm}} = T_\epsilon(N),$$

provided we can decide on a unique (m, n) split for every N. Noether [28] gives such a split, and so T need only be read from Appendix Table 5, multiplied by W, and the limits for μ are done!

To *compare two samples*, we may more conveniently use their *sums* than their *means*, and the corresponding statistic would then be multiplied by N.

Slope confidence limits

For confidence limits on β we must alter the slope of our line, but always passing it through the centroid $(x., y.)$ of all the data points. If the data points are plotted (as they usually are when division into three groups is attempted), we may lay down a trial line by a T-square and triangle, noting the value of the intercept on some convenient vertical line—perhaps the y axis. Then we shift the line *parallel* to itself until the line has passed over all the points of one of the groups except the last one. When it contains the last one, we note the intercept on our standard ordinate. Do the same for all four extreme deviates, two for each of the groups. The differences between the intercepts for the two extreme deviates in each group give the ranges of the two groups *for the slope we are trying*. Also project the mean values of these two groups, which were found in fitting the best slope. The test is

$$u_\epsilon(2, p) = \frac{|x_1. - x_2.|d_p\sqrt{p}}{\dfrac{w_1 + w_2}{2}\sqrt{2}} \equiv \frac{|x_1. - x_2.|}{w_1 + w_2} d_p\sqrt{2p},$$

where $u_\epsilon(2, p)$ is tabled by Lord [23] and w_1 and w_2 are the two ranges. For our purposes we may rewrite the test as

$$\frac{|x_1. - x_2.|}{w_1 + w_2} \geqslant \frac{u_\epsilon(2, p)}{d_p\sqrt{2p}} = r_\epsilon(p).$$

The statistic $r_\epsilon(p)$ is given briefly in Appendix Table 6. To use it, we multiply the sum of the two ranges by $r_\epsilon(p)$ and then adjust our slope until the difference between the projections of the two mean values is equal to this product. The symbol ϵ is the percentage chance of making a mistake if we assert that β is too far from the best value to be credible, and p is the number of points in each of the two groups whose means are being compared. For our problem,

$$p = 3$$
$$r = 0.487$$
$$w_1 = 0.16 \qquad w_2 = 0.10$$
$$x_1. - x_2. = 0.127$$

so that graphically we find

$$B_1 = 0.9882 \quad \text{and} \quad B_2 = 0.9966.$$

Although the two ranges, w_1 and w_2, are functions of the fitted slope, b, they change very slowly near the correct value for b and probably need be computed at most twice unless a large scatter in the data causes the limits for β to be rather wide.

It should also be noted that for large numbers of data ($p \geqslant 15$) we may wish to use the multiple division of *each* group into m subgroups of n—thus leading to a test of

$$u_\epsilon(2m, n) \leqslant \frac{|x_1. - x_2.| \sqrt{2p}\, md_n}{W_d},$$

where

$$W_d = W_1 + W_2 = \sum_i^{2m} w_i,$$

which may be usefully rearranged into

$$\frac{|x_1. - x_2.|}{W_d} \geqslant \frac{u_\epsilon(2m, n)}{d_n m \sqrt{2p}} = R_\epsilon(p)$$

and $R_\epsilon(p)$ is tabled in the Appendix (Table 7).

If this work is being done numerically, it is necessary to compute $Y_i = m + B(x_i - x.)$ or perhaps $Y_i = A + Bx_i$ for each x_i and to subtract this from the actual y_i, giving a column of $y_i - Y_i$ to be examined for a largest and smallest in each group, thereby producing a range for each group. The test may then be performed using either differences of the *means* of each group of $y_i - Y_i$, or the *sums*, the factor of p being absorbed into the significance test. Wallace [34] has prepared a table for this use of Lord's tests, and it differs from the table of r_ϵ in this book merely by being

$$p\, r_\epsilon(p) \equiv \sqrt{\frac{p}{2}} \frac{u_\epsilon(2, p)}{d_p}.$$

Low-Arithmetic Methods

In the arsenal of the practical statistician we find several extremely simple analytical techniques known as *Low-Arithmetic Methods*. They use less than one arithmetic operation per datum. Again the normal assumption underlies their structure, but their simplicity makes them attractive for some applications, and we feel that this is a good place to introduce two of the appropriate tests.

The midrange test

If we wish to set confidence limits on μ, the mean value of the true line, we consider the group of residuals projected down the best line that we can fit (or projected across to the y axis after a reasonably good approximate line has been removed). The problem then is to decide just how far the population mean may reasonably be from the location of the sample mean. The previous tests used the arithmetic mean (or sum) and the range in an analogue of the classical t test. Here we use the midrange, the average of the extreme values, as our central measure, and again use the range as the measure of scatter. Walsh [39] has given tables for various improbable levels of the statistic

$$D = \left(\frac{x_n + x_1}{2} - \mu_0\right)\Big/ w$$

(where x_1 is the smallest observation and x_n the largest in a sample of n), and Tukey [34] has modified these tables so that it is unnecessary even to compute the midrange; rather we set the limits, M, by measuring off from the extreme variates themselves. We reproduce this table in the Appendix (Table 8), giving the factor $s_\epsilon(n)$ by which the range, w, must be multiplied to produce a distance which we lay off from the extreme values to give confidence limits for the mean of the sample. For small samples these distances are laid off outside the sample, i.e., away from the center, while for the larger samples we get closer limits so that the distances must be laid off *toward* the center from the extreme value. The table clearly indicates which direction must be taken.

The simplification follows from noting that Walsh's quantity Dw is to be laid off from the midrange and hence the upper limit becomes

$$\frac{x_1 + x_n}{2} + Dw = \frac{2x_n - (x_n - x_1)}{2} + Dw = x_n + (D - \tfrac{1}{2})w.$$

If we wish to start at x_n, we must lay off $(D - \tfrac{1}{2})w$, proceeding away from the center of the sample. Similarly $(\tfrac{1}{2} - D)w$ is to be laid off toward the center for larger samples. Our tabled quantity, $s_\epsilon(n)$, is $(D - \tfrac{1}{2})$ or $(\tfrac{1}{2} - D)$. The instability of the extreme values in larger samples restricts the usefulness of this test.

In our example n equals 10 and at the 10 per cent level of significance $s_{10}(10)$ is 0.28—and is to be applied inside the extreme values. Multiplying by our range 0.260, we find that the distance 0.073 gives the confidence limits -0.092 and 0.022 for the population mean, which is estimated by a midrange of -0.035 in a scale translated so that y. is zero. Since the efficiency of this test drops rather rapidly as n increases beyond 6 or 8, we do not recommend using it for samples larger than the 10 provided for in the table.

In addition to this test, which is particularly simple to apply, there are others of the same type with slightly greater complexity. Walsh [39] lists several, two of which we quote here as typical. For a sample of 6, limits on the population mean may be set by

$$\left. \begin{array}{l} \mu_{\text{upper}} = 0.63x_6 + 0.37x_5 \\ \mu_{\text{lower}} = 0.63x_1 + 0.37x_2 \end{array} \right\} \text{ giving symmetrical 5 per cent limits}$$

$$\left. \begin{array}{l} \mu_{\text{upper}} = 1.06x_6 - 0.06x_1 \\ \mu_{\text{lower}} = 1.06x_1 - 0.06x_6 \end{array} \right\} \text{ giving symmetrical 2 per cent limits}$$

where x_6 is the largest variate value, x_1 the smallest. Both of these tests are about 98 per cent efficient on normal populations, and the significance level for the first one is always between 3.1 per cent and 6.2 per cent for *any symmetrical* population provided the observations are independent. The observations do not even have to come from the *same* symmetrical populations. These tests, then, dispense with the normality requirement at the cost of letting the significance level slide about a bit.

The gap test for slope

For our second low-arithmetic test we consider a method for setting limits on slopes of lines. Since the fundamental test is whether or not two groups of data could have arisen from populations with the same mean, we remove the middle third of our data points and then ask whether the two end thirds form groups with the same mean when they are projected down the fitted line onto the y axis. The critical slopes are those that will just cause the two end groups of points to appear significantly different when they are projected along these slopes to the y axis. The geometry of this test is precisely the same as in the rangized test utilizing the statistic $r_\epsilon(p)$, but the low-arithmetic test is simpler to apply—if harder to explain!

If two samples are arranged along a scale, and if they do not overlap, we suspect that they did *not* come from the same population, more precisely, that they did not come from populations with identical means. A measure of the separation of the two samples is k, the distance between the interior extreme values of the two samples (see Figure 25 for two con-figurations, the first sample being plotted above the line and the second below it). Since no simple nomenclature seems to be available to describe exactly which two extreme values are meant (although a glance at a picture makes this immediately clear), we shall refer to *crossovermost* values. This terminology becomes especially descriptive when the samples are large and—although different—overlap slightly so that the distance k becomes a negative number. The statistic to be computed is

$$k = \frac{y_{21} - y_{1p}}{w_1 + w_2}$$

where y_{1p} and y_{21} are the crossovermost values of the two samples and w_1 and w_2 are the ranges of the two samples—both of which have p members.

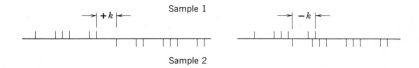

Figure 25

Tables have been computed by Link [34] which are reproduced in this book (Appendix Table 9) giving critical values of $k_\epsilon(p)$. If

$$y_{21} - y_{1p} \geq (w_1 + w_2)k_\epsilon(p),$$

our assertion that the two samples are different will be wrong less than ϵ per cent of the time. In our problem p is 3 and $k_{10}(3)$ is 0.00 so that the gap between the crossovermost values should be exactly zero to achieve significance at the 10 per cent level (symmetrical 5 per cent limits). We therefore look for those slopes through the mass center of our data that just allow the extreme data from the projected end groups to coincide. Thus we find 10 per cent confidence limits for β to be 0.9883 and 0.9972.

Non-parametric Methods

If we are seriously bothered by the assumption that the residual variation about the true regression line is a random variable which is *normally* dis-tributed, we can seek the solace of non-parametric methods. The price we pay is a lower statistical efficiency—more data are needed for the same degree of assurance than would be needed if the normal assumption could be made. This is to be expected, however, as the more information we assume, the more there is to be extracted. If our assumptions are realistic, our conclusions will be valid and valuable; if our assumptions are grossly incorrect, the conclusions we reach will bear a warped reflection of that wrong information.   Any good method of data analysis will strive in the right direction; not only will it give an honest answer to an honest question, but it will also attempt to give an honest answer to a warped question. The degree of influence that the warping has on the answer varies widely with the methods.   In non-parametric techniques this influence is quite small, because the specific assumptions are both rather more general and more frequently satisfied than are those of the classical normal model.

More specifically, with non-parametric methods we must answer the same questions as before: From what sort of reasonable population could this sample have arisen?   And again, is it credible that these two samples came from a common population?   But whereas we previously character-ized those underlying populations by the mean and variance of a normal distribution, we now tend to rely on medians as measures of central tendency; and dispersion is not measured directly for the population but is only referred to in specific samples where it is apt to be measured by the range.   Thus we often find tests restricted to symmetrical populations with continuous frequency functions, a very general class of distributions indeed, although certainly not all-inclusive.   Order statistics tend to replace variates—a datum is valued only for its position in the sample rather than for exactly how far up or down on a scale it occurs.   This allows a class of tests which are rather insensitive to the shape of the popu-lation frequency function, as long as it satisfies rather general require-ments of good behavior (like symmetry, perhaps).   Since we frequently know our data cannot reasonably follow a normal distribution, we grate-fully use these other tests, although they may be of less power and occasionally require as much labor as the classical ones.

The sign test for limits on μ

The most generally useful test for comparing two samples, or one sample with a hypothetical population, is the sign test.   If we wish to test the hypothesis that a sample of n came from a population with a zero median, we see how many values, r, in the sample exceed zero.   Since, if the hypothesis is true, the probability of obtaining a sample with exactly r such values is $\binom{n}{r}\left(\frac{1}{2}\right)^n$, the probability of obtaining a sample with r_ϵ or more values greater than zero is

$$\Pr\left(r > r_\epsilon\right) = \sum_{=r_\epsilon}^{n} \binom{n}{j}\left(\frac{1}{2}\right)^n = \epsilon.$$

If n is small, this probability can be easily computed, or we may refer to tables of the cumulative binomial distribution which are now generally available.*

This technique may be used to set confidence limits for μ in our straight-line fitting if we are willing to accept the *median* of our distribution as equivalent to the *mean* (which it is for any symmetrical distribution). After removing the best line from the data (or an approximate line) and projecting the plotted residuals over to the y axis, we ask how far this group of points could be moved up or down until it is no longer reasonable to expect them to have been drawn from a population having zero for a

median. In other words, for what value of r_ϵ is $\sum\limits_{j=r_\epsilon}^{n} \binom{n}{j} \left(\frac{1}{2}\right)^n$ equal to ϵ?

If we wish symmetrical 10 per cent limits, then ϵ is 0.05, and a glance at a binomial table will show that for $n = 10$, r_ϵ lies between 8 and 9, interpolation giving 8.1. Thus, if the median is really zero, we could expect to find 8.1 or more of our 10 observations greater than zero 5 per cent of the time merely by random chance. Any greater number of positive observations would occur less than 5 per cent of the time, so—at the 5 per cent level—we would reject the hypothesis if our sample contained more than 8.1 positive observations. By the same argument, 1.9 *or fewer* positive observations (i.e., 8.1 or more negative ones) are equally improbable and will again cause the hypothesis to be rejected at the 5 per cent level.

To set confidence limits, M, on the mean, μ, of the unknown true line, we may slide our fitted line parallel to itself until 8.1 of the residual points are above the line. Then it is just credible (at the 5 per cent error level) that such a value for μ is possible. The other limit is found by sliding the fitted line until 8.1 points lie below the line. The two values are symmetrical 10 per cent confidence limits for μ.

Appendix Table 10 instructs us to count in from the end datum, calling that one *zero*, until we reach the tabular value (1.9 for our example). This curious method of counting arises from an apparent indeterminacy common to all order statistics tests. Our sign test table was computed by asking, "What is the probability that no more than one observation out of a sample of n will fall by chance to the right of the population median?" The binomial theorem answered this question, as well as the several others for zero, two, three, etc. observations out of n. Then an interpolation to the required levels of probability gave the figures in Appendix Table 10.

If we look at Figure 26, we see that a contemplated median, M, can be placed

* *Tables of the Binomial Probability Distribution*, U.S. National Bureau of Standards, AMS 6 (1950).

anywhere between the two adjacent sample values and still give rise to the same probability answer to the question, "What is the chance that this sample would have been observed if the true median is located at M?" A sample of ten points will have one or none to the right of M about 1.1 per cent of the time, whereas *two* or fewer can occur naturally in about 5.5 per cent of such samples. The reader may wonder whether to place 5.5 per cent limits at the second or third points from the right in a sample of ten—or somewhere between—since the probability of observing such a sample is the same wherever the true median may be located within this range.

This apparent indeterminacy may be removed by reverting to the definition of a confidence limit. If we choose to place our limit at M, and then assert that the true median lies to the left, this statement can be wrong only if the median lies to the right of M_1. But then *one* point at most lies to the right of the median —a configuration which occurs naturally about 1.1 per cent of the time—and

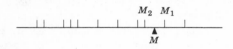

Figure 26

hence M_1 is a 1.1 per cent confidence limit. The same argument shows M_2 to be the 5.5 per cent confidence limit. Therefore some sort of interpolation (linear is presumably good enough for practical work) will yield 5 per cent limits slightly to the right of M_2.

For our numerical example, the sign test brackets the population mean with the values -0.077 and 0.082 at the 10 per cent error level on the reduced scale, corresponding to limits of 22.783 and 22.942 in the original.

The sign test is quick and easy to apply, but there are two objections to it. For small samples the number of available exact significance levels is very limited, and for large samples it extracts a rather small amount of the information available (64 per cent and up). In the discussion just given we have referred to the 1.9th value, an impossible statement if taken literally, but we meant that position given by linear interpolation between the first and second values. There are fine points about this interpretation which may be quibbled with, but no better procedure has been proposed and so we shall stick with this one. To some degree interpolation overcomes the small sample objection to the sign test by providing approximate significance levels between the exact ones at integer values of r. The large sample objection, inefficiency, is more serious because it is irremovable. Thus, if the sample size n is greater than ten, we are tempted to use a longer but more efficient test due originally to Wilcoxon [40] and modified by Tukey [34].

Confidence limits using Wilcoxon's procedure

Mathematically, this process requires that we form the arithmetic mean of *all possible pairs* from the sample whose parental population median is to be confidenced.   We then rank these means in order of magnitude and count in from either end by the number of means indicated in Appendix Table 11.   Again interpolation to fractional values is used in counting, the extreme mean is scored as *zero*, the next one as *one*, and so forth.   The critical values depend on the sample size and the degree of confidence desired.   Since we need count only a fairly small number from each end, we have only to find those means, and fortunately there is a graphical procedure which makes this feasible.   We arrange the sample of *n* points

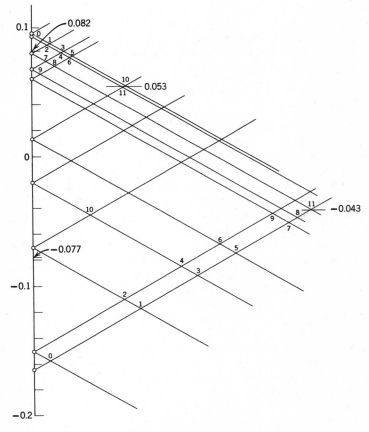

Figure 27. Wilcoxon's limits

along a scale (Figure 27) and then form the means graphically by laying off an array of parallel lines from all the points (or all the ones near the ends if the sample is large) at some convenient angle, say 45°.   Then we lay off another array of parallel lines at an angle to the scale supplementary to the first.   The intersections are the means required, and we need count in from the extreme only the number indicated in Appendix Table 11, remembering to tally the first point as zero.   In our problem, the 10 per cent critical value for a sample of 10 is 10.8.   We thus establish our limits at −0.043 and 0.053.   If we alter m, we merely shift the entire pattern, so that by making m equal to 22.816 or 22.914 we find that one of our limits for the population median has become zero.   Thus we establish these values of m as limits for μ.   This Wilcoxon procedure is laborious when compared with the sign test, but it is 95 per cent efficient or better, i.e., it gives limits as close as would be obtained by the t test with only 95 per cent as many points, assuming that we compare the two tests on a normal population.   It is somewhat less work than the t test, is almost as efficient, and is denormalized.

Confidence limits for β

To obtain denormalized confidence limits for β we have a number of techniques available.   If we are to follow our previous philosophy, we must test two batches of points—residuals from the two end thirds of the data—to see whether we believe them to come from a common population. This hypothesis may be examined by several methods.   Before we look at these procedures, however, we shall leave our previous philosophy and consider a new one—that the value of x does not affect the value of a residual if the proper slope has been removed.   Using this hypothesis, we then see that if *all possible pairs of residual points* are connected by line segments, these segments should slope positively or negatively with equal probability.   Thus a generalization of the sign test can be used on these slopes.   If we change all the residuals by removing a line with a different slope, the *slopes of the line segments* connecting the residuals will all be changed by the *same* amount, i.e., the slope of the line removed.   This suggests a procedure in which we lay off such slopes from a common origin, done most expediently on thin graph or tracing paper, and then count in from each end by a critical value found in Appendix Table 12. Again this is a procedure in which the counting begins with zero for the extreme slope, one for the next, etc.   Tukey [34] calls this the *Kendall-slope* method.   Note that we cannot use this method when we have several values of y and one value of x unless some modification is made, as the presence of the vertical slopes becomes embarrassing.   By the same

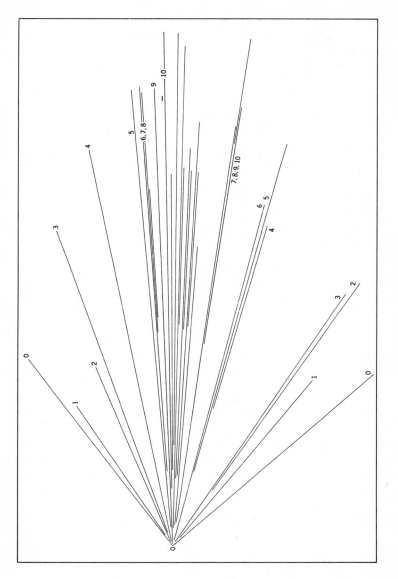

Figure 28. Kendall slope

token, data in which the x values occur closely clustered in several groups do not recommend themselves for this type of analysis. Perhaps the median of each cluster could be used instead of the individual points, but we know no formal procedure for this purpose. In our example Figure 28 shows the graphical treatment in which we have replaced the last two points by their mean value, and 10 per cent limits (9.6 for $n = 9$) lead to confidence slopes of -0.0076 and 0.0011 for the line fitting the residuals, or 0.9848 and 0.9935 for β.

Comparing two samples—Kendall sum

There is a procedure for comparing two samples suspected of originating in the same population that bears a great resemblance to the Kendall slope. It is the Kendall sum and is based on the hypothesis that the sample in which any particular datum happens to find itself has no influence on the value of that datum. We therefore form *all possible* pairs, provided one datum of each pair is in each sample. Graphically, we may think of the two samples as plotted vertically on nearby ordinates, and then the various pair comparisons correspond to the slopes of the lines connecting them. Again, all possible slopes are to be laid off from a common origin, and again a table (Appendix Table 13) is to be entered, but with the sizes of both samples this time, and the factor read that is to be used in counting in from the extreme slopes. Again the extreme slope tallies as zero, the next as one, etc. If the confidence limits thus achieved do not enclose the horizontal line, we conclude that the two samples are different. By shifting the two samples until one or the other of the confidence lines is horizontal, we measure the possible discrepancy between the two population medians, i.e., we set confidence limits for their difference. In our example, this shifting corresponds to removing a line with a different slope, which not only will shift the projections of the two end groups of residuals but will also warp them slightly—so that a simple shift is not an exact test. Rather than replot the residuals for a number of different lines, however, we depend on the smallness of this warping to let us ignore it—a smallness that is realistic if the line being shifted is nearly horizontal.

Thus the Kendall-sum procedure may be used to compare the residuals from the two end thirds of the data points analogously to the low-arithmetic and rangized methods used earlier. Also we have here no objection to multiple values of y for a given x, and bunching is not considered embarrassing. Slightly more labor is involved, as the two groups must be projected to the common ordinates. We do not know the relative power of the two procedures but suspect that no serious discrepancy will be found between them. Our example has only three points in each group, and the minimum for which critical tables exist is four, so we have not applied the Kendall-sum technique here.

Run test and rank order tests

An entirely different type of test which could be used to compare the two samples of residual points (end thirds of the data) is a run test. If we rank these two samples together on a single ordinate, keeping track from which sample each datum comes, we obtain a single array possessing several properties useful for testing the hypothesis that both samples spring from similar parent distributions. One such statistic is the number of runs, or number of sequences of adjacent points from the same sample, which are found in the whole roster (Figure 29). Clearly if these are too

Figure 29. Two samples plotted on the same scale showing ten runs.

few, the samples will tend to be different. If the samples are nearly the same, the data from one sample will be interspersed with those from the other sample, creating numerous runs. This test is sensitive to both location and scale (dispersion) differences between the parent populations. If the medians of the two populations are widely different, we would get only two groups of points, the first sample, then the second. Also, if the first population were much more compact than the second, we would tend to get most of the first sample bunched closely together in the middle of the roster, again reducing the number of runs. This type of test has been tabled by Swed and Eisenhart [31], but it does not seem suitable for setting confidence limits, as there is no easy way to predict the changes in the number of runs obtained when the two samples are slipped slowly past one another—the procedure used to obtain all our confidence limits for two-sample comparisons.

The other statistic is obtained by giving a rank order number to each datum in the combined sample and then separating the points into their original group and tallying the scores they now carry, the smaller number being the one we examine. Again critical values are available (Mann and Whitney [25], Wilcoxon [40]), and again, for the same reasons as before, it seems difficult to use the procedure to set confidence limits, although to test a specific pair of samples once is not too laborious.

Joint distribution-free confidence regions

If we want to construct a joint confidence region for the two line parameters without invoking any particular error distribution, we may assume
only that individual data points will fall above or below the true line with
equal probability. If we divide all observed points into two groups by
their median x value, and if we then contemplate a trial line, the number of
points *above* the line in each half will measure how well the contemplated
line fits. Specifically, since the expected number of points above the line
in each group is $n/4$, either

$$A = \frac{8}{n}\left[\left(r_1 - \frac{n}{4}\right)^2 + \left(r_2 - \frac{n}{4}\right)^2\right]$$

or

$$B = \frac{2}{\sqrt{n}}\left[\left|r_1 - \frac{n}{4}\right| + \left|r_2 - \frac{n}{4}\right|\right]$$

will become too large as the contemplated line is shoved or wiggled too
far from its most plausible position. Critical values for A can be obtained
by noting that for moderately large n the value is a χ_2^2 variate with two
degrees of freedom. Critical values of B—again for n fairly large—are
2.24 at the 5 per cent level and 2.81 for a 1 per cent error rate. The test
is due to Brown and Mood [6].

Although these criteria certainly define joint confidence regions for the
unknown line parameters, α and β, they are not easy to use. For a reasonable number n of data points the limits on A or B quickly define a small
set of number pairs, r_1 and r_2, of points which should be above (or below)
the contemplated line on each side of the median value of x. We must
then shove the contemplated line around into all the possible limit configurations defined by these number pairs, thereby generating an envelope
of lines which is a non-parametric confidence region for the entire true
line in the (x, y) plane. If we want the (α, β) confidence region, it seems
necessary to plot the values of α and β for these limiting lines and then draw
the convex region in the (α, β) plane defined by these points. Such a procedure is too laborious to be attractive, although it has the mathematical
virtue of being uniformly more efficient on samples from normal populations than Daniels' alternative procedure which is to be described. (The
powers of A and B, as well as his m test, are discussed in Daniels' [10]
article.)

It is geometrically obvious that a line which is displaced parallel to its
optimum position will quickly lose data points from both groups (line 1
in Figure 30), as will a line rotated about the mass center of all the points
(line 2). Thus against these alternatives the A and B criteria are quite

powerful. Much less satisfactory is the power of A or B against lines that pass through the mass center of (say) the left half of the data points (line 3). Such lines inflate only one of the terms in the A statistic and hence, for this set of alternatives, the A statistic can take on only a rather small maximum value, a value that may be small enough to cause us to consider all such lines as plausible parents for our data.

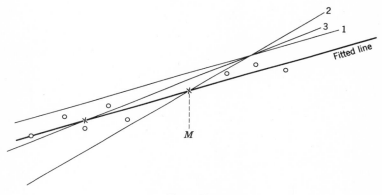

Figure 30

To remedy this defect H. E. Daniels has suggested an alternative procedure which yields (α, β) confidence regions directly. The equation

$$y = \alpha + \beta x$$

is rewritten as

$$\alpha = y_i - \beta x_i$$

so that each datum (x_i, y_i) defines a line in the (α, β) plane. These lines are plotted from the sample in hand, thereby fencing in several convex polygons. Since the most plausible values for (α, β) lie in the "center" of these polygons, Daniels suggests that each polygon be given a score, m, which is the *minimum* number of lines that must be crossed to get completely outside. He gives a table of probabilities that the minimum number of lines, m_0, is less than or equal to, i.e.,

$$\Pr (m \leqslant m_0)$$

for various values of m_0 and n. With this table it is possible to choose the polygons in the (α, β) plane that must be regarded as plausible joint regions for the parameter values. Thus, for 4 and 11 per cent error rates we must accept regions bounded by at least m_0 fences (counting the first

fence as *zero*, as usual with these combinatorial limits) with the error rates
shown in Table 4.   The tabular entries are *n*, the number of data points.

Like the sign test, this distribution-free confidence procedure has a
rather sparse set of probability levels for small values of *n*.   Thus, for
nine data points, the largest enclosed region will fail to contain the population parameters less than 3.5 per cent of the time, and the next smaller

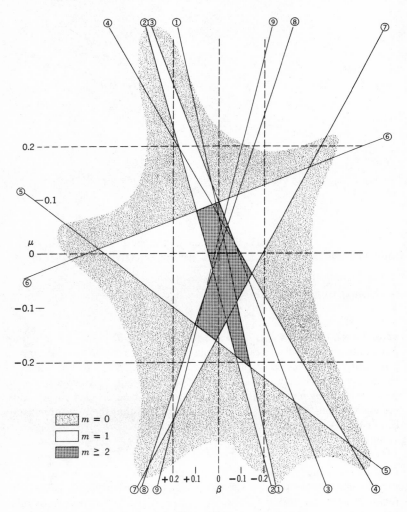

Figure 31

TABLE 4

m_0	0.04	0.11
0	9	7
1	13	11
2	16	14
3	18.5	17
4	22.5	20

region (*m* greater than or equal to *two*) will give an *error rate of* 24.6 *per cent.* Interpolation restores the sign test to usefulness, but no intuitively attractive two-dimensional interpolation scheme seems available here, and we conclude that this lack must remain a serious detriment to the process.

Note: When we tried the *m* test on our standard example (Figure 31), we quickly discovered that the technique is much easier to apply to the orthogonal form of the equation

$$\mu = y_i - (x_i - x.)\,\beta$$

than to the form given in the exposition because the slopes in the (μ, β) plane are both positive and negative, whereas in the (α, β) plane only negative slopes are possible.

SECTION 4: TWO LINES OR ONE; X WITHOUT ERROR

An additional set of data

We shall now return to our original problem of determining by chemical analyses the amounts of calcium oxide in ten known samples. This time, however, *two* methods of analysis are used on each sample, with the result that we have two values of y for each value of x, two lines that ideally should pass through the origin and have a slope of 45°. The complete data appear in Table 5.

Although we can ask the same questions of the new data as we did of the old (whether the true intercept could be *zero* or the true slope *one*), a more interesting investigation is whether or not the two methods yield equivalent results. Statistically we are asking, "Could the same true but unknown line have given rise to both these sets of data?" Since the y values occur in pairs (with identical x's), this question may be conveniently rephrased by considering the differences between the y data. If both y's arose from the same unknown parent value, ζ, and if we are making the same assumptions about the nature of the fluctuations as we did before (constant variance about the unknown true line), the difference between two y values for the same x should be normally distributed about

TABLE 5

CaO Present, mg.	Old Method, mg.	CaO Found, New Method, mg.	Difference, mg.
4.0	3.7	3.9	0.2
8.0	7.8	8.1	0.3
12.5	12.1	12.4	0.3
16.0	15.6	16.0	0.4
20.0	19.8	19.8	0.0
25.0	24.5	25.0	0.5
31.0	30.7	31.1	0.3
36.0	35.5	35.8	0.3
40.0	39.4	40.1	0.7
40.0	39.5	40.1	0.6
232.5	229.0	232.3	3.6

zero as a mean and with a variance of *twice the variance of either y separately.* Symbolically:

$$(y_2 - y_1) \Rightarrow N(0; 2\sigma_\eta^2).$$

Thus we may reduce this two-line problem to a one-line version, and a rather trivial line at that; we need merely test

$$z = y_2 - y_1$$

as a linear function of x.   Our null hypothesis says that this line has a true slope of zero and a true mass center of zero.   These assertions may be checked either separately or jointly by using the techniques described earlier.   As a matter of personal preference I feel that the elliptical joint confidence region in the parameter space (β, μ) displays the whole picture rather well in Figure 32.   (Note the expanded horizontal scale for β.) From these data a true slope of zero is a very tenable hypothesis, and it is equally clear that the true mean value of z is probably *not* zero.   In general we can conclude that these data are consistent with several hypotheses, the most attractive of which are:

1. The new chemical analysis gives values about 0.36 units larger than the old, regardless of the amount of CaO found.

2. The new analysis gives values which are 0.36 units larger on the average than the old, but which tend to be slightly bigger for larger amounts of CaO in the samples.

3. The two lines start together (at an x of zero) but diverge slightly as x increases—about 0.01 units/(unit of x).

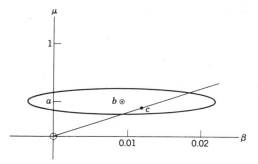

Figure 32

The first of these hypotheses corresponds to the point a on the diagram, the second to the fitted point b, and the third to some such point as c on the sloping line which is the hypothesis that the intercept α is zero. The variable α occurs in the non-orthogonal form of the equation

$$z = \alpha + \beta x \equiv \mu + \beta(x - x.).$$

The arithmetic leading to the elliptical confidence region is most easily followed by fitting a straight line to the values of z and x:

$$x. = 23.25 \qquad\qquad Sxx = 1{,}568.625$$
$$z. = 0.360 \qquad\qquad Sxz = 14.250$$
$$\qquad\qquad\qquad\quad\ Szz = 0.364$$
$$m = z. = 0.360 \qquad\quad SSR = 0.23455$$
$$b = \frac{Sxz}{Sxx} = 0.009084 \quad MS = 0.02932 = s^2$$

On 8 degrees of freedom $s = 0.1712$. Since $F_{2,8}(0.05)$ is 4.46, the interior of the ellipse is given, for the 5 per cent error level, by

$$4.46 \geqslant \frac{8}{2}\left[\frac{(\mu - 0.36)^2(10) + (\beta - 0.009084)^2(1{,}568.625)}{0.23455}\right],$$

which may be rewritten in the standard form

$$1 \geqslant \frac{(\mu - 0.36)^2}{\left[\dfrac{(4.46)(0.05864)}{10}\right]} + \frac{(\beta - 0.009084)^2}{\left[\dfrac{(4.46)(0.05864)}{1{,}568.625}\right]}$$

or

$$1 \geqslant \frac{(\mu - 0.36)^2}{(0.162)^2} + \frac{(\beta - 0.009084)^2}{(0.0129)^2}$$

which quickly gives the ellipse, center at $(0.009, 0.36)$ and semiaxes of 0.0129 and 0.162 respectively.   The line arises from setting α equal to zero in the equation

$$\alpha = \mu - \beta x.$$

so that we find

$$\mu = 23.3\beta$$

to be the equivalent form of the hypothesis that the true intercept is zero.

The decision that the two processes are indeed different, that there are two different lines in these sets of data, is made easy by the pairwise grouping of the y values.   This grouping allows us to work directly with the differences and thus reduce our manipulations to the simplicities of the one-line problem.   It is only in the final interpretation that we have to deal with two lines.   When the two sets of data do not have common x values, our procedure is necessarily different.   It is a little more complicated and needs to be viewed in a rather different light, although the conclusions may rather resemble our present example.

Unpaired data

In studying bond dissociation energies of aromatic compounds, Ladaski and Szwarc [21] give the data of Table 6 on temperature and rate constant. The authors plotted all these data on a single graph without regard to a third variable, time, which they also recorded.   We have arbitrarily divided these data into two groups, t less than or greater than *one*—a more or less

TABLE 6

$t > 1$		$t < 1$			
T, °K.	$k.10^2$ sec^{-1}	T, °K.	$k.10^2$ sec^{-1}	T, °K.	$k.10^2$ sec^{-1}
1,014	2.32	1,030	3.55	1,084	19.6
1,019	4.28	1,031	4.91	1,086	21.9
1,024	3.31	1,033	5.36	1,091	28.9
1,029	5.64	1,034	4.83	1,093	26.7
1,046	7.55	1,037	5.12	1,094	32.7
1,048	7.96	1,041	6.85	1,100	39.9
1,061	13.2	1,044	6.85	1,104	43.0
1,080	23.3	1,052	8.04	1,108	50.1
1,081	23.2	1,053	8.00	1,119	73.5
1,085	27.0	1,054	7.84	1,121	75.0
		1,065	12.4	1,125	79.8
		1,076	15.9	1,133	90.2
				1,133	97.6

natural gap in their table of t values. We now inquire whether we feel that these two sets of data are satisfied by the same line, or whether two lines are needed. As with all such rate-temperature data, the linear relation is between $1/T$ and $\log k$, which variables we hereafter designate as x and y.

If we compute the sums of squares and cross products for the deviations from both the grand mean and the means for the two groups separately (i.e., fit one line to each group and a third to both sets), we find the values given in Table 7, the last line of which is unusual. It is the sum of the

TABLE 7

t	n	$10^4 x.$	$y.$	$10^8 Sxx$	$10^3 Sxy$	Syy
Both	35	9.361	3.942	3.1696	-2.1540	158.3956
$t > 1$	10	9.541	3.070	0.5426	-0.4229	35.9696
$t < 1$	25	9.289	4.291	2.1718	-1.5111	111.7716
—	Sum	—	—	2.7144	-1.9340	147.7412

two preceding lines and represents the pooled squared deviations of all the data after removing separate means. The single slope that we will calculate from this line is the slope that best fits the two sets of data after replotting them so that their x and y means coincide. Likewise the residual sum of squared deviations shows the variability that would remain in this translated plotting of the data after removing the best single line. Two fitted means and one slope leave 32 degrees of freedom to this Sum of Squares.

The slopes, reductions, and residuals are given in Table 8. If we wish

TABLE 8

t	n	$b = Sxy/Sxx$	SSReg	SSR	DF
Both	35	$-67,961$	146.3897	12.0059	33
$t > 1$	10	$-77,937$	32.9580	3.0116	8
$t < 1$	25	$-69,577$	105.1351	6.6365	23
—	Sum	$-71,248$	137.8916	9.8496	32

to find how much reduction in the unexplained variability is effected by fitting two lines instead of one, we examine the difference of SSR for

TABLE 9

			MS
SSR (both)	12.0059	33 DF	
$SSR_1 + SSR_2$	9.6481	31 DF	0.3112
Reduction	2.3578	2 DF	1.1789

$F = 1.1789/0.3112 = 3.79$

both lines and for each line separately (Table 9). This reduction, at 2 and 31 degrees of freedom, is not quite significant at the 5 per cent error level when compared to the pooled residuals about the two lines. If this were the only analysis we could perform, the writer would reluctantly decide that he was not justified in using two lines, but he would harbor a strong suspicion that further data might well disclose that two lines are warranted.

Fortunately such discomfort is unnecessary, since we can break down the two degrees of freedom for fitting an additional line into individual ones attributable to differences in *means* between the two sets of data and differences in slope. We compare the SSR for the pooled variability about two lines with that for the pooled variability about the common-line-if-the-means-were-the-same (Table 10).

TABLE 10

SSR common means	9.8496	32
$SSR_1 + SSR_2$	9.6481	31
Reduction due to slope	0.2015	1

Our final analysis of variance table now reads

			MS
Total SSR about a common line	12.0059	33	
Reduction for separate means	2.1563	1	2.1563
Reduction for separate slopes	0.2015	1	0.2015
Pooled SSR about two lines	9.6481	31	0.3112

$F = 2.1563/0.3112 = 6.93$

We thus see that almost all the reduction gained in fitting separate lines to the two groups of data accrues from the different means. When separate slopes are allowed, no significant additional reduction occurs. The reduction for the mean, however, is quite significant (at about the

2 per cent error level), and we therefore conclude that the two sets of data do indeed deserve two lines—with the same slope, to be sure, but displaced parallel to one another.　What the physical meaning of this displacement may be is a question which the statistician must toss back to the experimental man, but he is denying some information contained in his data when he uses only one line to represent these points.

CHAPTER 3

Regression with Several Values of y for Each Known x

Let us suppose we are given several values of y at each of n values of x, where x is still assumed to be known accurately. We are now in a position to test two of the assumptions which had to be accepted blindly when we had only one y for each x. The repeated values of y allow us to estimate the y variability directly at each of the several points, and thus allow us to see whether we believe that this variance is constant, as we have been assuming, or is really a function of x. Also, since we have sampled a little distribution at each of the x values, we may test the hypothesis that the variability in the *location* of these distributions is greater than that allowed by the variability of the y values themselves.

In other words, we can decide whether the assumption that the y distribution means fall on a straight line is one justified by the data. If the true curve is parabolic, or if another uncontrolled variable strongly dependent on our x value is affecting our y values, the true distribution may not be sitting on a line in the (x, y) plane. Of course the means of the observed values will not lie exactly on a line, but the essential question concerns how far they deviate from the best line, i.e., whether or not the deviation of the y means are too large to have happened merely because of the inherent variability of the y data and we should therefore suspect that other factors are augmenting the usual discrepancies. These two forms of non-linearity are illustrated in Figures 33 and 34, respectively.

In Chapter 7 we shall handle the first type of non-linearity by fitting other functional forms. It is the second type, however, that is more common and more interesting. For an example, let us say an electrical resistance has had various voltages, x, applied to it, and the current, y, has been measured. This was done several times for each value of the voltage, but the experimenters were not too careful in their design, and so they allowed considerable time to elapse between the measurements at one level of x and the next. During this interval the temperature in the laboratory changed, humidity changed, and perhaps even the observer and the meters used were changed, so that other variables entered into the experiment but were not recorded. We might wish to discover whether or not a straight line adequately accounts for such data, the slope being the conductance of the circuit, and if we find that it does not explain the observed variation, we should try to break down that residual variance into its respective components. How far we can do this depends to a considerable extent on what additional data may have been recorded. All too often there are no other pertinent data available, and the extractable information is correspondingly meager. This subject and its ramifications are known as the *analysis of variance* and have already been treated by Snedecor [29], Brownlee [7], and others. It is so large a subject that we here only explore the vicinity of those places where it joins our regression problems.

To illustrate some of the problems that arise when repeated values of y are available at each of several values of x, we examine data of Stone and Eichelberger [30] giving the titration of oxygen dissolved in water at

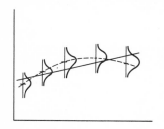
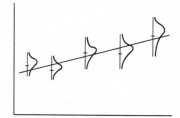

Figure 33   Figure 34

various temperatures. The calibration curve is not linear in these units, but there is some reason to hope that the logarithm of the titer will be linear in the reciprocal absolute temperature. Accordingly, in Table 1 we present $10^6/°K. - 3,200$ as x and $-10^4 \log$ (cc. titer) as y. The average y values are given at the foot of the table.

If we wish to fit a line by minimizing the sum of squares of residuals in the vertical direction when there are several (k_i) values of y_{ij} for each of the x_i's, we see that we require

$$\sum_{i=1}^{n} \sum_{j=1}^{k_i} [(y_{ij} - m) - b(x_i - x.)]^2$$

to be a minimum. If we differentiate with respect to m and b, and if we write $\sum_{j=1}^{k_i} y_{ij} = k_i y_i.$, we get, on equating those derivatives to zero,

TABLE 1

T, °C.	15.0	25.3	27.2	31.2	31.8	38.1
x	270	150	129	85	79	12
y	458	1,158	1,314	1,549	1,612	1,918
	434	1,169	1,349	1,549	1,630	1,918
	434	1,163	1,325	1,549	1,630	1,904
	482	1,169	1,319	1,530	1,624	1,911
	472	1,163	1,325	1,537		1,925
	491	1,158	1,308			
			1,319			
			1,331			
			1,319			
k_i	6	6	9	5	4	5
$y.$	461.83	1,163.33	1,323.22	1,542.80	1,624.00	1,935.2

$$\left. \begin{array}{l} \sum_{ij} [(y_{ij} - m) - b(x_i - x.)] = \sum_i k_i[(y_i. - m) - b(x_i - x.)] = 0 \\ \sum_{ij} [(y_{ij} - m) - b(x_i - x.)][x_i - x.] \\ \qquad = \sum_i k_i[(y_i - m) - b(x_i - x.)][x_i - x.] = 0. \end{array} \right\} \quad (1)$$

Note that the second of each pair of equations is exactly the equation that would have been obtained had we decided to use only one point, the mean value $y_i.$, for each x_i, but to weight that point in proportion to the number of original data points whose average it is. The first equation contains the undefined symbol $x.$. If we now define this as the weighted average of the x_i by the relation $\sum_i k_i x_i = Nx.$, where $\sum_i^n k_i = N$, the first equation gives us

$$m = \frac{\sum_i k_i y_i.}{N} = y.. \quad (2)$$

and the second equation yields

$$b = \frac{\sum_i k_i(y_i - y..)(x_i - x.)}{\sum_i k_i(x_i - x.)^2} = \frac{Sy_i.x_i}{Sx_ix_i}. \quad (3)$$

It is not until we break up the sum of the squares of the residuals from an arbitrary line,

$$Y_i = M + B(x_i - x.),$$

that we obtain the material for significance tests. Here

$$\sum_{ij} (y_{ij} - Y_i)^2 \equiv \sum_{ij} \{(y_{ij} - y_{i\cdot}) + [(y_{i\cdot} - m) - b(x_i - x_\cdot)]$$
$$+ (b - B)(x_i - x_\cdot) + (m - M)\}^2$$
$$\equiv \sum_{ij} (y_{ij} - y_{i\cdot})^2 + \sum_{i} k_i[(y_{i\cdot} - m) - b(x_i - x_\cdot)]^2 \qquad (4)$$
$$+ (b - B)^2 \sum_{i} k_i(x_i - x_\cdot)^2 + \sum_{ij} (m - M)^2$$
$$\equiv \sum_{ij} (y_{ij} - y_{i\cdot})^2 + \sum_{i} k_i[(y_{i\cdot} - m) - b(x_i - x_\cdot)]^2$$
$$+ (b - B)^2 Sxx + N(m - M)^2.$$

The cross products disappear on summation, for the usual *algebraic* reasons. If the arbitrary line is now assumed to be the *true* line, we notice that only the last two sums of squares are affected, when B becomes β and M becomes μ. Thus these terms may be used to set limits for credible values of β and μ—the F test being appropriate between any pair of the given sums of squares.

We choose to define the symbol s^2 by rewriting the last line of the identity once more as

$$\sum_{ij} (y_{ij} - Y_i)^2 \equiv (N - n)s^2 + (n - 2)s^2 + (b - B)^2 Sxx + N(m - M)^2.$$

If our hypothesis that the y's fluctuate about a common line with a common variance is correct, the s^2 in both the first and the second sums of squares of residuals provides estimates of the variance, σ^2, of y. The first one is a direct estimate in the sense that only variations of y about its mean at each value of x_i are used, whereas the second one is actually the variation of these mean values about the fitted line. If the mean values fluctuate too much, the second estimate will be too large, which we may F-test by comparing the ratios of the two sums of squares divided by their respective degrees of freedom. Here, the second sum of squares is based on n values $y_{i\cdot}$, but two parameters have been fitted, so $n - 2$ degrees of freedom remain. The first sum is based on N points, y_{ij}, minus n fitted means, $y_{i\cdot}$, leaving $N - n$ degrees of freedom. Since each of the terms in equation (4) are sums of squares of normally distributed variates; $N(0; \sigma^2)$, they are themselves distributed as $\sigma^2\chi^2$ with the appropriate degrees of freedom. If we divide these Sums of Squares by their Degrees of Freedom, we obtain Mean Squares, whose ratio follows the familiar F distribution, from which the unknown σ^2 has conveniently disappeared.

In our example we fit a line to the weighted y means, obtaining the usual sums of squares and cross products displayed below. The SSD term represents the amount by which the y means fluctuate about the fitted line.

$$Sxx = \sum_i k_i(x_i - x.)^2 \qquad = \qquad 210{,}025.886$$

$$Sxy = \sum_i k_i(x_i - x.)(y_i. - y..) = -1{,}216{,}073.629$$

$$Syy = \sum_i k_i(y_i. - y..)^2 \qquad = \qquad 7{,}062{,}672.66$$

$$\text{SSReg} = b^2 Sxx \qquad = \qquad 7{,}041{,}203.82$$

$$\text{SSD} = Syy - \text{SSReg} \qquad = \qquad 21{,}468.84$$

$$b = Sxy/Sxx \qquad = \qquad -5.790113$$

$$x. = \qquad 128.057$$

$$y. = 1{,}301.314$$

We must also look at the mean y values to see whether they depart from the line because they lie on a parabola (or some other simple curve) as in Figure 33 or whether they embody some less obvious form of fluctuation which we shall hopefully term *random*. We see from Table 2 that the fitted values and the values of the discrepancies (fitted—actual) suggest

TABLE 2

			Fitted y Means		
479.45	1,174.26	1,295.85	1,550.62	1,585.36	1,973.30

			Discrepancies = (Fitted—Actual)		
17.62	10.92	−27.37	7.82	−38.64	38.10

that any parabolic element may be neglected in comparison to the "random" fluctuations. It is clearly our duty to examine these data further to determine, if possible, whether the fluctuations of the mean y's are merely those that might reasonably arise from the wobble present in the individual y values or whether, this explanation proving untenable, we must look for another.

A direct measure of y variability is the pooled sum of squares of variation about the fitted group means. Thus we find

$$\text{SSW(ithin)} = \sum_{ij} (y_{ij} - y_i.)^2 = 5{,}431.32 \qquad \text{DF} = 29$$

$$s^2 = 187.287 \qquad \text{or} \qquad s = 13.68.$$

If we wish formal sanctification of the obvious, we may examine the estimate of s^2 obtained from the SSD in the light of this newer estimate. Here

$$s^2 = 21{,}468.84/4 = 5{,}367.21$$

is to be compared via the ratio

$$5,367.21/187.287 = 28.66$$

for 4 and 29 degrees of freedom—a "significant" F value at anybody's level of confidence.

Even this breakdown of the sum of squares is coarser than it need be. We could separate the first term of equation (4) into

$$\sum_j (y_{ij} - y_{i.})^2 = (k_i - 1)s_i^2$$

for each value of i, thus obtaining estimates of σ^2 at each value of i. We are then in a position to examine each of these for variation with x, systematic or random, to see whether our assumption of homoscedasticity is justified.

For our data, the six estimates of s^2 and s are:

s^2	684.97	24.27	137.69	78.2	72.0	63.7
s	26.17	4.93	11.74	8.84	8.49	7.98.

Certainly our first reaction is to suspect that these are not data from a homogeneous experiment. The first group seems to be rather more variable than the others.

Testing for homoscedasticity

If we have a group of mean squares all purporting to estimate the same variance component, the quickest test that they do so is Hartley's [19] maximum F ratio. In this test we take the ratio of the largest mean square to the smallest (look in Appendix Table 15 for the 5 per cent critical value for this ratio), provided we have k estimates and each has ν degrees of freedom. If our ratio exceeds the tabular entry, we conclude that the variances are significantly different, and this conclusion will be wrong 5 per cent of the time. This test assumes that all k of the estimating mean squares have ν degrees of freedom apiece. Hartley apparently feels that the sensitivity of the test is not seriously dependent on this assumption and suggests using it as a rough test even if the ν_i are different, entering the table with $\nu.$, the mean of the ν_i's.

A warning must be added here. Unfortunately the three tests for homoscedasticity given in this paragraph are peculiarly susceptible to non-normality in the underlying distributions (see Box [5]). Thus two samples that seem to have different variances may really arise from non-normal populations. The assumption of normality underlies most of our useful statistical tests, but fortunately most of the tests are not particularly sensitive to mild departures from normality. Such a test is said to be robust. No robust test for non-homoscedasticity is known. For our data, Hartley's statistic is 685/24.3 or 28.2 for 6 mean squares at about 5.8 degrees of freedom. The 5 per cent is about 13.8, and our ratio is considerably larger. Another quite similar test for heterogeneity of variances was proposed by Cochran [8]. This test again demands v degrees of freedom in each of k mean squares and tests the ratio of the largest mean square to the sum of all the mean squares. A 5 per cent table is given in the reference.

If the v_i are seriously different, Bartlett's test [3] must be used. This is somewhat inconvenient, as it involves the computation of

$$M = N \ln \left(\frac{\sum\limits_i v_i s_i^2}{N} \right) - \sum_i v_i \ln s_i^2, \tag{5}$$

$$c_1 = \sum_i \frac{1}{v_i} - \frac{1}{N}, \qquad c_3 = \sum_i \frac{1}{v_i^3} - \frac{1}{N^3}$$

$$N = \sum v_i,$$

and possibly interpolation in a triple-entry table. The test is quite general, however, and permits treatment of cases where the other procedures fail or are questionable.

If on applying one of these tests we find we may treat the individual variances as equal, we then pool these sums of squares into the estimate given in equation (4) with $N - n$ degrees of freedom and go on to test the linearity assumption. If the linearity assumption holds, the first two terms of (4) may be pooled to give a still better estimate of σ^2 with $N - 2$ degrees of freedom which should be used to set limits on μ and β via the F ratios (or t, if the square root is taken, since the numerators have only one degree of freedom in these tests) as we did previously.

If the earlier test for homoscedasticity fails, indicating non-homogeneous variances, we should compute the individual estimates of σ^2 and examine them for systematic variation with x, possibly leading to a transformation that will reduce the data to homoscedastic form (Chapter 8). If a non-systematic change in the variance appears plausible, we look to the original experiment to see whether some physical reason can be found—some way in which the experiment can be run better next time so as to yield more information, since the limits which *this* experiment will be able to set on μ and β will probably not be very good. Inhomogeneity of the error variances usually points either to poor experimental technique or to *poor experimental design*. (The variability of a biological experiment, for instance, is not always under our control, but the experiment can frequently be designed to prevent this variability from obscuring the desired information.)

If the second test fails, indicating that the means are displaced from the line more than the normal variance of y can explain, we should examine these points to see whether the discrepancies suggest another functional form—say a parabola—or perhaps, again, variation caused by other variables whose sources and effects are to be sought in the unrecorded data of the experiment rather than in the numbers at hand.

Components of variance

In all our work thus far, we have been interested in testing the proposition that variances are equal, or that additional variation is not present, as our basic hypotheses assert. When a test shows that one of these hypotheses is untenable, that there is additional (if unwanted) variation, we shall desire to measure that additional component. To do this it is necessary to know the expected value of the mean squares we have been using in our various F tests. The logic involved and the algebraic manipulations used are similar in all cases, so that we feel they could profitably be displayed in detail at least once. Thereafter a statement of the results should suffice, and the reader should be in a position to work out his own components of variance for the many designs he must use which are not given in this book. We have chosen this model of several y values for each accurately known x as having sufficient complexity to be realistic, without—we hope—completely overwhelming the uninitiated. (Note that we do *not* demand all the subgroups to be of the same size, a simplification which would not render our task much easier.)

At this point it is necessary to state the underlying mathematical model we are assuming. A useful one seems to be

$$y_{ij} = \mu + \beta(x_i - x.) + \gamma_i + \epsilon_{ij} \qquad \begin{matrix} i = 1, ..., n \\ j = 1, ..., k_i \end{matrix} \qquad (6)$$

where γ_i is an independent random variable distributed with a zero mean and variance σ_γ^2

and ϵ_{ij} is an independent random variable distributed with a zero mean and variance σ^2.

This means that the expected value of γ_i [written $E(\gamma_i)$] is zero, as is $E(\epsilon_{ij})$. Note that although

$$E(\gamma_i^2) = \sigma_\gamma^2 \qquad \text{and} \qquad E(\epsilon_{ij}^2) = \sigma^2,$$

nevertheless

$$E(\gamma_i\gamma_j) = 0, \quad E(\gamma_i\epsilon_{jk}) = 0, \qquad \text{and} \qquad E(\epsilon_{ij}\epsilon_{k1}) = 0,$$

provided the subscripts are such as to prevent the arguments degenerating into a perfect square. The γ_i are thought of as errors that are constant for any particular x_i, that vary with x, and that are apt to be zero on the average, when all x are considered. They do not, however, depend on the other errors. The ϵ_{ij} are thought of as errors that are different for every observation, having an average value of zero, and are not dependent on the x, the γ_i, or the previous errors.

We have to decide whether our experiment demands a model in which the γ_i are randomly drawn from an infinite population, a moderate population, or perhaps one of only n members, all being used at random—one with each of the x_i. We have a similar decision for ϵ_{ij}. For the present we shall take the algebraically simplest and most familiar choice, the infinite population for both γ and ϵ, leaving the complications of a finite population for a later exposition.

We begin by finding the expected value of the first sum of squares in (4), an almost trivial operation:

$$
\begin{aligned}
E \sum_{ij} (y_{ij} - y_{i.})^2 &= \sum_{ij} E(\epsilon_{ij} - \epsilon_{i.})^2 \\
&= \sum_{ij} [E(\epsilon_{ij}^2) - 2E(\epsilon_{i.}\epsilon_{ij}) + E(\epsilon_{i.}^2)] \\
&= \sum_{ij} \left(\sigma^2 - \frac{2\sigma^2}{k_i} + \frac{\sigma^2}{k_i} \right) = \sum_{ij} \sigma^2 \left(1 - \frac{1}{k_i} \right) \\
&= \sigma^2 \sum_i k_i \left(1 - \frac{1}{k_i} \right) = \sigma^2 (N - n).
\end{aligned} \tag{7}
$$

The value of $E(\epsilon_{i.}\epsilon_{ij})$ is found from

$$
E(\epsilon_{i.}\epsilon_{ij}) = E\left[\frac{\epsilon_{ij} \sum_{r=1}^{k_i} \epsilon_{ir}}{k_i} \right] = \frac{1}{k_i} \sum_{r=1}^{k_i} E(\epsilon_{ij}\epsilon_{ir}) = \frac{\sigma^2}{k_i} \sum_{r=1}^{k_i} \delta_{jr} = \frac{\sigma^2}{k_i}
$$

where

$$
\delta_{jr} = \begin{cases} 0 \text{ when } j \neq r \\ 1 \text{ when } j = r \end{cases}.
$$

(Throughout this section an average over an i subscript will be a *weighted* average; thus $Nx. = \sum k_i x_i$ where $\sum k_i = N$.) Equation (7) shows the algebraic reason for the degrees of freedom, rather than the heuristic explanation given earlier in terms of numbers of points minus the fitted constants.

We now need

$$
E \sum_{i=1}^{n} k_i [y_{i.} - m - b(x_i - x.)]^2.
$$

This expected value is difficult, since the bracket contains the random variables implicitly not only in y_i. but in m and in b, which are fitted parameters and may be expressed in terms of the y_i. We give the derivation starting on page 110 in the Supplement to this chapter. The expected value is

$$(n - 2)\sigma^2 + \left[\left(N - \frac{\sum k_i^2}{N}\right) - \frac{\sum k_i^2(x_i - x.)^2}{Sxx}\right]\sigma_\gamma^2.$$

This expression shows that the expected value for the sum of squares of fluctuation of the means about the regression line is equal to $(n - 2)\sigma^2$ if $\sigma_\gamma^2 = 0$ (i.e., *if the γ_i are all equal*). This is the hypothesis we are testing with our F ratio of MSB(etween groups)/MSW(ithin groups). If this test fails we may estimate σ_γ^2 by subtracting off $[(n - 2)/(N - n)]$ SSW(ithin groups) from the SSB(etween) and then dividing by the coefficient

$$\left[\left(N - \frac{\sum k_i^2}{N}\right) - \frac{\sum k_i^2(x_i - x.)^2}{Sxx}\right].$$

Note that this coefficient simplifies:

1. If $x_i = x.$, only $N - \dfrac{\sum k_i^2}{N} = k_0$ remains, a definition frequently found in examples of analysis of variance with a single classification and unequal subgroups—which this problem really is after the line has been removed.

2. If the subgroups all have equal numbers of points, i.e., $k_i = k$ for all i. Then we get $N - 2k = (n - 2)k$. Thus, in this case, the expected value of the SSB is $(n - 2)(\sigma^2 + k\sigma_\gamma^2)$, a greatly simplified formula, although alas not more easily derived.

We may conveniently summarize these and similar statements in tabular form, showing the Sums of Squares, Mean Squares, Components of Mean Squares, Average Mean Squares, and Average Components of Mean Squares, as well as the appropriate Degrees of Freedom. This table (Table 3) is an extension of the classical analysis of variance (anova) table and is a useful way to record the essential information and to summarize the computations.

Returning to our numerical example, if we are willing to assume that in addition to the basic y variability there is a second random fluctuation—peculiar to each group—being added to each datum, the variance of this second fluctuation may be estimated from the formula

$$s_\gamma^2 = \frac{\text{SSD} - \left(\dfrac{n - 2}{N - n}\right)\text{SSW}}{N - \dfrac{\sum k_i^2}{N} - \dfrac{\sum k_i^2(x_i - x.)^2}{Sxx}}$$

TABLE 3

Analysis of Variance Table for Regression with Unequal Subgroups

Item	DF	SS	$MS = \dfrac{SS}{DF}$	AMS
Mean	1	$N(m - M)^2 \equiv (N(y_{..} - Y_{.})^2$	$N(m - M)^2$	$\sigma^2 + \dfrac{\sum k_\gamma^2}{N}\sigma_\gamma^2 + N(\mu - M)^2$
Slope	1	$(b - B)^2 Sxx$	$(b - B)^2 Sxx$	$\sigma^2 + \dfrac{\sum k_i^2(x_i - x_.)^2}{Sxx}\sigma_\gamma^2 + (\beta - B)^2 Sxx$
Deviations	$n - 2$	$\sum k_i[y_{i\cdot} - m - b(x_i - x_.)]^2$	$s^2 + k_0 s_\gamma^2$	$\sigma^2 + \dfrac{1}{n-2}\left[N - \dfrac{\sum k_i^2}{N} - \dfrac{\sum k_i^2(x_i - x_.)^2}{Sxx}\right]\sigma_\gamma^2$
Within	$N - n$	$\sum\limits_{ij}(y_{ij} - y_{i\cdot})^2$	s^2	σ^2

$$\text{where } k_0 = \left[N - \frac{\sum k_i^2}{N} - \frac{\sum k_i^2(x_i - x_.)^2}{Sxx}\right]\frac{1}{n-2}$$

so that

$$s_y{}^2 = \frac{21{,}468.84 - \frac{4}{29}(5{,}431.32)}{35 - 6.26 - 5.54} = 893.1$$

or

$$s_y = 29.88$$

A post-mortem on the numerical example

The absence of any noticeable quadratic factor in the mean y's but the undeniable presence of unexplained deviations from the line provokes a little speculation about possible causes. That the excessive variability should be singularly prominent in the one group of experiments conducted at less than room temperature (Los Angeles room temperature, that is) suggests that the temperature control was less successful for this set of readings than for the others, which presumably shared different thermostatic conditions. The authors list their temperatures as ± 0.3 °C., which translates into ± 4 of our x units or ± 23 y units. Thus our estimate of 30 units standard deviation is very comparable to the experimenters' own estimate of their temperature indeterminacy. We can only wish that they had controlled their temperatures more closely *or at least had recorded the temperatures of the individual observations.* Such a record merely to the nearest tenth of a degree might well have reduced the residual variability about the calibration line by an order of magnitude, thereby revealing the finer structure of this line. Since such data were not recorded, the interesting question about the straightness of the calibration line must remain effectively obscured. Although the geometry of this line was not the primary concern of these chemists, nevertheless we have here a good example of a careful investigation which might have been materially enhanced by the addition of a few easily available data. That our presumptions are correct cannot, of course, be tested, but the evidence—although circumstantial—is still strongly suggestive.

Limits for variance components

Let us restrict further discussion of the present model to exactly k data at each value of x. The anova table simplifies to Table 4 where the AMS are the expected values of the corresponding Sums of Squares divided by their degrees of freedom. Earlier in this chapter we have discussed the appropriate tests of significance which may be used to set confidence limits on β and μ. They are almost obvious if we glance at the AMS column of Table 4, where the Mean Square Deviations is seen to be the appropriate denominator in the F tests for β and μ, provided always that $\sigma_y{}^2$ has been shown to exist in a comparison of MSD with MSW.

TABLE 4[a]

	DF	SS	AMS
Mean	1	$nk(m - M)^2$	$nk(u - M)^2 + k\sigma_y^2 + \sigma^2$
Slope	1	$k(b - B)^2 \sum_i (x_i - x.)^2$	$k(\beta - B)^2 Sxx + k\sigma_y^2 + \sigma^2$
Deviations	$n - 2$	$k \sum_i [(y_i. - m) - b(x_i - x.)]^2$	$k\sigma_y^2 + \sigma^2$
Within	$n(k - 1)$	$\sum (y_{ij} - y_i.)^2$	σ^2

[a] In this table $Sxx = \sum(x_i - x.)^2$, and the common k appears explicitly.

We now suppose that we want an estimate of σ_y^2, as well as confidence limits for this parameter. The estimator is the Component of the Mean Square of (population) Deviations,

$$s_y^2 \equiv \text{CMSD} = \frac{1}{k}(\text{MSD} - \text{MSW}),$$

whose expected value is exactly σ_y^2. This is an unbiased estimate, and all is lovely. It is not until we try to set confidence limits on σ_y^2 that we encounter trouble. Both the MSD and the MSW are χ^2 variates, but with different numbers of degrees of freedom. Their difference does not have a conveniently tabled distribution, so we are forced to seek approximate limits from the F table. Bross has given such limits in the form of two numbers, $\underline{L}$ and $\bar{L}$, which are to be multiplied by our best estimate of σ_y^2 to yield the lower and upper confidence limits.

5 *Per Cent Lower Limit* $= s_y^2 \cdot \underline{L}$

where
$$\underline{L} = \frac{F - F_{n_1, n_2}(0.05)}{F \cdot F_{n_1, \infty}(0.05) - F_{n_1, n_2}(0.05)},$$

$$F = \text{MSD/MSW},$$

$F_{n, m}(\alpha) = $ value from the F table at the αth level of probability, with the indicated numbers of degrees of freedom,

$n_1 = $ DF deviation, here $n - 2$,

$n_2 = $ DF within, here $n(k - 1)$ or $(N - n)$.

5 *Per Cent Upper Limit* $= s_y^2 \cdot \bar{L}$

where $\quad \bar{L} = \dfrac{F - F_{n_1, n_2}(0.95)}{F \cdot F_{n_1, \infty}(0.95) - F_{n_1, n_2}(0.95)} = \dfrac{F \cdot F_{n_2, n_1}(0.05) - 1}{\dfrac{F \cdot F_{n_2, n_1}(0.05)}{F_{\infty, n_1}(0.05)} - 1},$

$F_{n, m}(0.95) = 1/F_{m, n}(0.05)$ (note reversal of DF),

and the other symbols are as given for the 5 per cent lower limit. When $F \leqslant F_{n_1, n_2}(0,05)$, the lower limit is negative. Bross suggests that zero be used. In this same range of F, the upper limit also seems unsatisfactory, and Tukey [34] has proposed a Modified Upper Limit to be used for F in this limited region. The Modified Limit is not easily expressed as multiplier of the best estimate, but involves the MSD and the MSW explicitly. This

5 *Per Cent Modified* (*Bross*) *Upper Limit*, to be used when

$$F \leqslant F_{n_1, n_2}(0.05),$$

is

$$\frac{F_{\infty, n_1}(0.05)}{k} \left[\text{MSD} - \frac{\text{MSW}}{F_{n_2, n_1}(0.05)} \right],$$

where the symbols are already defined.

SUPPLEMENT ON FINITE POPULATIONS

Components of variance from finite error populations

Although the commonest regression models assume that the observations are disturbed by random errors from a large or infinite population, nevertheless many situations clearly call for different hypotheses. We frequently encounter physical problems in which the observations already contain all the possible errors of one type that we care to consider; i.e., we have sampled all of a very small population of errors. Analyses performed by each of the three chemists on a laboratory staff, for instance, will show the habitual biases of these men. If we are interested only in evaluating future work by these same analysts, clearly we do not wish to consider these three biases as a random sample of all possible analyst biases, but rather as the total population of biases present in our own rather restricted universe. The characteristic reactions to overheating of twenty types of radio tubes may all be represented in the errors of a large experiment—or perhaps only twelve of the twenty are present. In either case, we wish to consider a model far different from one postulating an infinite error population.

The algebra of these finite populations is messy. Fortunately a general pattern is visible to the initiated, so the detailed grinding out of an expected value for a Mean Square in the analysis of variance table can frequently be circumvented. Nevertheless, we know of no convenient illustration of the gruesome process and feel that a desirable completeness requires its inclusion at this point. Students may wish to peruse this section; men of faith or demonstrated ability will probably choose to skip it. We claim no elegance or particular conciseness in the exposition. We merely attempt to include enough of the steps to lead the timid and to guide the wary. The difficulties that are stressed are the ones encountered by the author in his first travail. He has resisted the impulse to make the derivations more sophisticated in the hope that they may remain more useful.

Sampling from a finite population

If we choose a sample of n, without replacement, from a population of size N, and if we let x_i be the symbol for the ith variate drawn, the formulae for the mean and *variance of the mean* of the sample of size n can be expressed in terms of the mean of the population, a, and the variance of the population, σ^2.

It has been conventional to define the variance of the population as $\frac{1}{N} \sum_{i=1}^{N} (x_i - a)^2$, and then that of the Sample Mean is $\frac{\sigma^2}{n} \cdot \frac{N-n}{N-1}$. (See Wilks, pp. 85, 86.)

We prefer to define the variance of the population as

$$\sigma^2 = \frac{1}{N-1} \sum_{i=1}^{N} (x_i - a)^2$$

where $a = \frac{1}{N} \sum_{i=1}^{N} x_i$, as before, since this leads to simpler algebra in the later analyses of variance.

The mean, $\bar{x}$, of the sample of n has an expected value of a. This is intuitively obvious but can be derived if we note that

$$E(x_1) = \sum_{i=1}^{N} x_i \operatorname{Pr}(X_1 = x_i).$$

Since $\operatorname{Pr}(X_1 = x_i) = 1/N$ (the x_i are assumed all different—not essential, but convenient), we see that

$$E(x_1) = \frac{\sum_{i=1}^{N} x_i}{N} = a;$$

then

$$E(\bar{x}) = \frac{1}{n} \sum_{i=1}^{n} E(x_i) = \frac{1}{n} \sum_{1}^{n} a = a,$$

as required. Further

$$n^2 \sigma_{\bar{x}}^2 = \sum_{\substack{i,j=1 \\ i \neq j}}^{n} \rho_{ij} \sigma_i \sigma_j + \sum_{i=1}^{n} \sigma_i^2.$$

(This follows from the linear combination of the x_i's leading to $\bar{x}$, which has weights of $1/n$ on each term. These weights are squared and the covariances summed.) The trick is to evaluate $\rho_{ij} \sigma_i \sigma_j$ and σ_i^2. For this purpose we note that

$$\sigma_i^2 = \mathrm{E}(x_i - a)^2 = \sum_{i=1}^{N} (x_i - a)^2 \, \mathrm{Pr}\,(X_1 = x_i)$$

$$= \frac{1}{N} \sum_{i=1}^{N} (x_i - a)^2 = \frac{N-1}{N} \left[\frac{\sum_{i}^{N} (x_i - a)^2}{N-1} \right],$$

so that $\sigma_i^2 = \dfrac{N-1}{N} \cdot \sigma^2$. This is the variance of one reading, x_i. The *covariance* requires the marginal probability $\mathrm{Pr}\,(X_1 = x_i, X_2 = x_j)$, which is $[N(N-1)]^{-1}$ since the first two values may be chosen in only one way, whereas the third has $N-2$ ways, the fourth $N-3$, etc.—but the total probability associated with any *one* value is $[N(N-1)(N-2) \ldots (N-n+1)]^{-1}$. By using the definition of covariance

$$\rho_{ij} \sigma_i \sigma_j = \mathrm{E}(x_i - a)(x_i - a) \sum_{\substack{i,j=1 \\ i \neq 1}}^{N} (x_i - a)(x_j - a) \, \mathrm{Pr}\,(X_1 = x_i, X_2 = x_j),$$

$$\rho_{ij} \sigma_i \sigma_j = \sum_{i=1}^{N} (x_i - a) \sum_{\substack{j=1 \\ j \neq i}}^{N} \frac{(x_j - a)}{N(N-1)}$$

$$= \sum_{i=1}^{N} \frac{(x_i - a)}{N(N-1)} \left[-(x_i - a) + \sum_{j=1}^{N} (x_j - a) \right]$$

$$= - \sum_{i=1}^{N} \frac{(x_i - a)^2}{N(N-1)} = - \frac{\sigma^2}{N}.$$

Now

$$n^2 \sigma_{\bar{x}}^2 = \frac{N-1}{N} \sum_{i=1}^{n} \sigma^2 - \frac{1}{N} \sum_{\substack{i,j=1 \\ i \neq j}}^{n} \sigma^2$$

$$= n\sigma^2 \frac{(N-1)}{N} - \frac{\sigma^2}{N} n\,(n-1)$$

$$= \frac{n\sigma^2}{N} (N - 1 - n + 1) = \frac{n\sigma^2}{N} (N - n),$$

so that

$$\sigma_{\bar{x}}^2 = \frac{\sigma^2}{nN} (N - n) = \frac{\sigma^2}{n} \left(1 - \frac{n}{N} \right) = \sigma^2 \left(\frac{1}{n} - \frac{1}{N} \right).$$

This last form is much pleasanter in the subsequent analyses of variance than is the more conventional one. Both forms are asymptotically correct: $N \to \infty$ gives $\sigma_{\bar{x}}^2$ or σ^2/n. Also, if the sample size, n, is a sample of *one*,

$$\sigma_{\bar{x}}^2 = \sigma_i^2 = \sigma^2 \left(1 - \frac{1}{N}\right), \text{ as required.}$$

Simple regression—analysis of variance

We assume the model for our (unknown) line to be

$$y_i = \alpha + \beta x_i + \epsilon_i, \qquad i = 1, 2, \ldots n, \tag{9}$$

where the x_i are known accurately, and the ϵ_i are drawn from a population of N members, whose mean is zero and whose variance is σ^2. We have n data points from which we fit our line by minimizing $\sum_{i=1}^{n} (y_i - a - bx_i)^2$, which gives

$$\left. \begin{array}{l} \sum_i (y_i - a - bx_i)(x_i) = 0 \quad \text{or} \quad b = \dfrac{\sum(x_i - x.)(y_i - y.)}{\sum (x_i - x.)^2} \\ \text{and} \\ \qquad \sum_i (y_i - a - bx_i) = 0 \quad \text{or} \quad a = y. - bx. \end{array} \right\} \tag{10}$$

Now if we take an *arbitrary trial line*, $Y_i = A + Bx_i$, and consider the Sums of Squares which are usual in the analysis of variance, then

$$\begin{aligned} \sum_i (y_i - Y_i)^2 &\equiv \sum_i [(y_i - a - bx_i) + (b - B)(x_i - x.) \\ &\qquad\qquad + x.(b - B) + (a - A)]^2 \\ &\equiv \sum_i [(y_i - a - bx_i) + (b - B)(x_i - x.) \\ &\qquad\qquad + (y - Y.)]^2 \\ &\equiv \sum_i (y_i - a - bx_i)^2 + (b - B)^2 Sxx + n(y. - Y.)^2. \end{aligned} \tag{11}$$

The cross terms vanish because of the definition of $x.$ as the arithmetic mean—and not because of any probability assumptions. The model (Greek letters) has not yet been involved—only *algebraic* identities.

These Sums of Squares are all computable from the data (including the assumed constants A and B) and are commonly called the Sums of Squares for the *residual, slope,* and *mean*, respectively.

We shall now examine the expected values of these quantities.

First:

$$\begin{aligned} n(y. - Y.)^2 &= n(\alpha + \beta x. + \epsilon. - A - Bx.)^2 \\ &= n[(\alpha - A) + (\beta - B)x. + (\epsilon. - 0)]^2. \end{aligned}$$

If we take expected values, the only term which is affected is the $\epsilon.$; thus

$$E[n(y. - Y.)^2] = n[(\alpha - A) + (\beta - B)x.]^2 + n\, E(\epsilon.^2).$$

Now it can be shown that

$$E(\epsilon_i^2) = \left(1 - \frac{1}{N}\right)\sigma^2$$

$$E(\epsilon.^2) = \left(\frac{1}{n} - \frac{1}{N}\right)\sigma^2$$

so that

$$E[n(y. - Y.)^2] = n(y_\Delta - Y.)^2 + \left(1 - \frac{n}{N}\right)\sigma^2, \tag{12}$$

where the subscript Δ means the average over the whole population (of N).

Next:

$$E[(b - B)^2 Sxx] = Sxx\, E(b - B)^2.$$

Here we may begin by considering

$$bSxx = \sum_i (x_i - x.)(y_i - y.)$$

$$= \sum_i (x_i - x.)[\beta(x_i - x.) + (\epsilon_i - \epsilon.)]$$

$$= \beta Sxx + \sum_i (x_i - x.)(\epsilon_i - \epsilon.)$$

so that $Sxx(b - \beta) = \sum_i (x_i - x.)(\epsilon_i - \epsilon.)$.

By taking expected values after squaring,

$$Sxx\, E(b - \beta)^2 = \frac{1}{Sxx}\, E[\sum_i (x_i - x.)(\epsilon_i - \epsilon.)]^2 \tag{13}$$

$$= \frac{1}{Sxx}\, E\left[\sum_{i,j}^{n} (x_i - x.)(x_j - x.)(\epsilon_i - \epsilon.)(\epsilon_j - \epsilon.)\right]$$

$$= \frac{1}{Sxx}\left[\sum_i (x_i - x.)^2\, E(\epsilon_i - \epsilon.)^2 \right.$$

$$\left. + \sum_{i,j}' (x_i - x.)(x_j - x.)\, E(\epsilon_i - \epsilon)(\epsilon_j - \epsilon.)\right]$$

where $\sum_{i,j}'$ means that $i = j$ is omitted from the summation.

If we know $E(\epsilon_i - \epsilon.)(\epsilon_j - \epsilon.)$, etc., this can be evaluated. But

$$E(\epsilon_i - \epsilon.)^2 = E(\epsilon_i^2) - 2E(\epsilon_i \epsilon.) + E(\epsilon.^2)$$

$$= \left[\left(1 - \frac{1}{N}\right) - 2\left(\frac{1}{n} - \frac{1}{N}\right) + \left(\frac{1}{n} - \frac{1}{N}\right)\right]\sigma^2$$

$$= \left(1 - \frac{1}{n}\right)\sigma^2,$$

and for $i \neq j$

$$E[(\epsilon_i - \epsilon.)(\epsilon_j - \epsilon.)] = E(\epsilon_i \epsilon_j) - 2E(\epsilon_i \epsilon.) + E(\epsilon.^2)$$

$$= \left[-\frac{1}{N} - 2\left(\frac{1}{n} - \frac{1}{N}\right) + \left(\frac{1}{n} - \frac{1}{N}\right) \right]\sigma^2$$

$$= -\frac{\sigma^2}{n}. \tag{14}$$

By using these results,

$$Sxx\, E(b - \beta)^2 = \frac{1}{Sxx}\left(1 - \frac{1}{n}\right)\sigma^2 Sxx$$

$$+ \frac{1}{Sxx}\left(-\frac{\sigma^2}{n}\right)\sum_{ij}' (x_i - x.)(x_j - x.)$$

$$= \left(1 - \frac{1}{n}\right)\sigma^2 + \frac{\sigma^2}{n} = \sigma^2. \tag{15}$$

Using the relation

$$E(b - B)^2 = E[(b - \beta) + (\beta - B)]^2 = E(b - \beta)^2 + (\beta - B)^2,$$

we get

$$E[(b - B)^2 Sxx] = Sxx(\beta - B)^2 + \sigma^2. \tag{16}$$

Finally:

$$E\left[\sum_i (y_i - a - bx_i)^2\right]$$

$$= E\left[\sum_i (\alpha + \beta x_i - a - bx_i + \epsilon_i)^2\right] = E\sum_i [(\beta - b)(x_i - x.) + (\epsilon_i - \epsilon.)]^2$$

$$= E(\beta - b)^2\, Sxx + 2E(\beta - B)\sum_i (x_i - x.)(\epsilon_i - \epsilon.) + E(\epsilon_i - \epsilon.)^2\, n;$$

but

$$(b - \beta)Sxx = \sum_i (x_i - x.)(\epsilon_i - \epsilon.),$$

so that

$$-2E(b - \beta)\sum_i (x_i - x.)(\epsilon_i - \epsilon.) = -\frac{2E}{Sxx}\left[\sum_i (x_i - x.)(\epsilon_i - \epsilon.)\right]^2,$$

which is $= -2Sxx\, E(b - \beta)^2$ as shown in equation (13). Thus

$$E\left[\sum_i (y_i - a - bx_i)^2\right] = E(\epsilon_i - \epsilon.)^2 n - Sxx\, E(\beta - b)^2$$

$$= n\left(1 - \frac{1}{n}\right)\sigma^2 - \sigma^2 = (n - 2)\sigma^2. \tag{17}$$

This explains why we define s^2 by the relation

$$(n - 2)s^2 = \sum_i (y_i - a - bx_i)^2. \tag{18}$$

These derivations explain the terms appearing in the anova tables for this problem. Such a table is shown in Table 5 (also in the article by Tukey [35]).

Confidence limits are set with the ratios of appropriate Mean Squares—using the F test (which is the t^2 test if the numerator has one degree of freedom).

TABLE 5

Item	DF	SS	MS	CMS
Mean	1	$n(y. - Y.)^2$	$n(y. - Y.)^2$	$(y. - Y)^2 - \left(\dfrac{1}{n} - \dfrac{1}{N}\right)s^2$
Slope	1	$(b - B)^2 Sxx$	$(b - B)^2 Sxx$	$(b - B)^2 - s^2\{Sxx\}^{-1}$
Residue	$n - 2$	$(n - 2)s^2$	s^2	s^2

Item	AMS	ACMS
Mean	$n(y_\Delta - Y.)^2 + \left(1 - \dfrac{n}{N}\right)\sigma^2$	$(y_\Delta - Y.)^2$
Slope	$(B - \beta)^2 Sxx + \sigma^2$	$(\beta - B)^2$
Residue	σ^2	σ^2

DF = Degrees of Freedom
SS = Sums of Squares
MS = Mean Square
CMS = Component of Mean Square
AMS = Average Mean Square
ACMS = Average of Component of Mean Square

Repeated measurements at each value of x

Now we shall summarize a more complicated regression model. Suppose that we have repeated measurements at each of the x_i values, and suppose that there are two kinds of errors in y, those that depend on x_i and those that are independent of x_i:

$$y_{ij} = \alpha + \beta x_i + \xi_i + \epsilon_{ij} \qquad \begin{array}{l} i = 1, 2, ..., n \\ j = 1, 2, ..., k \end{array} \tag{19}$$

where the ϵ_{ij} come from a population (size N) of zero mean and variance σ_0^2 and the ξ_i come from a population (M) of zero mean and variance σ_1^2 and the ξ_i come from a population (M) of zero mean and variance σ_1^2 and are dependent on x_i. This model is identical with that treated earlier in this chapter except for the finiteness of the populations.

If there were a known systematic effect of x_i on the ϵ_{ij}^2, the best method of fitting should utilize this knowledge in its procedure—by some weighting scheme for the various values of x_i, perhaps. Since we do not wish to particularize the problem in this direction, we shall merely fit by the ordinary technique, using the means of the y's at each point as if they were the raw data. Since we supposed an equal number of data points at each value of x_i, this would be equivalent to minimizing $\sum_{ij} (y_{ij} - a - bx_i)^2$.

Thus we minimize

$$\sum_i (y_i - a - bx_i)^2$$

giving

$$a = y.. - bx.$$
$$bSxx = \sum_i (x_i - x.)(y_i. - y..). \tag{20}$$

Note that the equal number of data at each x allows k to come out through the summation. Thus we find ourselves using Sxx for $\sum_i (x_i - x.)^2$ instead of $k \sum_i (x_i - x.)^2$, which would have been strictly analogous to the previous example with unequal numbers.

If we suspect the arbitrary line

$$Y_i = A + Bx_i$$

to be the true line, we shall want to examine the sum of squares

$$\sum_{ij} (y_{ij} - Y_i)^2 \equiv \sum_{ij} [(y_{ij} - y_i.) + (y_i. - a - bx_i)$$
$$+ (b - B)(x_i - x.) + (y.. - Y.)]^2$$
$$\equiv \sum_{ij} (y_{ij} - y_i.)^2 + k \sum_i (y_i. - a - bx_i)^2$$
$$+ k(b - B)^2 Sxx + n\,k(y.. - Y.)^2$$

with the cross products disappearing on summation for the usual *algebraic* reasons. We shall now invoke our probability model to evaluate the expected value of each of these sums of squares.

First:

$$\text{E} \sum_{ij} (y_{ij} - y_i.)^2 = \text{E} \sum_{ij} (\epsilon_{ij} - \epsilon_i.)^2 = \text{E} \sum_{ij} (\epsilon_{ij} - \epsilon_i.)(\epsilon_{ij})$$

$$= \text{E} \sum_{ij} \epsilon_{ij}{}^2 - k\text{E} \sum_i (\epsilon_i.)^2$$

$$= n\,k\left(1 - \frac{1}{N}\right)\sigma_0{}^2 - n\,k\left(\frac{1}{k} - \frac{1}{N}\right)\sigma_0{}^2$$

$$= n\,k\,\sigma_0{}^2\left(1 - \frac{1}{k}\right) = n(k - 1)\sigma_0{}^2. \tag{21}$$

Second:

$$k\text{E} \sum_i (y_i. - a - bx_i)^2 = k\text{E} \sum_i [(\beta - b)(x_i - x.) + (\xi_i - \xi.) + (\epsilon_i. - \epsilon..)]^2$$

$$= Sxx\,\text{E}(\beta - b)^2 + k\text{E} \sum_i (\xi_i - \xi.)^2 + k\text{E} \sum_i (\epsilon_i. - \epsilon..)^2$$

$$+ 2k\text{E} \sum_i (\beta - b)(x_i - x.)(\xi_i - \xi.)$$

$$+ 2k\text{E} \sum_i (\beta - b)(x_i - x.)(\epsilon_i. - \epsilon..)$$

$$+ 2k\text{E} \sum_i (\xi_i - \xi.)(\epsilon_i. - \epsilon..). \tag{22}$$

Since we postulate zero correlation between ξ_i and ϵ_{ij}, the last term is zero.

Now consider

$$bSxx = \sum_i (y_i. - y..)(x_i - x.)$$

$$= \sum_i (x_i - x.)[\beta(x_i - x.) + (\xi_i - \xi.) + (\epsilon_i. - \epsilon..)]$$

$$= \beta Sxx + \sum_i (x_i - x.)(\xi_i - \xi.) + \sum_i (x_i - x.)(\epsilon_i. - \epsilon..),$$

so that

$$\text{E}\,Sxx(b - \beta)^2 = \frac{1}{Sxx}\,\text{E}\left[\sum_i (x_i - x.)(\xi_i - \xi.) + \sum_i (x_i - x.)(\epsilon_i. - \epsilon..)\right]^2$$

$$= \frac{1}{Sxx}\,\text{E}\left[\sum_{ij} (x_i - x.)(x_j - x.)(\xi_i - \xi.)(\xi_j - \xi.)\right.$$

$$\left. + \sum_{ij} (x_i - x.)(x_j - x.)(\epsilon_i. - \epsilon..)(\epsilon_j. - \epsilon..)\right]. \tag{23}$$

The cross terms disappear under the expectation, since $\xi_i \epsilon_i.$ correlation is zero.

Since

$$\beta - b = \frac{1}{Sxx}\left[\sum_i (x_i - x.)(\xi_i - \xi.) + \sum_i (x_i - x.)(\epsilon_i. - \epsilon..)\right],$$

the cross terms which did not disappear in equations (22) give

$$- \text{E} \frac{2k}{Sxx} \left[\sum_i (x_i - x.)(\xi_i - \xi.) \right]^2 - \text{E} \frac{2k}{Sxx} \left[\sum_i (x_i - x.)(\epsilon_i. - \epsilon..) \right]^2$$

(cross terms in $\xi_i \epsilon_{ij}$ again disappearing under E), which is equal to

$$- 2kSxx \, \text{E}(b - \beta)^2$$

by virtue of (23). Thus (22) becomes

$$kE \sum_i (y_i. - a - bx_i)^2$$

$$= kE \sum_i (\xi_i - \xi.)^2 + kE \sum_i (\epsilon_i. - \epsilon..)^2 - kSxx \, \text{E}(b - \beta)^2$$

$$= k \sum_i \text{E}(\xi_i - \xi.)^2 + k \sum_i \text{E}(\epsilon_i. - \epsilon..)^2 - kSxx \, \text{E}(b - \beta)^2. \qquad (24)$$

But

$$\text{E}(\epsilon_{ij}^2) = \left(1 - \frac{1}{N}\right)\sigma_0^2; \quad \text{E}(\epsilon_{ij}\epsilon_{ik}) = - \frac{\sigma^2}{N} \qquad j \neq k$$

$$\text{E}(\epsilon_i.^2) = \left(\frac{1}{k} - \frac{1}{N}\right)\sigma_0^2$$

and

$$\text{E}(\epsilon..^2) = \text{E}(\epsilon_i.\epsilon..) = \left(\frac{1}{nk} - \frac{1}{N}\right)\sigma_0^2,$$

so that

$$\text{E}(\epsilon_i. - \epsilon..)^2 = \text{E}(\epsilon_i.)^2 - \text{E}(\epsilon..)^2 = \frac{1}{k}\left(1 - \frac{1}{n}\right)\sigma_0^2.$$

Also

$$\text{E}(\xi_i - \xi.)^2 = \left(1 - \frac{1}{n}\right)\sigma_1^2; \quad \text{E}[(\xi_i - \xi.)(\xi_j - \xi.)] = - \frac{\sigma_1^2}{n} \qquad i \neq j$$

(and

$$\text{E}(\epsilon_{ij} - \epsilon_i.)^2 = \left(1 - \frac{1}{k}\right)\sigma_0^2; \quad \text{E}\left[(\epsilon_i. - \epsilon..)(\epsilon_j. - \epsilon..)\right] = - \frac{\sigma_0^2}{kn}\right] \quad i \neq j).$$

Thus

$$Sxx \, \text{E}(b - \beta)^2 = \frac{1}{Sxx} \left[\sum_{ij} (x_i - x.)(x_j - x.) \, \text{E}(\xi_i - \xi.)(\xi_j - \xi.) \right.$$

$$\left. + \sum_{ij} (x_i - x.)(x_j - x.) \, \text{E}(\epsilon_i. - \epsilon..)(\epsilon_j. - \epsilon..) \right]$$

$$= \frac{1}{Sxx}\left\{ \sum_i (x_i - x.)^2[\mathrm{E}(\xi_i - \xi.)^2 + \mathrm{E}(\epsilon_i. - \epsilon..)^2] \right.$$

$$+ \sum_{ij}' (x_i - x.)(x_j - x.)[\mathrm{E}(\xi_i - \xi.)(\xi_j - \xi.)$$

$$\left. + \mathrm{E}(\epsilon_i - \epsilon..)(\epsilon_j. - \epsilon..)] \right\}$$

$$= \left(1 - \frac{1}{n}\right)\sigma_1{}^2 + \frac{1}{k}\left(1 - \frac{1}{n}\right)\sigma_0{}^2 + \frac{\sigma_1{}^2}{n} + \frac{\sigma_0{}^2}{kn}$$

$$= \sigma_1{}^2 + \frac{1}{k}\sigma_{02}. \tag{25}$$

Returning to (17), we see that

$$k\mathrm{E}\sum_i (y_i. - a - bx_i)^2 = n\,k\left(1 - \frac{1}{n}\right)\sigma_1{}^2 + nk\frac{1}{k}\left(1 - \frac{1}{n}\right)\sigma_0{}^2 - k\sigma_1{}^2 - \sigma_0{}^2$$

$$= k(n - 2)\sigma_1{}^2 + (n - 2)\sigma_0{}^2$$

$$= (n - 2)(k\sigma_1{}^2 + \sigma_0{}^2).$$

Third:

$$\mathrm{E}[k\,Sxx(b - B)^2 = k\,Sxx\,\mathrm{E}(b - B)^2$$

$$= k\,Sxx\,\mathrm{E}[(b - \beta) + (\beta - B)]^2 \tag{26}$$

$$= k\,Sxx[(\beta - B)^2 + \mathrm{E}(b - \beta)^2]$$

$$= k\,Sxx(\beta - B)^2 + k\sigma_1{}^2 + \sigma_0{}^2.$$

Last:

$$nk\,\mathrm{E}(y.. - Y.)^2 = nk\,\mathrm{E}[(\alpha + \beta x. + \epsilon. + \epsilon..) - Y.]^2.$$

Only the $\epsilon..$ and $\xi.$ have probabilistic character, and their mean values are zero, so only terms of second order in these will be affected by E. Thus

$$nk\,\mathrm{E}(y.. - Y.)^2 = nk\,\mathrm{E}[(\alpha + \beta x. - Y.) + (\xi. + \epsilon..)]^2$$

$$= n\,k(y_\varDelta - y.)^2 + nk\,\mathrm{E}(\xi.^2 + 2\xi.\epsilon.. + \epsilon..^2).$$

If we demand that ξ_i and ϵ_{ij} be uncorrelated, the middle term of the second bracket disappears, and we must evaluate only

$$\mathrm{E}(\xi.^2) = \left(\frac{1}{n} - \frac{1}{M}\right)\sigma_1{}^2$$

$$\mathrm{E}(\epsilon..)^2 = \left(\frac{1}{nk} - \frac{1}{N}\right)\sigma_0{}^2,$$

so that

$$nk\,\mathrm{E}(y.. - Y.)^2 = n\,k(y_\varDelta - Y.)^2 + k\left(1 - \frac{n}{M}\right)\sigma_1{}^2 + \left(1 - \frac{nk}{N}\right)\sigma_0{}^2. \tag{27}$$

TABLE 6

Item	DF	SS	$MS = \dfrac{SS}{DF}$	CMS	AMS	ACMS
Mean	1	$nk(y_{..} - Y_.)^2$	$nk(y_{..} - Y_.)^2$	$a(y_{..} - Y_.)^2 - \left(\dfrac{1}{n} - \dfrac{1}{M}\right)s_1^2 - \left(\dfrac{1}{nk} - \dfrac{1}{N}\right)s_0^2$	$nk(y_\Delta - Y_.)^2 + k\left(1 - \dfrac{n}{M}\right)\sigma_1^2 + \left(1 - \dfrac{nk}{N}\right)\sigma_0^2$	$(y_\Delta - Y_.)^2$
Slope	1	$k(b - B)^2 Sxx$	$k(b - B)^2 Sxx$	$\dfrac{1}{kSxx}[MSS(\text{lope}) - MSD(\text{eviation})]$	$k(\beta - B)^2 Sxx + k\sigma_1^2 + \sigma_0^2$	$(\beta - B)^2$
Deviation	$n - 2$	$k\sum_i (y_{i.} - a - bx_i)^2$	$ks_1^2 + s_0^2$	$\dfrac{1}{k}[MSD(\text{eviation}) - MSW(\text{ithin})]$	$k\sigma_1^2 + \sigma_0^2$	σ_1^2
Within	$n(k - 1)$	$\sum_{ij}(y_{ij} - y_{i.})^2$	s_0^2	s_0^2	σ_0^2	σ_0^2

a CMSM(ean) could also be written, if M and N were sufficiently large, $\dfrac{1}{nk}$ [MSM(ean)—MSD(eviation)]

We sum these formulae up in Table 6.   Note that CMS is that Combination of Mean Squares which will have, on the average, the value of the variance (or a group of parameter variances) which we wish to measure.

Thus CMSD(eviation) is, on the average, equal to $\sigma_\xi^2 \equiv \sigma_1^2$ and CMSW(ithin) is, on the average, equal to $\sigma_\epsilon^2 \equiv \sigma_0^2$, whereas CMSS(lope) is equal to, on the average, $(\beta - B)^2$ and measures how much variance is contributed by a bad guess for B.

Confidence limits with finite populations

When it comes to setting limits, several questions confront us: The fairly obvious test for slope would be

$$\frac{\text{MSS}}{\text{MSD}} = F_{1,\,n-2} = t_{n-2}^2.$$

The test for the mean, if M and N are large, is the same, but if they are small, a denominator of

$$\left(1 - \frac{n}{M}\right)\text{MSD} + n\left(\frac{1}{M} - \frac{k}{N}\right)\text{MSW}$$

seems to be suggested.*   Then the question of appropriate degrees of freedom for this denominator arises.   In fact, the question of whether or not such a composite denominator may be used in anything approximating an F test can be raised.   The examination of ratios of this type showed that they were apt to be least reliable when negative coefficients were involved, and Cochran proposes the use of a different ratio as an F test, so as to eliminate all minus signs.   Here the simplest one would be

$$F' = \frac{\text{MSM} + \dfrac{n}{M}\,\text{MSD} + \dfrac{nk}{N}\,\text{MSW}}{\text{MSD} + \dfrac{n}{M}\,\text{MSW}}. \tag{28}$$

In either case the appropriate number of degrees of freedom is to be determined by the formula

$$\nu = \frac{\left(\sum\limits_i a_i \text{MS}_i\right)^2}{\sum\limits_i \dfrac{a_i^2(\text{MS}_i)^2}{n_i}} \tag{29}$$

where the summation is over the mean squares in the linear combination for which an equivalent degree of freedom is desired, the a_i are the coeffi-

* W. Cochran, *Biometrics* 7 (1951), 20.

cients of the MS_i in the linear combination, and the n_i are the degrees of freedom for MS_i. The essential points to notice from Tables 5 and 6 are:

1. The finiteness of the error populations in a linear regression problem with one variate in error affects only our tests for the mean.

2. If, in Table 6, the deviations of the group means from the line have been completely sampled, then $M = n$ and σ_1^2 does not appear in the AMS for the mean. The appropriate F comparison is then MSD. By the same argument, if the variations within the populations have been completely sampled (an experimentally less probable situation), then $N = nk$ and σ_0^2 does not appear in AMSM(ean). If M is infinite, the appropriate F comparison for MSM(ean) might be (MSD $- \dfrac{nk}{N}$ MSW), but this has the objectionable negative sign. Alternatively, we could use (MSM $+ \dfrac{nk}{N}$ MSW) versus MSD, the appropriate degrees of freedom being calculated from equation (29).

3. If either of the errors are drawn from a finite population that is only partially sampled, the appropriate F tests are not exactly known, but a working procedure has been outlined above.

4. If the deviations of the population mean ξ_i are completely sampled but if those that are independent of $x_i(\epsilon_{ij})$ come from a large or infinite supply, Table 6 looks very similar to Table 5 where there was no question of deviations of the population means from the structural line—and, indeed, the F tests for the means are identical in the two cases. The slope tests, of course, differ.

The derivation of an expected value

Earlier in Chapter 3 we needed to find

$$E \sum_{i=1}^{n} k_i[y_i. - m - b(x_i. - x.)]^2.$$

The difficulties arise because the brackets contain the random variables implicitly in m and b as well as in $y_i.$. We omit the range of summation as it can cause no confusion. Using

$$bSxx = \sum_i k_i(x_i - x.)(y_i. - y..)$$

and $m = y.. = \mu + \gamma. + \epsilon..$, we obtain

$$E \sum_i k_i \Big[(\gamma_i - \gamma.) + (\epsilon_i. - \epsilon..) + \beta(x_i - x.) - \frac{x_i - x.}{Sxx} \sum_r k_r(x_r - x.)(y_r. - y..) \Big]^2.$$

By eliminating the y's from the last parentheses,

$$E \sum_i k_i \Big\{ (\gamma_i - \gamma.) + (\epsilon_i. - \epsilon..)$$

$$- \frac{(x_i - x.)}{Sxx} \sum_r k_r [x_r - x.][(\gamma_r - \gamma.) + (\epsilon_r. - \epsilon..)] \Big\}^2.$$

If we now square the largest bracket and move the expectation symbol through the summation on i, placing it immediately in front of all Greek letter products, we see that all terms in which an ϵ is multiplied by a γ vanish. Most of the others will disappear also, but in order not to make any mistakes while juggling with subscripts, we shall write down all the other terms explicitly. We thus obtain

$$\sum_i k_i \Big\{ E(\gamma_i - \gamma.)^2 + E(\epsilon_i. - \epsilon..)^2$$

$$+ \frac{(x_i - x.)^2}{Sxx^2} \sum_{rs} k_r k_s (x_r - x.)(x_s - x.)[E(\gamma_r - \gamma.)(\gamma_s - \gamma.)$$

$$+ E(\epsilon_r. - \epsilon..)(\epsilon_s. - \epsilon..)] - \frac{2(x_i - x.)}{Sxx} \sum_r k_r (x_r - x.)$$

$$[E(\gamma_r - \gamma.)(\gamma_i - \gamma.) + E(\epsilon_r. - \epsilon..)(\epsilon_i. - \epsilon..)] \Big\}.$$

At this point we must evaluate expressions like $E(\gamma_r - \gamma.)(\gamma_s - \gamma.)$, and the values we obtain will depend on the population model assumed. With our infinite population $E(\gamma_r - \gamma.)(\gamma_s - \gamma.) = E(\gamma_r \gamma_s) - E(\gamma_r \gamma.) - E(\gamma_s \gamma.)$

$+ E(\gamma^2.) = \left(\delta_{rs} - \frac{k_r}{N} - \frac{k_s}{N} + \theta \right) \sigma_\gamma^2$, where δ_{rs} is defined above and

$\theta = \frac{1}{N^2} \sum k_r^2$, a constant that does not involve either subscript. The computation of $E(\gamma_r \gamma.)$ is similar to that of $E(\epsilon_{ij} \epsilon_i.)$, as are the other expectations required. We may summarize the results by noting that

$$E(\gamma_i - \gamma.)^2 = \left(1 - \frac{2k_i}{N} + \theta \right) \sigma_\gamma^2,$$

$$E(\epsilon_r. - \epsilon..)(\epsilon_s. - \epsilon..) = \left(\frac{\delta_{rs}}{k_r} - \frac{1}{N} \right) \sigma^2,$$

$$E(\epsilon_r. - \epsilon..)^2 = \left(\frac{1}{k_r} - \frac{1}{N} \right) \sigma^2.$$

In the summation $\sum_{rs} k_r k_s (x_r - x.)(x_s - x.) \left(\delta_{rs} - \frac{k_r}{N} - \frac{k_s}{N} + \theta \right)$, only the first term will produce anything, as the other three all give $\sum k_t(x_t - x.)$ as a factor—and this is identically zero by definition of $x.$. The expectation just given reduces to

$$\sigma_y^2 \sum_i k_i \left[\left(1 - \frac{2k_i}{N} + \theta \right) + \frac{(x_i - x.)^2}{(Sxx)^2} \sum_{r,s} k_r k_s (x_i - x.)(x_s - x.) \right.$$
$$\left. \left(\delta_{rs} - \frac{k_r}{N} - \frac{k_s}{N} + \theta \right) - \frac{2(x_i - x.)}{Sxx} \sum_r k_r(x_r - x.) \left(\delta_{ri} - \frac{k_r}{N} - \frac{k_i}{N} + \theta \right) \right]$$

$$+ \sigma^2 \sum_i k_i \left[\left(\frac{1}{k_i} - \frac{1}{N} \right) + \frac{(x_i - x.)^2}{(Sxx)^2} \sum_{r,s} k_r k_s (x_r - x.)(x_s - x.) \right.$$
$$\left. \left(\frac{\delta_{rs}}{k_r} - \frac{1}{N} \right) - \frac{2(x_i - x.)}{Sxx} \sum_r k_r(x_r - x.) \left(\frac{\delta_{ir}}{k_r} - \frac{1}{N} \right) \right],$$

and further

$$\sigma_y^2 \sum_i k_i \left\{ 1 + \theta - \frac{2k_i}{N} + \frac{(x_i - x.)^2}{(Sxx)^2} \sum_r k_r^2(x_r - x.)^2 - \frac{2(x_i - x.)}{Sxx} \right.$$
$$\left. \left[k_i(x_i - x.) - \frac{1}{N} \sum_r k_r^2(x_r - x.)^2 \right] \right\}$$
$$+ \sigma^2 \sum_i k_i \left[\frac{1}{k_i} - \frac{1}{N} + \frac{(x_i - x.)^2}{Sxx} - \frac{2(x_i - x.)^2}{Sxx} \right],$$

which becomes

$$\sigma_y^2 \left[N + N\theta - 2N\theta + \frac{1}{Sxx} \sum_r k_r^2(x_r - x.)^2 - \frac{2}{Sxx} \sum_r k_r^2(x_r - x.)^2 \right]$$
$$+ \sigma^2(n - 1 + 1 - 2).$$

Finally we see that

$$E \sum_i k_i [y_i. - m - b(x_i - x.)]^2$$
$$= (n - 2)\sigma^2 + \left[\left(N - \frac{\sum k_i^2}{N} \right) - \frac{\sum k_i^2(x_i - x.)^2}{Sxx} \right] \sigma_y^2.$$

CHAPTER 4

Samples from Bivariate Normal Populations

We now wish to depart from the strict topic of this book, the analysis of straight-line data, to consider the lines that may be found underlying data from a bivariate population. Since our aim is to set forth only those features that affect our main straight-line problem, we shall not deal exhaustively with this topic and usually we shall confine our remarks to samples drawn from a bivariate *normal* population. We hasten to remark that this interlude is proffered in the hope of lessening the confusions which have occurred in the literature, where the term *regression line* has been used to denote almost any kind of a line as long as it has arisen from one or more distributed variables. There is considerable generic difference between a chemical analysis in which the quantity being analyzed is under the control of the chemist and the heights of several fathers and their sons where presumably we must take the sample we get. It is possible to consider these two models each from the point of view of the other, but more information can be extracted by treating each as the individual problem that it is.

In the subsequent chapters we shall examine straight-line models in which both variables are subject to errors. Taken by themselves, these errors will have some bivariate distribution, and so the present material is germane to this later discussion. Also, when we discuss "degenerate" models in Chapter 5, we are talking about structural lines on which have been superimposed large distributions other than those of the measurement errors, and this addition gives the model some of the attributes of the bivariate-normal regression problems. Thus the clear-cut distinction made here will ultimately be broken down, but nevertheless we feel it is a useful one.

Bivariate populations seldom appear in the physical sciences with the same dominance that they enjoy in the biological ones. A greater control in physics, chemistry, and engineering allows us to design experiments which relegate bivariate distributions to the smaller parts of the analysis and bury them (we hope) under the main effects we wish to estimate. We like such situations, as they make our analyses easier. Occasionally, however, we cannot arrange an experiment in such a convenient way. Indeed, we may not be able to arrange it at all. If we examine the effect of sunspots on radio wave propagation, we may observe the number of sunspots and measure some quality of radio reception. These variables are not under our control and exhibit variations containing strong random elements. Lacking an adequate time-series understanding of these phenomena, we shall probably choose to regard such data as random samples from a bivariate population—and then see what information we can extract.

In biological experiments, the number, size, and body weight of the offspring cannot be preselected, and so we accept these additional dominant random elements in our experimental structure.

The mathematical model

A pictorial representation of our bivariate-normal model is given in Figure 35. Here the total volume under the mountainous surface is unity

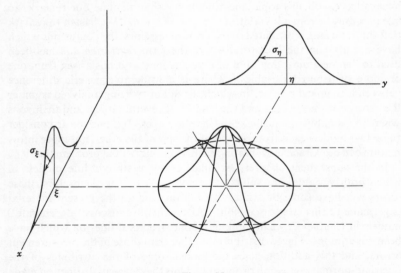

Figure 35

and thus the volume of the right cylinder over any particular region in the (x, y) plane represents the probability of finding a datum in that area rather than somewhere else. If we draw a truly random sample from the population distribution depicted and plot the sample as a three-dimensional histogram, this histogram will approximate the shape of the population distribution. ("Approximate" can be given operational meaning in one of several reasonable ways, and the approximation will be better the larger our sample.) More precisely, as the sample size increases toward ∞, the probability will approach *one* that the sample distribution is closer than ϵ to the population distribution (ϵ being in the units of our measure of closeness of fit). Thus, from the sample data we can estimate the parameters of the usually unknown parent population.

The bivariate normal distribution has five parameters, two locating the center (ξ, η), two measuring the dispersion (σ_ξ, σ_η), and one giving the degree of correlation $\rho_{\xi\eta}$.

If we consider the mountain to be made of a uniform material, and then —with a bulldozer—push it parallel to the x axis, onto the (y, z) plane, allowing it to pile up higher where it will but not to spread out, we get a normal curve for the one variable, y. For pictorial elegance we normalize it so that the maximum ordinate is the same height as the mountain peak. Its mean is η and the distance from this mean to its inflection point is σ_η, so it is precisely the old familiar normal curve of Chapters 2 and 3. Similarly, by projecting parallel to y we get a frequency function for x alone with mean ξ and variance σ_ξ^2. These two one-dimensional curves are the *marginal distributions* of y and x respectively. Analytically, they are obtained by integrating out the unwanted variable from the bivariate frequency function. Thus four of the five parameters may be thrown back into the more familiar one-dimensional framework, and further discussion becomes superfluous.

These marginal distributions are not the only one-dimensional normal curves lurking in our picture. Not only may we project the whole mountain onto *any* vertical plane to get a normal distribution, but *any vertical section* of the mountain is also a normal curve. Note that the marginal distribution obtained with the bulldozer is usually *not* the optical projection of the mountain profile onto a wall, such an optical projection being only a particular vertical section through the center. The bivariate *normal* distribution, however, has the unusual property that these two operations lead to identical results. If we look at the sampling consequences of these properties, we see that the marginal distributions are found by looking at all the data for one variable without considering the other at all. A section through the mountain parallel to the y axis, however, corresponds to *repeated sampling of* y *at the same constant value of* x. If our population is a true bivariate one, we can seldom take data in this form, but given a sufficient quantity of bivariate data, they can frequently be arranged at least approximately in this manner. A section along a diagonal line in the (x, y) plane would correspond to a sampling distribution in one of two coordinates which are simple rotations of the present ones.

If we examine the sections of our mountain for each of the several values of x, we find that their maxima fall on a straight line in the (x, y) plane. *This is called the regression line for* y *on* x, and represents our best guess for the unknown value of y if we are given a particular value of x. Similarly, the maxima of the sections taken parallel to the x axis define the *regression line for* x *on* y. *These two lines are not the same.* If we now note that level contours of our mountain are geometrically similar ellipses with a common center (ξ, η), we also see that the y on x regression line must cut the ellipses at their left and right extrema, as in Figure 36, and that the x on y line must cut at the top and bottom. The less eccentric

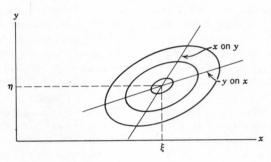

Figure 36

the ellipses, the farther apart are the two lines; the extreme case of circles yields vertical and horizontal regression lines (Figure 37) which show that for this extreme no information about y is contributed by knowledge of x and vice versa. It is not necessary for the ellipses to degenerate into circles, however, before the regression lines become parallel to the axes and thus contribute no information. Any ellipse, however eccentric, if oriented with its major and minor axes parallel to the coordinate system, will yield such regression lines. Indeed the regression lines coincide with the axes of the ellipse in this special configuration. See Figure 38.

Thus *the amount of information transmitted by the regression lines is a function of both the eccentricity of the level contours and their degree of tilt* with respect to the coordinate system. This amount of information is measured by the fifth parameter, the correlation coefficient, ρ. It is the only essentially new parameter which is introduced by the two-dimensionality of the bivariate normal distribution. The range of ρ is from -1 through 0 to $+1$, the limiting cases corresponding to mountains which have narrowed down to straight ridges through the origin; in other words, x determines y completely.

The analytical expression for the ordinate of the bivariate normal distribution is

$$
\frac{1}{2\pi\sigma_\xi\sigma_\eta(1-\rho^2)^{1/2}}
$$
$$
\exp\left\{-\frac{1}{2(1-\rho^2)}\left[\left(\frac{x-\xi}{\sigma_\xi}\right)^2 - 2\rho\left(\frac{x-\xi}{\sigma_\xi}\right)\left(\frac{y-\eta}{\sigma_\eta}\right) + \left(\frac{y-\eta}{\sigma_\eta}\right)^2\right]\right\} \quad (1)
$$

where ξ, η are the means of the x, y variables respectively, σ_ξ^2, σ_η^2 are the variances of the marginal distributions of x, y, and $\rho_{\xi\eta}$ is the correlation coefficient.

A not quite trivial exercise in integral calculus will convince the skeptic that integration of (1) over the entire (x, y) plane gives exactly unity.

If we draw a random sample of paired (x, y) measurements from a population we believe to be normally distributed, we will usually like to estimate the five parameters of the parental population and, if possible,

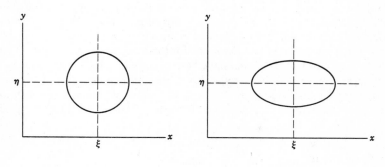

Figure 37   Figure 38

to establish confidence limits for them.   We may also want to know where an additional y value might plausibly lie for a given value of x, as well as wanting to know the answers to the other questions asked in the straight-line models of Chapters 2 and 3.   Although the questions are similar and to the casual observer the models bear a generic resemblance to each other, nevertheless the answers are *not* necessarily the same.   Note that here there is no immediate question of our data's being measured erroneously.   We assume this sample to be accurately measured and recorded.   If we attempt to allow for errors of measurement, we then create little bivariate error distributions around each datum point.   If these little distributions are nearly normal, we find them dissolving imperceptibly into the large distribution, thereby merely inflating it.   The separation of the error effect from the structural distribution is, in this case, quite impossible.

Further questions arise when we are confronted by two samples from assertedly the same population, an allegation we choose to examine. Before this model can be treated we must make the hypothesis more definite by deciding that:

1. All but one of the parameters are to be assumed equal, and we are to test only that other critical one; or

2. All but n of the parameters are to be assumed equal, and we are to test only those critical n.

These problems can become complicated even without much experimental confusion, and we can only hope to treat them briefly, if at all.

A genetic example

In a study by S. B. Holt [20], the data of Table 1 are presented to show the hereditary similarities in finger markings. The combined dermal ridge counts for the little fingers of both hands in pairs of parents and children were recorded and examined for their degree of correlation. (The counts, groups 0–4, 5–9, etc., have been replaced by their midvalues 2, 7, etc., which have then been coded for computational convenience by subtracting 27 and dividing by 5. Both the coded values and the original data groupings appear at the top of Table 1.)   The marginal totals suggest

TABLE 1

Children

	−5	−4	−3	−2	−1	0	1	2	3	4	5	
Classes	0–4	5–9	10–14	15–19	20–24	25–29	30–34	35–39	40–44	45–49	50–54	Totals
5								1	1	1		3
4				1								1
P 3								2	2	2		6
a 2		1	1	1	2	3	5	10	3	3	1	30
r 1		1		1	2	3	5	8	3			23
e 0	3	1	2	6	10	9	4	4				39
n −1		2	1	6	7	17	6	7				46
t −2	1		3	4	6	5	1	2				22
s −3	4	2	3	5	2	1	1		1		1	20
−4	2	3	1	1	4	2		1				14
−5		2	1	1	3			1				8
Totals	10	12	12	26	36	40	22	36	10	6	2	212

that the distributions may be slightly skewed—a distinct possibility because the measurements are necessarily positive. The abnormality is, however, slight, and the expository values of this chapter would not be materially enhanced by transforming to a logarithmic scale which the experimenter clearly did not intend. (The equally spaced groupings of the data imply the use of these original counts.)

The statistics we naturally compute from such a bivariate table are, in units of the coded variables,

$$x. = -0.594 \qquad Sxx = 951.1$$
$$y. = -0.302 \qquad Syy = 1{,}072.7$$
$$(n = 212) \qquad Sxy = 517.0$$

where the symbols are defined in the next paragraph. The estimates for the standard deviation of the marginal distributions are

$$s_\xi = 2.123 \qquad s_\eta = 2.255,$$

again in coded units. Finally the sample correlation coefficient is

$$r = 0.512,$$

which suggests a rather appreciable connection between the finger ridges of the parents and their children. Just how strongly we should believe this estimate of the population correlation coefficient will be examined later in the chapter.

Estimation of the parameters

From our data we may compute the means and the variances of our samples by the already familiar one-dimensional formulae:

$$x. = \frac{1}{n}\sum x_i \qquad\qquad y. = \frac{1}{n}\sum y_i$$

$$s_\xi^2 = \frac{1}{n-1}\sum(x_i - x.)^2 = \frac{Sxx}{n-1} \quad s_\eta^2 = \frac{1}{n-1}\sum(y_i - y.)^2 = \frac{Syy}{n-1}. \quad (2)$$

These sample statistics are also unbiased estimators of the corresponding population parameters. The sample correlation coefficient, r, is computed from

$$r_{\xi\eta} = \frac{Sxy}{\sqrt{SxxSyy}}, \qquad (3)$$

and this statistic estimates the population coefficient, $\rho_{\xi\eta}$.

Confidence limits for ξ and η are found quite simply by the usual t test. This is natural, since the x data alone give the x marginal distribution which contains only the two parameters ξ and σ_ξ. We can thus isolate these parameters from the rest of the problem and extract any information here that could be obtained in the corresponding one-dimensional model. Thus the limits for ξ are given by the two values of X from

$$\pm \frac{(x. - X)\sqrt{n}}{s_\xi} \equiv \frac{\sqrt{n(n - 1)}(x. - X)}{\sqrt{Sxx.}} \leqslant t_{n-1}. \tag{4}$$

The symmetric 10 per cent limits for ξ in our example are -0.834 and -0.354. A similar estimate is available for η (-0.556, -0.048). Unless the population correlation is zero, however, these two separate confidence regions for ξ and η are not independent, and we may not draw a rectangle in the (ξ, η) plane with these intervals as its sides and then use the product of the two separate levels. A correct joint region will be discussed later.

Confidence limits on σ_ξ and σ_η separately can be found from the χ^2 distribution, exactly as in the one-dimensional problem. Since

$$\frac{\sum(x_i - x.)^2}{\sigma_\xi^2} \equiv \frac{Sxx}{\sigma_\xi^2} \Rightarrow \chi^2_{n-1}, \tag{5}$$

we have only to look up, say, 5 per cent and 95 per cent points of χ^2_{n-1}, substitute these for the right-hand side of (5), and solve for the two critical values of σ_ξ^2. For our data, the two 5 per cent limits are 3.74 and 5.48, with the best estimate being 4.51 (which is not halfway between because of the skewness in the χ^2 distribution). Again, joint limits on σ_ξ^2 and σ_η^2 together are not found this way. Not only is statistical independence lacking, but the second-order cross moments enter essentially into the statistical theory. The exact distribution is known as the Wishart distribution, but the three population parameters enter in such a computationally unpleasant manner that it has not been tabled, nor is any simple method of using such a table apparent even if one did exist.

The sample correlation coefficient, r, has a distribution which depends only on that of the population, ρ, and the size of the sample n. It has been tabled by David [11] and is generally available. To set a lower limit on ρ we simply inquire whether a particularly low value of ρ could plausibly have given rise to a value of r as large as or larger than the one observed. If the chance (from David's tables) is, say, more than 5 per cent, we accept this value of ρ as a possible parent and try a still smaller one, until we get one that seems sufficiently implausible. We then repeat with large trial values of ρ until we find one that could have given rise to our observed value of r or a still smaller one 5 per cent of the time by random chance. The two limits must be found separately because the distribution of r is highly skewed for values of ρ near ± 1, so no symmetry can be invoked to simplify the labor. For our example these limits are 0.422 and 0.585.

The analytical expression for the frequency function of r is

$$f_n(r, \rho) = \frac{n - 2}{\pi}(1 - \rho^2)^{(n-1)/2}(1 - r^2)^{(n-4)/2} \int_0^1 \frac{x^{n-2}\, dx}{(1 - \rho rx)^{n-1}(1 - x^2)^{\frac{1}{2}}}.$$

David tables both $f_n(r_0, \rho)$ and $\int_0^{r_0} f_n(r, \rho)\, dr$, so that these tables may be used to set up confidence limits for ρ if we know r and n. She also includes charts to simplify the construction of such intervals.

If we cannot refer to David's exact tables, we may use a normal approximation by the transformations

$$z = \frac{1}{2} \log \frac{1 + r}{1 - r} \quad \text{and} \quad \zeta = \frac{1}{2} \log \frac{1 + \rho}{1 - \rho}.$$

Then z is distributed approximately

$$N\left(\zeta + \frac{\rho}{2(n - 1)};\, \frac{1}{n - 3}\right),$$

so that $\left[z - \zeta - \dfrac{\rho}{2(n - 1)}\right] \cdot \sqrt{n - 3}$ is almost a standard normal variate. Since n and z are known from the sample values and the whole variate is given by the normal table, we may solve for the two confidence limits on ρ. This approximation is very good for n greater than 25 and can certainly be used, in emergencies, for much smaller values. Our example gives 0.421 and 0.589 for confidence limits on the population correlation coefficient.

The special case ρ equals zero, i.e., when the population variables are uncorrelated, deserves particular attention. We frequently wish to test the hypothesis that our variables are uncorrelated, but of course any *sample* will exhibit some correlation which must be judged significant or insignificant. For this test no correlation tables are needed, since a simple transformation of $f_n(r, \rho)$ gives the t distribution with $n - 2$ degrees of freedom. We need merely set

$$\frac{r^2(n - 2)}{1 - r^2} \leqslant F_{1,\, n-2} \tag{6}$$

and determine the limits by substituting critical F values on the right-hand side. Our degree of correlation is significantly different from zero at the 0.1 per cent point—as could be judged by the lower confidence limit just given.

Confidence limits for $\sigma_\xi^2/\sigma_\eta^2$

The distribution of the sample correlation coefficient, r, from uncorrelated populations may be used to set confidence limits on the unknown ratio of the unknown population variances. The connection between the correlation coefficient and the ratio of the variances may be seen if we note that knowledge of σ_ξ/σ_η would allow us to transform our data to new variables which are uncorrelated and independent. If we define

$$\omega = \frac{\sigma_\xi^2}{\sigma_\eta^2}, \quad w = \frac{Sxx}{Syy}, \quad r^2 = \frac{Sxy^2}{SxxSyy},$$

we can show that

$$\frac{(n-2)(w-\omega)^2}{4(1-r^2)w\omega} \Rightarrow F_{1,\,n-2} \tag{7}$$

is distributed like $F_{1,\,n-2}$. Since n, w, and r are sample statistics, they are definite numbers in any specific problem, and we only have to equate (7) to the critical F value and solve for the limiting values of ω. However, because the numerical example of this chapter is highly correlated, the technique of this paragraph is not applicable.

Let us take a bivariate normal population with its means at zero, since this introduces no essential change in our problem, and transform from (x, y) to (u, v) variables via the linear equations

$$u = \frac{x}{\sigma_\xi} + \frac{y}{\sigma_\eta}, \quad v = \frac{x}{\sigma_\xi} - \frac{y}{\sigma_\eta}.$$

Then, the Jacobian being constant,

$$\frac{1}{2\pi\sigma_\xi\sigma_\eta(1-\rho^2)^{1/2}} \exp\left\{ -\frac{1}{2(1-\rho^2)}\left[\left(\frac{x}{\sigma_\xi}\right)^2 - 2\rho\left(\frac{x}{\sigma_\xi}\right)\left(\frac{y}{\sigma_\eta}\right) + \left(\frac{y}{\sigma_\eta}\right)^2\right]\right\}$$

becomes

$$\frac{1}{2\pi\sigma_\xi\sigma_\eta(1-\rho^2)^{1/2}} \exp\left(-\frac{u^2}{4(1+\rho)} - \frac{v^2}{4(1-\rho)}\right).$$

Because this may be written as the product of a term containing only u with a term containing only v, these variables are statistically independent. The variance of u is $2(1+\rho)$, and that of v is $2(1-\rho)$. The correlation between u and v is clearly zero, but a sample from such a population will exhibit a correlation due to random fluctuations. Let us designate such a sample correlation by R. Now

$$R = \frac{Suv}{\sqrt{SuuSvv}} \equiv \frac{\sum\left(\frac{x}{\sigma_\xi} + \frac{y}{\sigma_\eta}\right)\left(\frac{x}{\sigma_\xi} - \frac{y}{\sigma_\eta}\right)}{\sqrt{\left[\sum\left(\frac{x}{\sigma_\xi} + \frac{y}{\sigma_\eta}\right)^2\right]\left[\sum\left(\frac{x}{\sigma_\xi} - \frac{y}{\sigma_\eta}\right)^2\right]}},$$

so that

$$R \equiv \frac{\dfrac{Sxx}{\sigma_\xi^2} - \dfrac{Syy}{\sigma_\eta^2}}{\sqrt{\left(\dfrac{Sxx}{\sigma_\xi^2} + \dfrac{Syy}{\sigma_\eta^2}\right)^2 - \dfrac{4Sxy^2}{\sigma_\xi^2\sigma_\eta^2}}} \equiv \frac{\dfrac{Sxx}{Syy} - \dfrac{\sigma_\xi^2}{\sigma_\eta^2}}{\sqrt{\left(\dfrac{Sxx}{Syy} + \dfrac{\sigma_\xi^2}{\sigma_\eta^2}\right)^2 - \dfrac{4Sxy^2\sigma_\xi^2}{Syy^2\sigma_\eta^2}}}.$$

By making the substitutions indicated above,

$$R = \frac{w - \omega}{\sqrt{(w + \omega)^2 - 4r^2 w\omega}} \, .$$

But

$$\frac{(n - 2)R^2}{1 - R^2} \Rightarrow F_{1, \, n-2},$$

so that

$$\frac{(n - 2)(w - \omega)^2}{4(1 - r^2)w\omega} \Rightarrow F_{1, \, n-2}.$$

Joint confidence region for (ξ, η)

If our aim is to locate the center of our bivariate population, some joint region for (ξ, η) is needed. If we know σ_ξ, σ_η and $\rho_{\xi\eta}$ (most unusual indeed), one such region is furnished by all values of (ξ, η) which make the exponent of the bivariate distribution smaller than some critical value, when $x.$ and $y.$ have been substituted for x and y. In fact

$$\frac{n}{(1 - \rho^2)} \left[\left(\frac{x. - \xi}{\sigma_\xi} \right)^2 - 2\rho \left(\frac{x. - \xi}{\sigma_\xi} \right) \left(\frac{y. - \eta}{\sigma_\eta} \right) + \left(\frac{y. - \eta}{\sigma_\eta} \right)^2 \right] \leqslant \chi_2^2(\alpha)$$

is a χ^2 variate with two degrees of freedom, so the elliptical region given by this formula is found by substituting a critical χ^2 value on its right-hand side.

In practice it is usually necessary to estimate σ_ξ, σ_η, and $\rho_{\xi\eta}$ by their sample statistics, and some "Studentized" procedure is desirable, analogous to the t distribution. If we define T^2 by the formula

$$T^2 = \frac{n(n - 1)}{(SxxSyy - Sxy^2)} [Syy(x. - \xi)^2 - 2Sxy(x. - \xi)(y. - \eta) \\ + Sxx(y. - \eta)^2], \qquad (8)$$

then

$$P(T^2 \geqslant x_0^2) = \left(1 + \frac{x_0^2}{n - 1} \right)^{1 - \frac{n}{2}} . \qquad (9)$$

This statistic is due to Hotelling, and may be found in standard texts. Thus we substitute a critical probability (say 0.10) for the left-hand side of (9) to get a critical value, x_0^2, which T^2 shall not exceed except with this probability. If we substitute this value for T^2 in (8), we have a quadratic expression in (ξ, η)—all the other terms are available from the sample— which defines an elliptical (90 per cent) confidence region for (ξ, η). The connection between (8) and the χ^2 variate becomes clearer if we divide the right-hand side of (8) by $SxxSyy$ inside the brackets and multiply by the same terms outside. Absorbing the $n - 1$ inside at the same time, we have

$$T^2 = \frac{n}{1 - r^2}\left[\left(\frac{x. - \xi}{s_\xi}\right)^2 - 2r\left(\frac{x. - \xi}{s_\xi}\right)\left(\frac{y. - \eta}{s_\eta}\right) + \left(\frac{y. - \eta}{s_\eta}\right)^2\right]$$

where r, s_ξ, and s_η are the usual sample statistics. For 10 per cent error limits, we find that T^2 should not exceed 4.56, so that the critical region for ξ and η is an ellipse whose equation is

$$0.0159 = \left(\frac{\xi + 0.594}{2.123}\right)^2 - 1.022\left(\frac{\xi + 0.594}{2.123}\right)\left(\frac{\eta + 0.302}{2.255}\right) + \left(\frac{\eta + 0.302}{2.255}\right)^2.$$

This ellipse is, of course, tilted in the (ξ, η) plane but can be plotted by standard analytic geometric methods.

The straight lines in the bivariate distribution

If we know the x value of a number pair from a bivariate normal distribution, in general we have some information about its y value even without having that other number explicitly available. From Figure 35 we see that the most probable value of y lies along a straight line, being the trace of the maxima of cross sections of the bivariate surface when the cuts are taken parallel to the y axis. This line is called the *regression of* y *on* x. If we choose to look at our bivariate normal surface as the contour map of Figure 36, where it appears as a nested set of similar ellipses, the *regression of* y *on* x is the line through the center that cuts all the ellipses at their right and left extremities.

In an analogous manner, if we know a value of y for a number pair, our most probable guess for its x value will be at the maximum of the bivariate surface along that known value of y, i.e., along a section parallel to the x axis at the given value of y. The line of such most probable x values is called the *regression of* x *on* y, and in general it is different from the other regression line. On our contour map it passes through the center and through the top and bottom extremities of the ellipses.

Although historically these lines are the ones to which the term *regression* was first applied, over the years we find all types of straight-line fitting being called regression, so that now some caution is required when reading the literature to ascertain exactly what type of problem the author is choosing to consider.

It is geometrically obvious that a rotation of coordinate axes can turn them parallel to the axes of the ellipses, in which configuration the common axes of the ellipses become the two regression lines. In this new coordinate system the two variables are uncorrelated, i.e., knowledge of x gives no special information about y and vice versa.   As was pointed out earlier, lack of correlation also occurs when the contours are circles, so the degree of correlation is seen to depend both on the eccentricity of the ellipses and on their orientation with respect to the axes.   It is this subtle dependence of the degree of correlation on the orientation of the coordinate system, as well as the scale factors, that requires considerable caution in interpreting correlation coefficients from physical experiments.   It is, for example, quite easy to produce almost *no* significant correlation by confining the population sampled to rather narrow limits—thus giving an almost circular (actually square) distribution cut out of the center of what may be a quite strongly correlated bivariate surface.   Restricting a psychological or educational test to a narrow range of intelligence or educational experience, for instance, will usually produce this phenomenon. Thus the degree of correlation can be strongly influenced by the population we are choosing to consider; any correlation coefficient so found should always be accompanied by an explicit statement showing the restricted population to which it applies.

These remarks about correlation coefficients apply equally well to regression lines, for their slope is a direct function of ρ.   Specifically, the equations of the two regression lines are

$$y = \rho \frac{\sigma_\eta}{\sigma_\xi} x \equiv \beta_{21} x \qquad \text{and} \qquad x = \rho \frac{\sigma_\xi}{\sigma_\eta} y \equiv \beta_{12} y$$

for y on x and x on y respectively, the identity defining the β's.   If we wish to estimate the β's from our sample, it is only necessary to substitute the corresponding sample statistics.   Thus

$$b_{21} = \frac{rs_\eta}{s_\xi} = \frac{Sxy\sqrt{Syy}}{\sqrt{SxxSyy}\sqrt{Sxx}} \equiv \frac{Sxy}{Sxx} \qquad (0.543),$$

a result which shows the regression coefficient to be algebraically identical with the slope of the one-variate-in-error least-squares fit of our first straight-line problem.   The analogous formula holds for b_{12}:

$$b_{12} = \frac{rs_\xi}{s_\eta} \equiv \frac{Sxy}{Syy}, \qquad (0.482).$$

Confidence limits for these regression coefficients may easily be found from Student's t distribution.   We have

$$\pm \frac{s_\xi\sqrt{n-2}}{s_\eta\sqrt{1-r^2}} (b_{21} - \beta_{21}) \Rightarrow t_{n-2} \qquad \begin{matrix} (0.440) \\ (0.646) \end{matrix}$$

and

$$\pm \frac{s_\eta\sqrt{n-2}}{s_\xi\sqrt{1-r^2}} (b_{12} - \beta_{12}) \Rightarrow t_{n-2} \qquad \begin{matrix} (0.390) \\ (0.574) \end{matrix},$$

$$(10)$$

so that it is only necessary to substitute critical values of t on the right-hand side of (10) and solve for the limiting values of β, the other terms being the available sample statistics. Again, the analogy to the one-variate-in-error fitting problem becomes apparent if we square and rewrite the first of these expressions as

$$\frac{(b_{21} - \beta_{21})^2 Sxx}{\dfrac{Syy - \dfrac{S^2xy}{Sxx}}{n - 2}} \equiv \frac{(b_{21} - \beta_{21})^2 Sxx}{\dfrac{\text{SSR}}{n - 2}}.$$

Doubtless it is this close parallelism that has caused the transferal of nomenclature between these two classes of problems, but the parallelism is a limited one and tends to confuse the issues when we get beyond the simpler fitting problems.

The equation for the regression of y on x may be simply derived from the definition of the conditional distribution,

$$f(y|x) \equiv \frac{f(x, y)}{\int_{\infty}^{\infty} f(x, y)\, dy}.$$

This is the distribution followed by y when x is specified. The conditional distribution of y given x is found by dividing the joint (x, y) distribution by the marginal distribution of x, the latter being found by integrating out y from the joint distribution. For the bivariate normal, with some algebra, we get

$$f(y|x) = \frac{1}{\sigma_\eta \sqrt{2\pi(1 - \rho^2)}} \exp\left\{ -\frac{1}{2\sigma_\eta^2(1 - \rho^2)}\left[(y - \eta) - \frac{\rho\sigma_\eta}{\sigma_\xi}(x - \xi)\right]^2 \right\}.$$

Note that this is a one-dimensional normal distribution with its mean located along the (regression) line

$$y = \eta + \rho\frac{\sigma_\eta}{\sigma_\xi}(x - \xi),$$

but with a variance $\sigma_\eta^2(1 - \rho^2)$ *which is not a function of* x. In effect, the normalizing denominator has blown up our mountain peak into a uniform ridge whose backbone lies along the regression line. Any cross section of this ridge is the same normal distribution with its mean displaced along the line. This picture is almost identical with our original one-variate-in-error geometric model, and hence the formulae are also nearly the same. The only difference is the scale factor $(1 - \rho^2)$ applied to the variance.

Stratified and random samples

In order to obtain valid estimates of all five parameters in the bivariate distribution, it is necessary that our sample be *random in both variables*— any value from the population must have its proper chance of being included. It is not always possible to take our sample in this way. If we are observing sunspot densities, our instruments may not detect very small spots, so we may consistently underestimate the activity, or the instruments may be affected by very strong activity and fail to work, this cutting out of our sample all values greater than a certain amount (a truncated sample).

Or perhaps we only have access to data already recorded and classified for another purpose. Perhaps they have been recorded according to specific values of x, exactly fifteen readings being recorded at each of six values of x. The rest, if they were ever recorded, have been lost. Here, the random element of sampling has been preserved for the y data, but it has been hopelessly lost for x. Under this circumstance we can still estimate the slope of the regression line, since we may treat the data as a straight-line fitting problem with all the error in y. Further, except for an unknown factor $1 - \rho^2$, we will get an estimate of σ_η^2 from our SSR. We cannot, of course, gain any insight about the location of the mean (ξ, η) except to remark that it probably lies on our regression line (confidence limits could be obtained in the form of a hyperbolic strip about this line, if desired), and certainly no information about σ_ξ can be extracted as it is not present in the data. Without random sampling on x, no information about ξ or σ_ξ can be extracted except for the small part about ξ which sneaks in by the back door from its correlation with η. When faced with determining the line y on x from a bivariate population, the experimenter has the choice of trying to get a sample random in both dimensions to yield the greatest possible amount of information, or of limiting his efforts to specific ranges of x—perhaps even specific values of x—and being satisfied with the lesser knowledge. Experimental necessity may dictate the choice, but more frequently mere expediency will decide. Since it is usually cheaper in the long run to gather all the needed information from one experiment, if possible, random samplings for the x variable should not be sacrificed lightly. A little extra care in planning the experiment and designing the equipment here may save running an entire second experiment if it should become apparent that the information about the statistical nature of x will ultimately be needed.

Truncated distributions

It seems to be the peculiar experimental nature of bivariate records that they are seldom complete. We give college entrance examinations to a fairly good random sample of high school graduates, but the *college* records of these are available only for those who did well enough to be admitted to college, i.e., y exists only for x greater than some critical value, although x was fairly sampled.   Analogously, initial chemical process data are frequently available for a whole range of quality of the starting materials, but subsequent performance records are lost because batches were "unsatisfactory" and were dumped out, their reactions never being carried to completion.   Perhaps they could not be carried out because of chemical limitations or perhaps operators considered such effort useless; in either case the data are incomplete, the distributions have been truncated.

At first glance a bivariate distribution truncated on x seems little more informative than one in which x has been sampled systematically.   The slope of the regression line is available, it is true, but we can get only a rather slippery grasp on σ_η^2, and σ_ξ^2 seems quite beyond our reach. Fortunately, appearances here are deceiving.   Cohen [9] has given methods for estimating ξ and σ_ξ^2, as well as the variances of these estimates, from a truncated normal distribution.   If we apply these, we find ourselves possessed of three functions of the distribution parameters. They are:

$$\sigma_\xi^2 = a \qquad \text{from the truncated distribution fit}$$

$$\left.\begin{aligned} \sigma_\eta^2(1 - \rho^2) &= b \\[2mm] \rho^2 \frac{\sigma_\eta^2}{\sigma_\xi^2} &= c \end{aligned}\right\} \quad \text{from the regression line fitting procedure.}$$

Thus

$$\rho^2 \sigma_\eta^2 = ac, \qquad \sigma_\eta^2 = b + ac,$$

and

$$\rho^2 = \frac{ac}{b + ac} = \frac{1}{\dfrac{b}{ac} + 1}.$$

Also our estimate of ξ may be combined with the fitted line to yield an estimate of the center point (ξ, η).

CHAPTER 5

Regression with both x and y in Error

In our previous discussions we have assumed that x was known without error, a mathematical fiction which simply means that any errors in x are sufficiently small to be ignored when compared with the errors in y. When such an assumption is justified, the uncomplicated formulae and procedures already given extract the essential information from the data efficiently and with a minimum amount of effort on the part of the analyst. Unfortunately most experiments do not conform to the model we desire. The Fifth Law of Thermodynamics, sometimes known as the Innate Cussedness of Inanimate Objects, often does not permit our experimenter to force his operations into the no-error-in-x mold, and so we seek a more realistic model, a less restrictive set of assumptions from which we can analyze our data. Since most experiments deserve, nay rather *demand*, such analysis, the reader may ask why we took up so much space with an unrealistic model. The answer is the expository one. It is easier to introduce the various concepts of tests of significance and confidence limits when only one dimension contains random elements. Then, too, occasionally we might be lucky enough to obtain data where x is without error, and the formulae may be helpful.

In the earlier chapters we discussed a model in which some sort of distribution of y values was observed for each fixed value of x. That is, if we imagine fixing x and taking repeated measurements on y, we obtain a mound of probability, as illustrated in Figure 5 (Chapter 2). If we now allow x, as well as y, to contain errors, we must introduce a new variable to hold fixed while generating a comparable distribution, this time a two-dimensional one. Accordingly, our underlying general model shall suppose there is a functional relationship connecting the true but unobserved variables ξ and η, and in general we shall assume this relationship to be linear. Thus

$$\eta = \mu + \beta(\xi - \xi.)$$ (1)

or

$$\eta = \alpha + \beta\xi, \tag{2}$$

depending on which form may be more convenient.   If we imagine that ξ is held fixed while repeatedly measuring x and y, we shall generate a two-dimensional mound of an experimental distribution on the (x, y) plane which might appear, schematically, as shown in Figure 39.   If we change

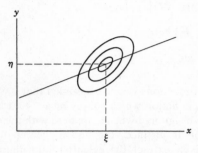

Figure 39

ξ, and hence η also, we move the mound, but the center will remain close to the unknown straight line [equation (1)], although the shape may change—by spreading out in almost any direction, or shrinking toward a spike, or perhaps rotating, to mention several unpleasant possibilities.   In the one-dimensional case we assumed that the distribution from which y was sampled moved its mean value along a line as x changed, but that its width or dispersion was unaffected by the shift in location.   Here we hope for the same homoscedasticity (to use its formal title) by assuming that, if we change the true experimental variables ξ, η, we merely move a bivariate distribution along the true line *without changing its shape*.   For much of the classical theory we assume that this movable distribution is the bivariate normal one, in which case its shape is specified by $\sigma_u{}^2$, $\sigma_v{}^2$, and ρ_{uv} where u and v represent the differences between the observed and true values.   Thus

$$\begin{aligned} x &= \xi + u \\ y &= \eta + v. \end{aligned} \tag{3}$$

The correlation ρ_{uv} between errors in x and y measurements is a complication frequently and unrealistically ignored in experimental data analysis.   The case for lack of correlation between the errors must be made in the light of individual experiments, but we should like to point out that since u and v are errors, they usually contain parts that are common (such as scale errors due to temperature effects, or inaccuracies in the measuring instruments due to humidity levels, etc.—or the increased variability due to fatigue in the single observer who made both readings). These common parts mean that ρ_{uv} is seldom zero, and if we use a model which assumes it to be zero, we may distort our information. Except where it makes the formulae completely intractable, we shall retain ρ_{uv} and let the optimistic set it equal to zero when they dare.

An heuristic approach

There have been many attempts to fit straight lines to data when both variates contain errors, and the methods proposed vary widely in the information presumed to be known by the analyst, as well as in the amount of statistical substructure inferred or demanded by the assumptions. Some approaches choose to minimize a sum of squares without seeking any statistical support for the procedure. These are of doubtful value to us because they limit the analyst to blind fitting procedures and preclude the relatively more important problem of prediction and variance-component estimation. Others seek the solace of maximum-likelihood methods, a general approach to statistical estimation which has both led and misled experimenters to operational formulae, but which is important enough to warrant an exposition—and this chapter affords a convenient place. Some engineers and physicists have thought of fitting a line to points in terms of a mechanical model in which the points are replaced by unit masses, and then the weightless line is required to become an axis about which the system is statically stable and dynamically minimal in its rotational inertia. The first property causes the line to pass through the mass center of the points, and the second one requires the minimization of the sum of the squares of the *perpendicular* deviations from the line, thus placing this method in the category of least-squares procedures. Unfortunately, this is not a uniquely determined line; it is not invariant under simple transformations. We may, for example, stretch the graph in the x direction by doubling that scale, thereby shifting all the points in the line and causing the former perpendicular distances to be perpendicular no longer. In fact some other line will now be the one to minimize the new perpendicular distances. Since this physical model, as well as the simple least-squares one, does not contain any provision for denoting the relative magnitude of the errors in x and y (to say nothing of their correlation!), it fails us in this particular way. The failure suggests the remedy, i.e., to plot the data in units of their respective standard deviations, but we prefer to approach this partial answer, in which correlation still lurks unseen, from a more systematic point of view. Whether or not we use such a concept to derive a method, it is valuable in pointing out that some sort of knowledge beyond that of the (x, y) data themselves is needed to define the problem uniquely. In fact *it is necessary to know any two of the three quantities* σ_u, σ_v, *and* ρ_{uv} before a satisfactory least-squares line may be fitted. It is sometimes possible to estimate these quantities from the data themselves, especially if many points are available, but as we begin our discussion of regression with both variates in error, we prefer to continue our idealism for a short while by treating a model that is still unrealistic to the experimenter—unrealistic in that it will assume prior knowledge about the relative magnitudes of the errors in x and y and even the degree of correlation between them. This information the experimenter frequently does not possess in advance, and the data all too often are taken in a manner that prevents any satisfactory estimation of these relationships. But again for expository convenience, we shall first construct a mathematical model which assumes such *a priori* knowledge before we go on to the more difficult and less pleasant models that do not.

Maximum-likelihood estimation when both variables contain error

We shall assume, as mentioned earlier, that (ξ, η) are the coordinate values which (x, y) would take on were it not for the presence of errors. Further, we assume that (x, y) follow a bivariate normal distribution with center (ξ, η), variances σ_u^2, σ_v^2, and covariance $\rho_{uv}\sigma_u\sigma_v$. We avoid the expressions σ_x etc. as misleading; the variances are those of the *deviations* from ξ and η. The probability density function for (x, y) is

$$\frac{1}{2\pi\sigma_u\sigma_v\sqrt{1 - \rho_{uv}^2}}$$
$$\exp\left[-\frac{1}{2(1 - \rho_{uv}^2)}\left\{\left(\frac{y - \eta}{\sigma_v}\right)^2 - 2\rho_{uv}\left(\frac{y - \eta}{\sigma_v}\right)\left(\frac{x - \xi}{\sigma_u}\right) + \left(\frac{x - \xi}{\sigma_u}\right)^2\right\}\right],$$

where we postulate a linear relation

$$\eta = \mu + \beta(\xi - \xi.)$$

between ξ and η. The symbol $\xi.$ is a mean value of the various values of ξ which enter the problem, the precise kind of mean being left to our later disposal. Discovering the underlying functional relation means estimating μ and β and their reliability. The maximum-likelihood procedure is to take values of μ and β which maximize the likelihood of obtaining the sample actually observed. If we suppose the sample obtained consists of n groups of points of size $k_i(i = 1, ..., n)$, each group being taken at the same values of (ξ_i, η_i), $\sum k_i = N$ being the total number of points, we can then set up the following model.   The joint probability distribution function for the sample consists of the product of the probability distribution functions for each (x_i, y_i)—assuming independence of the sampling *errors* from one point to the next—so our job is to maximize with respect to μ and β the expression

$$\left(\frac{1}{2\pi\sigma_u\sigma_v\sqrt{-\rho_{uv}{}^2}}\right) \exp\left[-\frac{1}{2(1-\rho_{uv}{}^2)}\sum_{i=1}^{n}\sum_{j=1}^{k_i}\left\{\left(\frac{x_{ij}-\xi_i}{\sigma_u}\right)^2\right.\right.$$
$$\left.\left.-2\rho_{uv}\left(\frac{x_{ij}-\xi_i}{\sigma_u}\right)\left(\frac{y_{ij}-\eta_i}{\sigma_v}\right)+\left(\frac{y_{ij}-\eta_i}{\sigma_v}\right)^2\right\}\right].$$

We note that we maximize the logarithm of this function at the same time as the function itself, and that the constant in front of the exponential does not contain μ or β.   Unfortunately, although we are not particularly interested in the ξ_i and η_i, they enter into the maximum-likelihood expression, and we must include one set or the other with the parameters with respect to which the expression is to be maximum.   We choose the $\{\xi_i\}$ $(i = 1, ..., n)$.

Formal differentiation of

$$F(\sigma_u, \sigma_v, \rho_{uv}) - \frac{1}{2(1-\rho_{uv}{}^2)}\sum_{i=1}^{n}\sum_{j=1}^{k_i}\left[\left(\frac{x_{ij}-\xi_i}{\sigma_u}\right)^2\right.$$
$$\left.-2\rho_{uv}\left(\frac{x_{ij}-\xi_i}{\sigma_u}\right)\left(\frac{y_{ij}-\eta_i}{\sigma_v}\right)+\left(\frac{y_{ij}-\eta_i}{\sigma_v}\right)^2\right]$$

with respect to μ gives

$$-\sum_{i=1}^{n}\sum_{j=1}^{k_i}\left[\rho_{uv}\left(\frac{x_{ij}-\xi_i}{\sigma_u}\right)\left(\frac{1}{\sigma_v}\right)-\left(\frac{y_{ij}-\eta_i}{\sigma_v}\right)\left(\frac{1}{\sigma_v}\right)\right]$$
$$=\sum_{i=1}^{n}\frac{k_i}{\sigma_v{}^2}\left[(y_i.-\eta_i)-\frac{\rho_{uv}\sigma_v}{\sigma_u}(x_i.-\xi_i)\right].$$

If this is equated to zero we get

$$\sum_{i=1}^{n}k_i[(y_i.-\eta_i)-R(x_i.-\xi_i)]=0 \qquad (4)$$

where, for typographic convenience,

$$R=\frac{\rho_{uv}\sigma_v}{\sigma_u},$$

$$y_i.=\frac{\sum_{j=1}^{k_i}y_{ij}}{k_i},$$

and

$$x_i.=\frac{\sum_{j=1}^{k_i}x_{ij}}{k_i}.$$

If we carry out the summation with respect to i, again defining the symbols

$$\sum_{i=1}^{n} k_i y_{i\cdot} = y_{\cdot\cdot} N, \qquad \sum_{i=1}^{n} k_i \eta_i = \eta_{\cdot} N$$

and similarly for $x_{\cdot\cdot}$ and $\xi_{\cdot}$ respectively (here we define our $\xi_{\cdot}$ at last), we obtain

$$(y_{\cdot\cdot} - \eta_{\cdot}) = R(x_{\cdot\cdot} - \xi_{\cdot}). \tag{5}$$

Differentiation with respect to a particular ξ_r gives

$$\sum_{j} \left[\left(\frac{x_{rj} - \xi_r}{\sigma_u} \right) \left(\frac{1}{\sigma_u} \right) - \rho_{uv} \left(\frac{x_{rj} - \xi_r}{\sigma_u} \right) \left(\frac{\beta}{\sigma_v} \right) \right.$$
$$\left. - \rho_{uv} \left(\frac{y_{rj} - \eta_r}{\sigma_v} \right) \left(\frac{1}{\sigma_u} \right) + \left(\frac{y_{rj} - \eta_r}{\sigma_v} \right) \left(\frac{\beta}{\sigma_v} \right) \right],$$

which, on summing and equating to zero, gives

$$(y_r - \eta_r) = R(x_r - \xi_r)\theta \tag{6}$$

where

$$\theta = \frac{\beta - R/\rho^2}{\beta - R}.$$

If we substitute (6) into (4) we get

$$\sum_{i=1}^{n} k_i [R(x_{i\cdot} - \xi_i)(\theta - 1)] = 0$$

or

$$\sum_{i} k_i(x_{i\cdot} - \xi_i) = 0.$$

Thus

$$x_{\cdot\cdot} = \xi_{\cdot}$$

and, on substituting in (5),

$$y_{\cdot\cdot} = \eta_{\cdot} = \mu_{\cdot}$$

This last equality comes from multiplying $\eta_i = \mu + \beta (\xi_i - \xi_{\cdot})$ by k_i and summing.

Differentiating with respect to β gives

$$\sum_{i} \sum_{j} \left[\rho_{uv} \left(\frac{x_{ij} - \xi_i}{\sigma_u} \right) \left(\frac{1}{\sigma_v} \right) - \left(\frac{y_{ij} - \eta_i}{\sigma_v} \right) \left(\frac{1}{\sigma_v} \right) \right] \left[\xi_i - \xi_{\cdot} \right],$$

which, on summing with respect to j and equating to zero, yields

$$\sum_{i=1}^{n} k_i \{ [(y_{i\cdot} - \eta_i) - R(x_{i\cdot} - \xi_i)][\xi_i - \xi_{\cdot}] \} = 0. \tag{7}$$

If we substitute (6) into (7) we get

$$\sum_{i} k_i [R\theta(x_{i\cdot} - \xi_i) - R(x_{i\cdot} - \xi_i)][\xi_i - \xi_{\cdot}] = 0$$

or

$$\sum_{i} k_i(x_{i\cdot} - \xi_i)(\xi_i - \xi_{\cdot}) = 0. \tag{8}$$

In order to reduce this last equation to computational form, we need the two identities,

$$0 = y_r. - \eta_r - R\theta(x_r. - \xi_r)$$
$$= (y_r. - y..) - \beta(\xi_r - \xi.) - R\theta(x_r. - x..) + R\theta(\xi_r - \xi.),$$

so that

$$(\xi_r - \xi.) = \frac{(y_r. - y..) - R\theta(x_r. - x..)}{\beta - R\theta} .$$

Also,

$$x_r. - \xi_r \equiv (x_r. - x..) - (\xi_r - \xi.)$$
$$= (x_r. - x..) - \frac{(y_r. - y..) - R\theta(x_r. - x..)}{\beta - R\theta}$$
$$= -\frac{(y_r. - y..) - \beta(x_r. - x..)}{\beta - R\theta} .$$

Substituting these two expressions into (8), we simplify to obtain

$$0 = \sum_{i=1}^{n} k_i[(y_i. - y..) - \beta(x_i. - x..)][(y_i. - y..) - R\theta(x_i. - x..)] \qquad (9)$$

$$\equiv \sum_i k_i(y_i. - y..)^2 - (\beta + R\theta)\sum_i k_i(x_i. - x..)(y_i. - y..) + \beta R\theta \sum_i k_i(x_i. - x..)^2$$

$$\equiv Sy_i.y_i. - (\beta + R\theta)Sx_i.y_i. + \beta R\theta Sx_i.x_i.. \qquad (9')$$

Equation (9) is the important equation, with its alternate form (9') defining the symbolism and indicating the computational procedure. Note that (9) is a quadratic equation in β because of the β contained in θ. Since

$$\beta + R\theta = \frac{\beta^2 - \dfrac{R^2}{\rho^2}}{\beta - R}$$

and

$$\beta R\theta = \frac{\beta - \dfrac{R}{\rho^2}}{\beta - R} \cdot \beta R$$

then (9') may be written as

$$\beta^2(Sx_i.y_i. - RSx_i.x_i.) - \beta\left(Sy_i.y_i. - \frac{R^2}{\rho^2}Sx_i.x_i.\right)$$
$$- \left(\frac{R^2}{\rho^2}Sx_i.y_i. - RSy_i.y_i.\right) = 0. \qquad (10)$$

Equation (10) gives the maximum-likelihood estimate of the slope, β, of the functional relationship between ξ and η. To compute it, we need to know $R = \rho_{uv}\,\sigma_v/\sigma_u$ and ρ_{uv} itself, that is, the ratio of the error standard deviations and their correlation coefficient. (Note that R^2/ρ^2 is not a function of ρ, being merely σ_v^2/σ_u^2.) The other items are computable from the (x, y) data PROVIDED *we know to which of the* i *clusters of points each* (x_{ij}, y_{ij}) *belongs.* If the experimenter has kindly labeled his data, or if the separation of the clusters is enough greater than the errors so that the grouping is evident from a plot of the data, this information is available and no further difficulties beset us. If, however, the data are merely listed in order of magnitude and are almost equally dense throughout most of their range in the (x, y) plane, we are robbed of essential knowledge and must seek an approximation that does as well as can be expected under this handicap.

The balloon problem

The data of Table 1 give the heights of a tethered balloon as measured simultaneously by a theodolite x and by a rather precise altimeter carried

TABLE 1

x	y	x	y	x	y	x	y
59	58	78	75	113	110	130	125
56	55	79	77	109	112	133	128
55	53	81	77	108	108	126	130
51	52	82	79	104	104	131	134
49	54	79	78	106	104	132	134
52	53	79	78	104	104	134	133
54	55	87	87	110	110	131	131
58	60	81	82	110	108	130	133
56	54	77	79	117	110	136	131
57	57	83	80	114	110	135	132
547	551	806	792	1,095	1,080	1,318	1,311

on the balloon y. Ten measurements were made at each of four heights. Presumably the variations are due not only to errors in observations but also to changes in the barometric pressure (affecting y through the calibration of the altimeter) and to variations in the actual height of the balloon because of winds (affecting both x and y). Without an independent record of barometric pressure it is impossible to separate out that effect decisively, but some light may be shed if we examine the data for internal consistency in the within-group variabilities. For the present, however, we must content ourselves with computing the quantities needed in equation (10), all of which are found from the column averages (or totals). Thus

$Sx.x. = 10[(54.7)^2 + (80.6)^2 + (109.5)^2 + (131.8)^2 - (376.6)^2/4] = 33,930.5$
$Sx.y. = 33,468.6$
$Sy.y. = 33,029.7$

and we find our estimate of β from (10) to be 0.9867, using an *a priori* assumption of 0.60 for $\rho\sigma_v/\sigma_n$ and 0.75 for $\sigma_v{}^2/\sigma_u{}^2$. (Actually these error variances were suggested by the within-group variabilities, which are easily estimated since the data are neatly separated.)

When only one datum point is observed from each distribution, the k_i are all equal to one and the sums of squares in (10) become Syy, etc. We can always treat the clustered case as if this were the model, but then we obtain values for the sums of squares in (10) that are too large because they include variation about the local means which properly does not belong in the estimation of β but rather serves only to determine σ_u and σ_v. If our values of σ_u, σ_v, and ρ_{uv} are really good, the treatment of clustered data by formula (10) is accurate enough, but when our information is fragmentary or if we have no prior knowledge of these variabilities, we should use other techniques that will recover at least some of the knowledge otherwise lost. These will be discussed later as the *instrumental variate* cases.

Both variables in error, ρ_{uv}, $\sigma_u{}^2$ known *a priori*, uniform occurrence of ξ

It may happen that we know the error variance of one of the variables from our prior experience, but not that of the other. We suppose the known variance is that of the error in x (this is no limitation, since the problem is symmetrical in x and y). We must further assume prior knowledge of ρ_{uv}, the correlation between the two errors. Again experience might well supply such information.

Let us suppose that our data are given without obvious clusters or, better still, that they are known to have been taken at more or less uniform spacing in the true variable ξ and are close enough so that the errors run the groups of points together. In either case, the experimental probability mound is the mountain range type, with no clearly isolated peaks. We suppose further that no one has been nice enough to indicate which points might belong together in the sense that they are estimating the same true point (ξ, η). This situation is the same one previously exhibited, but with the slight difference that of the three quantities σ_u, σ_v, and ρ_{uv}, the first and last are known instead of the last and the *ratio* of the other two.

If we now take this geometric probability model and cut the mountain range parallel to the y axis (see Figures 2 and 6), we see that the apparent variance of y (assuming that all the mountain is due to errors in y) is greater than $\sigma_v{}^2$ because distributions with different (ξ, η) centers are contributing to the apparent variation in y at a fixed x. Only if the underlying true line is horizontal will this widening not occur, and the amount of spread depends on β. By integrating out ξ from the bivariate model under the assumption that it is uniformly sampled in our problem, we find the apparent variance of y to be

$$\text{Var } (y) = \sigma_v{}^2 - 2\beta\rho_{uv}\sigma_u\sigma_v + \beta^2\sigma_u{}^2 = \sigma_u{}^2\left(\beta^2 - 2\beta\rho_{uv}\frac{\sigma_v}{\sigma_u} + \frac{\sigma_v{}^2}{\sigma_u{}^2}\right).$$

This equation suggests that if we fit a best line under the simplest classical assumption of no error in x, we can use the fitted value of β and the estimate of the variance of y, together with our *a priori* values of $\sigma_u{}^2$ and ρ_{uv}, to solve for σ_v, or the ratio $\sigma_v{}^2/\sigma_u{}^2$, whichever we prefer. Now that we have obtained an estimate of the ratio $\sigma_v{}^2/\sigma_u{}^2$, we have the information required in our previous example, and a fit via those procedures is possible. We are not overly happy about such a technique, for it offers copious opportunity for bias to creep in. On the other hand, prior information about the variances is not necessarily valid to five decimal places either, and some laxity in procedure is perhaps defensible—especially if the choice is between a rough answer versus no answer at all.

Both variables in error, no prior knowledge of σ_u, σ_v, and ρ_{uv}, data taken in groups (replication)

If we have no previous experience to indicate the sizes of σ_u, σ_v, and ρ_{uv}, the best we can do is to estimate them from the data. In the happy situation where several measurements of (x, y) were taken for each true point (ξ, η), *and we know to which group each point belongs*, we are able to do this quite easily, as each group of points is drawn from a single bivariate population—which we are still assuming to be normal—and hence we have a number of independent estimates of $\sigma_u{}^2$, $\sigma_v{}^2$, and $\rho_{uv}\sigma_u\sigma_v$, in the form of

$$Sxx = \sum_j (x_{ij} - x_i.)^2 = (k_i - 1)s_u{}^2$$

$$i = 1, ..., n$$

$$Syy = \sum (y_{ij} - y_i.)^2 = (k_i - 1)s_v{}^2$$

$$j = 1, ..., k_i$$

$$Sxy = \sum_j (x_{ij} - x_i.)(y_{ij} - y_i.) = (k_i - 1)r_{uv}s_us_v.$$

For the balloon data of Table 1 the estimates of the SSW are found to be

z	1	2	3	4	Total
Sxx	92.1	76.4	164.5	75.6	408.6
Sxy	54.3	70.8	88.0	15.2	228.3
Syy	56.9	99.6	80.0	72.9	309.4

so that if they are considered to come from similar bivariate distributions, the overall estimates of the variances are found by combining

$$s_u{}^2 = 408.6/36 = 11.350$$
$$rs_u s_v = 228.3/36 = 6.342$$
$$s_v{}^2 = 309.4/36 = 8.594$$

where the divisor is the product of four groups each containing nine degrees of freedom (one mean having been fitted per group). We do not bother with a formal test of homogeneity since it is obvious by inspection that no one sample differs markedly from the others.

These estimates, one for each of the n clusters, may be tested to see whether or not we believe them to be approximately the same from cluster to cluster, this homogeneity being such a useful property that we usually postulate it if we cannot test it. If our hypothesis that the error distribution is unaffected by the location of its center is not disproved, we may combine these estimates into better ones based on more data (degrees of freedom), giving

$$\sum_i \sum_j (x_{ij} - x_i.)^2 = (N - n)s_u{}^2$$

$$\sum_i \sum_j (y_{ij} - y_i.)^2 = (N - n)s_v{}^2$$

$$\sum_i \sum_j (x_{ij} - x_i.)(y_{ij} - y_i.) = (N - n)r_{uv}s_u s_v.$$

These numbers have already appeared earlier. Armed with these estimates of the variances, we may now use any of the methods that presuppose such knowledge. The question of confidence limits is an uncomfortable one here, and we shall avoid it by saying that this is not the approach we favor for the data at hand, but we do not feel capable of plunging into the full-scale problem without giving some sort of introduction. The current paragraphs are introductory in the sense that they give physical meaning to sums of squares and cross products which will occur repeatedly in the larger problem, where recognition of any expression, however small, is a great pedagogical comfort.

A new example

Before analyzing the balloon data in detail, we should like to set forth for general discussion a more complicated set of (artificial) data on the thickness of a zinc coating on sheet steel as measured by magnigage y and as measured by stripping with acid for gravimetric determination x. These data have a structure similar to the balloon data, but with enough differences to make a parallel analysis instructive. Five sheets, each bearing a different nominal thickness of zinc, were cut up into 2-inch squares. Six of these squares from each sheet were then measured first by magnigage and then by stripping. The data appear in Table 2. We wish to estimate the structural calibration line which connects the measurements from each system. Here we have well-defined groups of points, one group from each sheet of steel. On a graph the groups may well lose their identities by overlapping, but we are supposing that the records show from which sheet each datum came.

TABLE 2

x	y	x	y	x	y
9.9	13.9	12.1	15.1	13.4	15.2
10.9	13.9	11.8	11.8	11.2	16.3
12.9	14.6	11.0	14.7	13.4	16.7
11.0	14.9	13.0	10.6	11.9	14.6
9.5	13.2	12.2	15.3	15.0	14.0
9.5	12.3	11.1	12.3	12.9	14.8
63.7	82.8	71.2	79.8	77.8	91.6

x	y	x	y
15.5	18.8	17.1	23.0
15.0	18.8	18.3	19.1
16.5	17.3	19.4	18.5
16.8	16.6	20.0	20.3
17.5	15.8	18.7	22.6
14.4	17.1	15.9	20.7
95.7	104 4	109.4	124.2

By almost any reasonable criterion, the best estimator of the structural line will pass through the center of gravity of the data. We shall therefore be concerned almost entirely with determining the slope of this line rather than its intercept. Our procedure for determining this slope and the confidence limits for it will depend very strongly on the several further assumptions we choose to make about our populations. In the one-variate-in-error models we could assume that the mean of each population falls on the unknown structural line, or that each population is a little different from this strict ideal and that each point therefore varies not only because of variations about the population means but also because of variations in those population means about the line. The same choice confronts us here when both x and y exhibit errors.

Should we decide that our individual population means would all fall on a structural line if we could only take enough data to suppress the fluctuations within each population, then we say that the *population (sheet) means degenerate along a line*. This model will frequently be referred to as *Model* 0. If we believe that the population means do not really lie on a structural line, i.e., that the model is non-degenerate, we must then decide exactly how we believe these means might deviate. Among the myriad of possible deviation patterns, two are especially plausible in experimental work. These will be designated as Models 1 and 2:

Model 1 assumes that each of the deviations of the n group means from the structural line is a sample from a very *finite population of size n*. Thus we have exhausted this population by our sample. *Model* 2 assumes that each deviation of a sheet mean from the structural line is a random sample from a very large population of deviations, perhaps an infinite one. Our sample does not even begin to exhaust this population. Readers familiar with the analysis of variance will recognize that the terms Model 1 and 2 have been taken over directly from that discipline.

If we consider the physical experiment, a particular sheet might give a mean point for its several magnigage and stripping readings that was not on the structural line because of a consistent bias introduced by all the chemical analyses' being performed by one man, whereas all the readings on the second sheet were made by a second analyst; and so on for exactly n analysts, which are all we have in our laboratory. Slightly less artificial might be the hypothesis that each different nominal thickness of zinc was achieved by a different process and that these processes affected the chemical stripping in a definite, consistent manner. Thus, having only n processes that we will ever encounter in our future measurements, we seek a calibration line within the framework of *Model* 1.

If, on the other hand, we feel that the deviations of the sheet means from the structural line are caused by variations in "standard" chemicals used in the stripping, chemicals which were consistent from one square to the next but which varied between sheets (since they were stripped on different days!), then we see that future analyses may encounter any one of a large population of "standard" chemicals of which we have here only a small random (we hope) sample. This point of view commits us to *Model* 2. When all possible factors are considered, some will turn out to be Model 1, some Model 2, and still others will fall in between. In the absence of an experiment specifically designed to separate these various factors and to estimate their relative importance, the experimenter must rely on his knowledge and physical intuition in determining which particular effect he considers to be dominant, thus classifying the calibration problem as Model 1 or Model 2.   Analysis of a problem lying between these models is beyond both the scope of this manual and the ability of its author.

Basic arithmetic

Having confessed our fell purpose, let us now form all the sums of squares that might seem appropriate in the light of our experience when only one variate contains errors.   This time, however, we shall perform our operations as symmetrically as possible on x^2, y^2, *and their cross product xy*.   There are really only two important sums (or three, depending on the point of view) for each quadratic variable, and the partition may be suggested if we use an analysis of (co)variance arrangement of our data.   We avoid, at this stage, the treatment of subgroups with different numbers of points.   Here $j = 1, ..., 6$ in all clusters.

Let us form $\sum_{ij} (x_{ij} - x_{i\cdot})^2$, $\sum_{ij} (y_{ij} - y_{i\cdot})^2$, $\sum_{ij} (x_{ij} - x_{i\cdot})(y_{ij} - y_{i\cdot})$ as before.   Also we shall compute $k \sum_{i} (x_{i\cdot} - x_{\cdot\cdot})^2$, $k \sum_{i} (y_{i\cdot} - y_{\cdot\cdot})^2$, $k \sum_{i} (x_{i\cdot} - x_{\cdot\cdot})(y_{i\cdot} - y_{\cdot\cdot})$.   Using the conventional names for these quantities, we designate them respectively as the Sums of Squares Within subgroups (SSW), and Sums of Squares Between subgroups (SSB).

Although these formulae show their structure, as is usual in statistics, they do not indicate the efficient computational technique.   This is easily found from the following identities:

$$\sum_{ij} x_{ij}^2 \equiv \sum_{ij} [(x_{ij} - x_{i\cdot}) + (x_{i\cdot} - x_{\cdot\cdot}) + x_{\cdot\cdot}]^2$$

$$\equiv \sum_{ij} (x_{ij} - x_{i\cdot})^2 + k \sum_{i} (x_{i\cdot} - x_{\cdot\cdot})^2 + nkx_{\cdot\cdot}^2$$

$$\equiv \quad \text{SSW} \quad + \quad \text{SSB} \quad + nkx_{\cdot\cdot}^2.$$

The terms to be calculated are

$$\sum_{ij} x_{ij}^2,$$

$$Nx_{\cdot\cdot}^2,$$

$$k \sum_{i} (x_{i\cdot} - x_{\cdot\cdot})^2,$$

leaving the SSW to be found by subtraction. The grand mean term, $Nx_{\cdot\cdot}^2 \equiv \frac{1}{N} \left(\sum_{ij} x_{ij} \right)^2$, is usually obtained at the same time as $\sum_{ij} x_{ij}^2$.   The SSB are computed from the usual identity:

$$k \sum_{i} (x_{i\cdot} - x_{\cdot\cdot})^2 \equiv k \left(\sum_{i} x_{i\cdot}^2 - nx_{\cdot\cdot}^2 \right) \equiv \frac{1}{k} \sum_{i} \left(\sum_{j} x_{ij} \right)^2 - Nx_{\cdot\cdot}^2.$$

We therefore compute $\sum_{ij} x_{ij}{}^2$, $\sum_{ij} x_{ij}$, and $\sum_i \left(\sum_j x_{ij} \right)^2$ and then combine to get SSB and SSW.

Since we are going to be carrying at least two and frequently three or more variables in all our future work, a standard notational form seems desirable. Some mathematicians have proposed standard matrix positions for our numbers, with the squares on the diagonals and the cross products at the intersections of the proper rows and columns. But Tukey [33], from whom much of this development is derived, prefers to place the squares in the first vertical column, on the grounds that they are the principal quantities of interest. The cross products then sit at the inter-sections of the appropriate diagonals:

$$(xx)$$
$$(xy)$$
$$(yy) \qquad (xz)$$
$$(yz)$$
$$(zz)$$

With our data, the computation of the sum of squares, the sum of the squares of the group means multiplied by k, and the grand mean gives the information in Table 3 where

$$(xx)$$
$$(xy)$$
$$(yy)$$

shows the arrangement of the numbers.

TABLE 3

	Balloon Data		Zinc Data	
$\sum w_{ij}{}^2$	388,908	385,253	6,089.52	6,932.88
	381,908		8,043.20	
$k\sum w_{i\cdot}{}^2$	388,499.4	385,024.7	6,051.1367	6,943.5267
	381,598.6		7,989.9067	
$Nw_{\cdot\cdot}{}^2$	354,568.9	351,556.1	5,818.5613	6,723.7295
	348,568.9		7,769.8613	

Thus we get the SSW and SSB of Table 4.

TABLE 4

	Balloon Data		Zinc Data	
	408.6		38.3833	
SSW		228.3		− 10.6467
	309.4		53.2933	
with	36 degrees of freedom		25 degrees of freedom	
	33,930.5		232.5754	
SSB		33,468.6		219.7972
	33,029.7		220.0454	
with	3 degrees of freedom		4 degrees of freedom	

The SSW are easily recognized as the components of the variance-covariance matrix for the individual populations, although still multiplied by $N - n$ in the form above. It is the SSB that contain all the useful information about the relationship between x and y in the large, i.e., everything about the functional form underlying these data. In addition, however, they contain information about whether or not the line adequately explains the data—whether or not the means of each group have a displacement from the best line which is too large to be explained away by the fluctuations displayed by the individual points.

Model zero—degeneracy along a line

If we choose to assume that all our population means lie *on* the structural line, the MSW estimate the variances of the fluctuations within the individual populations, whereas the MSB contain the effect of the structural line itself, plus some effect of the individual fluctuations. But the MSB is not inflated by the wobble of the population means around the line, simply because no such wobble exists. (The sample group means wobble about the line a little, but only because of the errors in individual observations.) If we can remove one degree of freedom for the slope, we can compare it with the MSW, just as in the one-variate-in-error examples —thereby giving a criterion for a plausible structural slope. Although this is not the only method to find such confidence limits, it is sufficiently important to warrant explanation of at least three methods for splitting out one degree of freedom for regression from the SSB.

1. We can behave as if the group means, $x_i.$, are equal to the unknown population (sheet) means. Here we treat the $(x_i., y_i.)$ pairs as data from

a one-variate-in-error situation, regressing y_i. on x_i. to fit the slope, b. The condition is simply

$$\sum[(y_i. - y..) - b(x_i. - x..)][x_i. - x..] = 0. \tag{11}$$

and b is merely the ratio of the (xy) and the (xx) components of the SSB. This b is our best estimate of β. In order to establish confidence limits on the unknown β, we may consider some other slope, B, to be the true value and vary B until the squared residuals about the trial line inflate to values that are obviously improbable when compared with the variation *within* the basic populations. The only trick is to pick the proper MSW with which to compare the residuals. We defer the details until mentioning the other methods. This procedure is powerful in that it extracts almost all the regression information from the SSB and puts it into a single degree of freedom, giving a powerful test. It suffers from the fact that the x_i. are *not* the population means but are in a fuzzy region near those unknown means, and thus the distribution of the b is unknown with that same degree of fuzziness. The use of an F test is therefore mildly dishonest. Frequently, however, this is the only semireasonable course open, and we must then take it. Note that if we had numerous additional x_{ij} values, even without their corresponding y_{ij}, our knowledge of x_i. would be better, and this procedure would be more nearly valid.

2. We can introduce the *rank order* of the populations (tetherings of balloons or the labels of the sheets of metal) as a third variable, z_i, and regress both x_i. and y_i. on this, thereby isolating a one-degree-of-freedom Sum of Squares for Regression. If the rank order is real, the procedure is completely honest (something the first can never be), but it may be considerably less powerful in the sense that some of the regression sum of squares may be left behind in the SSB.

3. We can make a rough estimate of β and of the shape of the elementary population distributions (i.e., we can estimate σ_x^2, σ_y^2, and $\rho_{xy}\sigma_x\sigma_y$ for each sheet). We then transform our (x, y) into new variables (u, v) in which β and ρ_{uv} are approximately zero. Then the SSB and SSW are nearly independent so that the distributions are once again nearly known. This procedure is more time-consuming, at least as powerful, and more nearly honest than the first. It has been dubbed 99.44 per cent pure—which title we shall occasionally use.

Before going into the details of these three methods, we shall pause to consider some elementary linear geometry which frequently occurs in these problems. If from a collection of (x, y) points we subtract a line of slope B through their mass center, the vertical SSR about that line may be expressed simply in terms of the three quantities Sxx, Sxy, and Syy.   We have

$$\text{SSR} \equiv \sum[(y_i - y.) - B(x_i - x.)]^2 \equiv Syy - 2BSxy + B^2Sxx.$$

Computing this type of residual corresponds to replotting the data so that the line of slope B now becomes the x axis, or—what is the same thing—it corresponds to projecting the data down the line of slope B to get their new y coordinate.   If our data have already been reduced so that their mass center is the origin of the coordinate system (as indeed they are after the first sum-of-squares calculation has been made), let us reduce them still further by removing $y = bx$ where b is the best line in the sense of equation (11).   Our picture is now Figure 40.

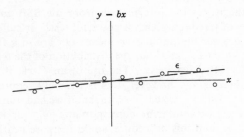

Figure 40

Consider the SSR about a line of slope ϵ.   Then, calculating the additional SSR about the ϵ slope line,

$$\text{SSR} = \sum[(y - bx) - \epsilon x]^2 - \sum(y - bx)^2 \equiv -2\epsilon\sum(y - bx)x + \epsilon^2 Sxx \quad (12)$$

But by the definition of b the first term on the right-hand side of equation (12) vanishes, so that

$$SSR = \epsilon^2 Sxx.$$

Now ϵ represents the arbitrary difference of slope between an arbitrary slope, B, and the best slope, b.   Thus the *reduction in the SSR achieved by fitting b instead of B is* $(b - B)^2 Sxx$.   Here b is a perfectly definite number, but B is at our disposal.

Regression on the group means

1. Returning to our first method of isolating a degree of freedom for regression, let us contemplate a value of B, tentatively asserting it to be the value of β, the true slope.   The change in the sum of squares as we go

from the true slope, B, to our fitted value, b, is to be compared with the MSW calculated while *assuming that B is the true slope*. This implies projecting along the direction B, i.e., computing

$$\text{MSW}(y - Bx) = \frac{\text{SSW}(y - Bx)}{N - n} = \frac{1}{N - n} \text{SSW}[(yy) - 2B(yx) + B^2(xx)]$$

$$= \frac{1}{N - n} [\Sigma(y_{ij} - y_{i.})^2 - 2B\Sigma(y_{ij} - y_{i.})(x_{ij} - x_{i.})$$
$$+ B^2\Sigma(x_{ij} - x_{i.})^2].$$

The test then becomes

$$\frac{(B - b)^2 k\Sigma(x_{i.} - x_{..})^2}{\text{MSW}(y - Bx)} \leqslant F_{1, \, N-n}. \tag{13}$$

We note that B occurs quadratically in both the numerator and denominator of (13), so that when the number from the F table is substituted on the right side of (13) the whole expression remains a quadratic. The solutions of this quadratic are the two confidence limits for β.

For the balloon data, this simplest method gives a slope

$$b = SSBxy/SSBxx = 33,468.6/33,930.5 = 0.986387$$

which is very close to the maximum-likelihood value of 0.9867. If we remember that the Within variability is quite small (the variances are approximately ten square units) and the separation Between is quite large (11,000·square units), clearly not much statistical wobble is possible and agreement between the two estimates should be good. More precisely, equation (13) becomes

$$(B - 0.986387)^2 = \frac{4.13}{(36)(33,930.5)} [309.4 - B(2)(228.3) + B^2(408.3)]$$

which gives limits for β

$$0.9575 \leqslant 0.9864 \leqslant 1.0164.$$

Identical calculations for the zinc data give

$$0.69 \leqslant 0.946 \leqslant 1.27$$

where the wider limits are to be expected on comparing the MSW (about 1.5 square units) with the MSB (about 55 square units).

Regression on the rank order

2. If we use the rank order of the populations as a less powerful but honest extractor of the regression sum of squares, we must compute the matrix

$$
\text{SSB} \left\| \begin{matrix} (xx) & & \\ & (xy) & \\ (yy) & & (xz) \\ & (yz) & \\ (zz) & & \end{matrix} \right\|
$$

where

$$
\text{SSB}(xz) = k \sum_i^n (x_i. - x..)(z_i - z.),
$$

for example. If the samples from the various populations had been of different sizes, k_i, we should have had to leave the k_i under the summation. In the present problem, each of the elements of the SSB matrix contains k as a factor, so it is frequently left out of the formulae in which it will later be canceled. Due caution should be exercised, as it occasionally does not cancel.

We now break the SSB for x and y up into two sums:

$$
\frac{(xz)^2}{(zz)} + \left[(xx) - \frac{(xz)^2}{(zz)} \right]
$$

$$
\frac{(xz)(yz)}{(zz)} + \left[(xy) - \frac{(xz)(yz)}{(zz)} \right]
$$

$$
\frac{(yz)^2}{(zz)} + \left[(yy) - \frac{(yz)^2}{(zz)} \right],
$$

which we may write as

$$
\text{SSB} \left\| \begin{matrix} (xx) & \\ & (xy) \\ (yy) & \end{matrix} \right\| = \text{SSReg} \left\| \begin{matrix} (xx) & \\ & (xy) \\ (yy) & \end{matrix} \right\| + \text{SSD} \left\| \begin{matrix} (xx) & \\ & (xy) \\ (yy) & \end{matrix} \right\|.
$$

Here we have removed from the SSB all the information that can be explained by z and have separated it out into a one degree of freedom matrix, SSReg, leaving a matrix with $n - 2$ degrees of freedom to describe the deviations of the population means which are not explained by a regression on z. Since z is intimately connected with the structural line, we suspect that most of our required information about the slope is in this first matrix. We shall reduce this matrix to a Mean Square (by dividing by *one*!), and then find the Components of the Mean Square for regression. These components will be unbiased estimators of the true population parameter matrix:

$$\left\| \begin{array}{cc} S\xi\xi & \\ & S\xi\eta \\ S\eta\eta & \end{array} \right\|.$$

Since $\beta = S\xi\eta/S\eta\eta$, we are going to use the ratio of our unbiased estimates of these quantities for b.   It is true that this b is not an unbiased estimator of β (the ratio of two unbiased estimators usually gives a slightly biased estimate of the ratio of the true parameters), but this defect is rarely of practical consequence.   The Components of the Mean Square are defined by

$$(Szz)(\text{CMSReg}) = (\text{MSReg} - \text{MSD}) \equiv \left(\text{MSReg} - \frac{\text{SSD}}{n-2} \right).$$

Note that these can still contain a factor $Szz = \sum_i k(z_i - z.)$ which will cancel in our formula for b.

Having found b, we may then get confidence limits on β by the identical procedure used earlier, i.e., by setting

$$\frac{(b - B)^2 Sxx}{\text{MSW}(y - Bx)} \leqslant F_{1,\,N-n} \qquad (14)$$

and solving the resulting quadratic in B.

The data of our two examples give

	SSB				SSReg				SSD	
	33,930.5				33,852.02				78.48	
		33,468.6		$\rightarrow$		33,409.68		$+$		58.92
Balloons	33,029.7		260.2		32,973.12				56.58	
		256.8								
	2.0					1 DF				2 DF

	232.5753				223.8802				8.6952	
		219.7972		$\rightarrow$		207.4610		$+$		12.3362
Zinc	220.0453		19.3167		192.2460				27.7993	
		17.9000								
	1.6667					1 DF				3 DF

so that we get

CMSB

Balloons	33,812.78	33,380.22	$\rightarrow b = \dfrac{33,380.22}{33,812.78} = 0.987207$
	32,944.83		

Zinc	220.982	203.349	$\rightarrow b = \dfrac{203.349}{220.982} = 0.920206.$
	182.9796		

The solution of equation (14) gives final limits on β of

$$0.952 \leqslant 0.9872 \leqslant 1.024$$

for the balloon slope and

$$0.66 \leqslant 0.9202 \leqslant 1.24$$

for the zinc data β.

The 99.44 per cent pure extractor

3. The third method involves estimating β crudely (by eye or any of the previous techniques), as well as the σ_ξ^2, σ_η^2, and $\rho_{\xi\eta}\sigma_\xi\sigma_\eta$ for the basic populations. The variances are computed by the standard MSW calculations described earlier. Geometrically, we now know the orientation and ellipticity of these basic distributions if, indeed, they are normal, as all this section assumes. The picture may look like Figure 41, where the unknowable population distribution means are assumed to be exactly on the unknowable line. We should like to reduce our data to a region near the x axis *and to scales in which the errors are uncorrelated.* If we plot $v = y - Bx$ versus x, the population means will be ranged along an unknown line near the x axis, but the elliptical contours of these distributions will, in general, be tilted as in Figure 41. Note that even if the

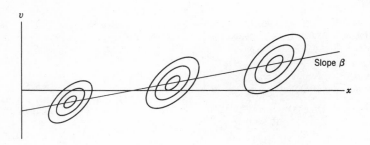

Figure 41

errors in x and y were uncorrelated, the removal of this line with slope B would usually introduce correlation, tilting the basic ellipses. We should like these contours to be ellipses with their axes parallel to the coordinate axes, so we replot once again, with

$$u = x + pv.$$

The constant p must be taken so that $-1/p$ is the slope in the (x, v) plane of the diameters of the ellipses conjugate to the direction β.   Figure 42 shows the theoretical configuration, assuming our approximations are reasonably good.   Now the errors in u and v are approximately uncorrelated, and any attempt to extract a single degree of freedom for regression (a small effect, to be added to the one already removed with the slope B) will not be complicated by statistical dependence between the SSW and SSB.   We may now use the first procedure: regressing $v_i.$ on $u_i.$ as if the $u_i.$

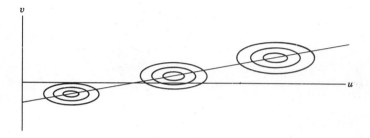

Figure 42

were exact.   If we really have the geometry pictured in Figure 42, errors in the $u_i.$ cannot introduce errors in the $v_i.$.   Even if we only approximate this geometry, the effects of such errors must be quite small.

If the ellipses in the (x, y) plane have equations

$$c = \left(\frac{y - \eta}{\sigma_\eta}\right)^2 - 2\rho\left(\frac{y - \eta}{\sigma_\eta}\right)\left(\frac{x - \xi}{\sigma_\xi}\right) + \left(\frac{x - \xi}{\sigma_\xi}\right)^2,$$

and if we remove a line of slope b_0, the diameters in the new (x, v) coordinates which are conjugate to the direction β have a slope

$$p = \frac{(b_0 + \beta)b_0 - \rho\frac{\sigma_\eta}{\sigma_\xi}(2b_0 + \beta) + \left(\frac{\sigma_\eta}{\sigma_\xi}\right)^2}{\rho\frac{\sigma_\eta}{\sigma_\xi} - (b_0 + \beta)} \qquad (15)$$

Here ρ, σ_η/σ_ξ refer to the original error distributions in the (x, y) plane, b_0 is the approximate slope (i.e., the slope of the line that has been removed from the y variates to give v), and β is the slope of the line fitted in the (x, v) plane.   *To a first approximation, $\beta = 0$.*   Thus, to the same approximation:

$$p = \frac{b_0{}^2 - \rho\frac{\sigma_\eta}{\sigma_\xi}2b_0 + \left(\frac{\sigma_\eta}{\sigma_\xi}\right)^2}{\rho\frac{\sigma_\eta}{\sigma_\xi} - b_0} \qquad (16)$$

Some of the labor of this procedure may be reduced by computing entirely from the SSB in the (x, y) coordinates, combining these to form the Suv, Suu, etc. The recomputation of the individual data in (u, v) coordinates is unnecessary. Since

$$v = y - b_0 x$$
$$u = v - px = y - (p + b_0)x \tag{17}$$

then

$$Suu = S\ddot{y}y - 2(p + b_0)Sxy + (p + b_0)^2 Sxx$$
$$Suv = Syy - (p + 2b_0)Szy + b_0(p + b_0)Sxx \tag{18}$$
$$Svv = Syy - 2b_0 Sxy + b_0^2 Sxx.$$

for both the SSB and the SSW. We may save some arithmetic labor if we choose our approximate slope, b_0, by the first of our three procedures by letting

$$Sxy = b_0 Sxx.$$

Then, for SSB, equations (18) become

$$\text{SSB}uu = Syy - b_0 Sxy + p^2 Sxx \equiv \text{SSD} + p^2\text{SSB}xx$$
$$\text{SSB}uv = Syy - b_0 Sxy \qquad\quad \equiv \text{SSD}$$
$$\text{SSB}vv = Syy - b_0 Sxy \qquad\quad \equiv \text{SSD}.$$

Since our incremental slope in the (u, v) plane is small and the errors nearly uncorrelated, we fit b as if there were no error in the u coordinate by using

$$b = \text{SSB}uv/\text{SSB}uu \equiv \text{SSD}/(\text{SSD} + p^2 Sxx). \tag{19}$$

A test that yields confidence limits on β is

$$\frac{(B - b)^2 \text{SSB}uu}{\text{MSW}(v - Bu)} \equiv \frac{(N - n)(B - b)^2 \text{SSB}uu}{\text{SSW}[(vv) - 2B(uv) + B^2(uu)]} \leqslant F_{1,\, N-n} \tag{20}$$

where the denominator terms come from the equations (18) applied to the SSW. If our arithmetic has been accurate, SSWuv will be identically zero—a convenient check. Although it is possible to throw (20) back into terms of (xy) sums, no real simplification occurs.

If we translate our fitted line into the original coordinates, we get

$$y = \left[b_0 + \frac{b}{1 - bp}\right] x \approx [b_0 + b(1 + bp)]x \approx (b_0 + b)x, \tag{21}$$

where the first equality is exact. The approximations are based on the smallness of b and get worse as we go toward the right. Confidence limits for β are found by substituting the two solutions, B, of (20) for the b in the bracketed expressions of (21)—the entire coefficient of x being the required limit.   The rough slope, b_0, is removed to reduce the size of the numbers, help uncorrelate the errors, and simplify the fitting formulae.

To treat the balloon data by the 99.44 per cent method, we need estimates of the Within variances.   These are

$$\frac{rs_\eta}{s_\xi} \equiv \frac{228.3}{408.6} = 0.558737$$

and

$$\left(\frac{s_\eta}{s_\xi}\right)^2 = \frac{309.4}{408.6} = 0.757220.$$

For convenience we take b_0 equal to the slope we found by our first method, 0.986387.   On substituting into (16) we find p to be -1.46830. Using equations (18) we get

$$\text{SSW}uu = 624.332$$
$$\text{SSW}uv = 0 \qquad \text{(a check on } p)$$
$$\text{SSW}vv = 256.567$$

and

$$\text{SSB}uu = 16.17 + (-1.4683)^2(33,930.5) = 73,167.47$$
$$\text{SSB}uv = 16.17$$
$$\text{SSB}vv = 16.17$$

Thus

$$b = 16.17/73,167.47 = 0.00022838$$

and limits on β are found as solutions of

$$(B - 0.00022838)^2 = \frac{4.13}{(36)(73,167.47)} [256.567 + B^2(624.332)]$$

which are -0.019838 and 0.020296.   When these numbers are fed back through equation (21) to get values in the (x, y) plane, we find

$$0.96595 \leqslant 0.986615 \leqslant 1.00610$$

for our balloon limits.   All three methods have used a critical $F_{1,\ 36}$ value of 4.13 for the balloon problem, which gives a 5 per cent error rate, so we may assert the true value of our slope to lie between the given limits with 95 per cent confidence.

The corresponding values for the zinc problem are

$$\frac{rs_\eta}{s_\xi} = -0.27738 \qquad \left(\frac{s_\eta}{s_\xi}\right)^2 = 1.38845$$

$$b_0 = 0.945058$$

$$p = -2.295304$$

$$\text{SSB} \left\| \begin{array}{cc} 214.544 \\ & 12.324 \\ 12.324 \end{array} \right\| \quad \text{and SSW} \quad \left\| \begin{array}{cc} 94.5212 \\ & 0 \\ 107.7093 \end{array} \right\|$$

$$b = 0.057444$$

$$(B - 0.057444)^2(214.544) = \frac{4.26}{25}[107.7093 + B^2(94.5212)]$$

$$B = -0.25254, 0.35211$$

The final (x, y) slope and 95 per cent confidence limits are

$$0.344 \leqslant 1.01008 \leqslant 1.140.$$

Confidence limits on β from the MSB

In the preceding paragraphs, we have been considering ways of isolating a single degree of freedom for regression from the Sum of Squares Between populations. If convenient, this is a powerful technique since it distills the essential information into as concentrated a package as possible, placing it where it can be scrutinized most closely. Frequently, however, a less cumbersome method will suffice. In the one-variable-in-error problem with several data at each x, the squared deviations are usually broken up into one of two equivalent forms,

$$\underset{n-1}{\text{SSB}} + \underset{N-n}{\text{SSW}} \qquad \text{or} \qquad \underset{1}{\text{SSReg}} + \underset{n-2}{\text{SSD}} + \underset{N-n}{\text{SSW}}$$

where the corresponding numbers of degrees of freedom are shown underneath each term. If the data really lie on a line with zero slope, the expected values of MSB, MSW, and MSD are all the same, so that improbably large departures of MSB or MSReg from MSW or MSD imply a non-zero slope for the regression line. If the extraction of the single degree of freedom for regression (SSReg) has been clean, the most powerful comparison we can muster is against the pooled SSD and SSW (which may be combined because they are equivalent by our degeneracy assumption that the true points really lie *on* a true line rather than merely *near* one). We frequently choose to remain skeptical, however, about this degeneracy assumption and insure ourselves by testing the SSReg against merely the

SSD, which contain any deviations of the cluster means from the true line (as opposed to the SSW which measure only the within-group scatter). The SSB contain the regression slope information, so if we really believe our degeneracy assumption, the ratio of MSB to MSW gives a statistically precise test.   Since the presence of obscuring information not pertinent to the question may weaken the test considerably, we usually avoid it by using one of the other exact tests.   In the two-variate problem, however, we have the danger that incomplete removal of a regression sum of squares from SSB may leave an SSD which is not independent of the single degree supposedly removed.   To avoid this lurking trouble we choose to test the single degree *or the entire* MSB against the MSW, the latter course being followed when it is too difficult to isolate the single degree of freedom.

In setting confidence limits via the MSB it is necessary to project down a contemplated line with contemplated slope, B, and to ask the usual F question.   Thus:

$$\frac{\text{MSB}(y - Bx)}{\text{MSW}(y - Bx)} \leqslant F_{n-1,\; n(k-1)} \equiv F_{n-1,\; N-n}. \qquad (22)$$

Note that MSB is SSB/$(n - 1)$ here, since the degree of freedom for regression is still contained therein.   Both the numerator and denominator of (22) are quadratic in B similar to (20), and hence the test gives two values for B.   This test is perfectly legitimate provided only that we make the correct separation of our data into populations.

Our balloon data give 95 per cent confidence limits of

$$0.9696 \qquad \text{and} \qquad 1.0582$$

whereas for the zinc data we get the much wider ones

$$0.6249 \qquad \text{and} \qquad 1.4581.$$

Post-mortem on balloons

By this time the gentle reader probably has a surfeit of confidence limits for the slope of a not-too-interesting structural line which, after all, only shows whether or not the altimeter and the theodolite are giving the same answers about the height of a balloon.   Every limit has included the perfect slope of *one*, and so we must conclude that the two measurement methods are equivalent—unless perhaps a constant bias exists, which will show only in the means.

Perhaps we can ask more interesting questions that have little to do with the line but more to do with the sorts of variation to be expected.   If we examine that finest category of variability, the SSW, for each of the balloon tetherings, we find that these points fall in little ellipses which are tilted. Two extreme mechanisms seem pertinent here:

1. If the balloon were perfectly still in the air, but the altimeter and theodolite exhibited uncorrelated errors, the points would define ellipses with their centers on the 45° line, their long axes being either vertical or horizontal according to which instrument had the greater variability. Correlation between these errors would somewhat tilt the ellipses.

2. If, on the other hand, no errors were present in the altimeter or theodolite, but the balloon bobbed in the wind, then each group of points would lie on a segment of the 45° line, said segment being a degenerate tilted ellipse.

Undoubtedly both phenomena occurred, and so the four groups of points define four tilted ellipses which are caused in part by the bobbing of the balloon and in part by the instrumental variability. If we are interested in the reliability of the instrument rather than in the stability of a tethered balloon, we should try to break down these SSW still further. We feel that the theodolite readings, x_{ij}, might be made up of several additive parts:

$$x_{ij} = \mu_i + \omega_{ij} + \delta_{ij}$$

where $\mu_i + \omega_{ij}$ is the actual height of the balloon—
μ_i being the mean height throughout the ith group of observations,
ω_{ij} being the wind perturbations around that mean—and
where δ_{ij} is the random error of the theodolite reading.

The altimeter reading, y_{ij}, would contain similar components, the μ and ω being the same as for the theodolite reading but the instrument error, ϵ_{ij}, would be the random error of the altimeter. Thus

$$y_{ij} = \mu_i + \omega_{ij} + \epsilon_{ij}.$$

If we consider either a single group of readings or the pooled SSW, the MSW are trying to be

$$\text{AMSW} = \left\| \begin{array}{cc} \sigma_\omega{}^2 + \sigma_\delta{}^2 & \\ & \sigma_\omega{}^2 + \rho\sigma_\delta\sigma_\epsilon \\ \sigma_\omega{}^2 + \sigma_\epsilon{}^2 & \end{array} \right\|.$$

Without further assumptions or data we cannot hope to separate the $\sigma_\omega{}^2$ from the instrumental variances. If, however, we are willing to assume the altimeter errors to be uncorrelated with those of the theodolite, then $\rho\sigma_\delta\sigma_\epsilon$ is zero and the cross term only estimates $\sigma_\omega{}^2$—and this estimate may then be subtracted off from the other two mean squares to give direct estimates of the instrument variances. From our data we compute Table 5. The obvious implication is that much of the Within variability

TABLE 5

z	1	2	3	4	Pooled Estimates
s_ω^2	6.03	7.87	9.67	1.69	6.897
s_δ^2	4.20	0.62	8.50	6.71	5.008
s_ϵ^2	0.29	3.20	-0.89^a	6.41	2.253

[a] Negative variance estimates occur because of sampling fluctuations.

was caused by the balloon bobbing on its string—so much that we wonder whether perhaps a different experiment might not be needed before we can understand the structure of the errors in these two methods for determining altitude.   These data suggest the altimeter to be less variable than the theodolite, but no known test for inhomogeneity of variances would support such an assertion on these few degrees of freedom.

Two-parameter confidence regions

Although the procedures already presented for finding confidence limits on each of the two structural parameters separately will probably suffice for most applications, it is occasionally more elegant to have some two-parameter confidence region delimiting the family of plausible structural lines from which the data might have sprung.   Rectangular or parallelographic regions can be found from the one-parameter limits, but we are also tempted to try for the analogue of the elliptical regions, which occurs so simply in the one-variate-in-error problems.

The elliptical regions in Chapter 3 arise from splitting out two degrees of freedom for a line from the sums of squares and then comparing this mean square with the SSR.   The analysis requires that the x values be accurately known if the theory is to be exact, and so the same approach is unprofitable when both variates are in error unless the errors are uncorrelated.   It seems safe in 99.44 per cent coordinates, but we doubt whether the added computational troubles are worth the small gain in elegance.

An alternative way of looking at these problems is to demand that the true structural line pass through an arbitrarily fixed point with arbitrary slope and then inquire how much reduction in the squared residuals would be achieved by using the best line we know how to fit.   A significant reduction rejects the arbitrary point and slope.   This argument leads precisely to the conditions we have already described in Chapter 2 (not surprising, since the contemplated line is quite arbitrary), but it seems usable when both x and y are in error.   Of course we have not changed anything basic; if extraction of two degrees of freedom for regression was suspect before, it is still suspect here, but the plausibility lent by this point of view suggests that perhaps we are too suspicious and that the separation of two degrees of freedom can be quite good in the original coordinate system.   Quantitative information is badly needed here.

Non-degenerate models—slope

If we admit that our population means need not fall exactly on a structural line but may exhibit deviations that cannot be explained by the effects of the sampling errors within the populations, we must also decide how this non-degeneracy enters our algebraic model.   Perhaps the simplest model is

$$x_{ij} = \xi_i + \delta_{ij}$$
$$i = 1, ..., n$$
$$y_{ij} = \eta_i + \gamma_i + \epsilon_{ij}$$
$$j = 1, ..., k$$
$$\eta_i = \mu + \beta(\xi_i - \xi.)$$

where the δ_{ij} and ϵ_{ij} are the data fluctuations of the ith population about their mean $(\xi_i, \eta_i + \gamma_i)$ and the means are almost constrained to lie on a line.   The γ_i represent the deviations of the population means from the structural line whose parameters we want to estimate.

More assumptions must be made about the statistical behavior of γ, δ, and ϵ before we can estimate them from our data.   We must decide whether they represent random samples from perhaps large populations of errors with normal distributions or possibly a complete sampling of a very small family (n members) of errors.   Or perhaps they fall somewhere in between.

Since the δ and ϵ are often errors of measurement not dependent on the differences in the populations, we shall choose in this example to take

TABLE 6

	SS	MS	AMS
Mean	$nky..^2$	$nky..^2$	$nk\mu + \left(1 - \dfrac{n}{N}\right)k\sigma_\gamma^2 + \sigma_\epsilon^2$
Between	$k \sum_i (y_i. - y..)^2$	$\dfrac{k}{n-1} \sum (y_i. - y..)^2$	$\dfrac{k}{n-1} S\eta\eta + k\sigma_\gamma^2 + \sigma_\epsilon^2$
Within	$\sum_{ij} (y_{ij} - y_i.)^2$	$\dfrac{1}{n(k-1)} \sum_{ij} (y_{ij} - y_i.)^2$	σ_ϵ^2

them as bivariate normal errors with zero mean. They may be correlated with each other, but we shall assume they are *not* correlated with the γ_i. Both ϵ_{ij} and γ_i will have zero for their expected values.

Let us examine the usual anova table for y^2, Table 6. If we consider the Average Mean Square for the Between (population) variance, writing down the terms for the (xx) and the (xy), as well as for the (yy), we see that the term with $\sigma_\gamma{}^2$ enters only from the (yy)—a fact which allows us to separate out its effect. We have

$$\text{AMSM} = \left\| \begin{array}{cc} nk\xi.^2 + \sigma_\delta{}^2 & \\ & nk\xi.\eta. + \rho_{\delta\epsilon}\sigma_\delta\sigma_\epsilon \\ nk\eta.^2 + \left(1 - \dfrac{n}{N}\right)k\sigma_\gamma{}^2 + \sigma_\epsilon{}^2 & \end{array} \right\|, \tag{23}$$

$$\text{AMSB} = \left\| \begin{array}{cc} \dfrac{k}{n-1}S\xi\xi + \sigma_\delta{}^2 & \\ & \dfrac{k}{n-1}S\xi\eta + \rho_{\delta\epsilon}\sigma_\delta\sigma_\epsilon \\ \dfrac{k}{n-1}S\eta\eta + k\sigma_\gamma{}^2 + \sigma_\epsilon{}^2 & \end{array} \right\|, \tag{24}$$

and

$$\text{AMSW} = \left\| \begin{array}{cc} \sigma_\delta{}^2 & \\ & \rho\sigma_\delta\sigma_\epsilon \\ \sigma_\epsilon{}^2 & \end{array} \right\|; \tag{25}$$

so that the Components of the Mean Square Between become

$$\text{CMSB} = \frac{1}{k}(\text{MSB} - \text{MSW}) = \left\| \begin{array}{cc} \dfrac{1}{n-1}S\xi\xi & \\ & \dfrac{1}{n-1}S\xi\eta \\ \dfrac{1}{n-1}S\eta\eta + \sigma_\gamma{}^2 & \end{array} \right\|. \tag{26}$$

Since by hypothesis ξ and η lie exactly on the structural line with unknown slope β, i.e., equation (2), our best estimators, b, of β are

$$b = S\xi\eta/S\xi\xi \qquad \text{and} \qquad b = S\eta\eta/S\xi\eta. \tag{27}$$

If we knew the three quadratic sums of ξ and η exactly, these estimates would be identical. Since we must use approximations for these sums, we prefer to invoke the first one, avoiding the possible complications inherent in the $\sigma_\gamma{}^2$ term of the *Syy*.

One of the first problems is to decide whether our data do indeed degenerate happily along a line or do they have this γ quantity cluttering up most of the Between Squares and all of the confidence limits? From (24) and (25) we see that

$$\text{AMSB}(y - bx) = \frac{k}{n-1}(S\eta\eta - 2bS\xi\eta + b^2 S\xi\xi) + k\sigma_\gamma^2$$
$$+ (\sigma_\epsilon^2 - 2b\rho\sigma_\epsilon\sigma_\delta + b^2\sigma_\delta^2)$$

which, if b is given both by $S\xi\eta/S\xi\xi$ and also by $S\eta\eta/S\xi\eta$, becomes

$$\text{AMSB}(y - bx) = k\sigma_\gamma^2 + \text{AMSW}(y - bx)$$

so that the ratio

$$\frac{\text{MSB}(y - bx)}{\text{MSW}(y - bx)}$$

will exceed unity only because of sampling fluctuations and the presence of σ_γ^2. The sampling fluctuations will cause this ratio to exceed $F_{\text{DFB, DFW}}(\alpha)$ only 100α per cent of those occasions we make the test, and so we may use it to decide whether σ_γ^2 is inflating our y variability. As with all such tests, our F allowance for statistical variability is often large enough to mask a real but small σ_γ^2—and so we may well be led to accept the hypothesis that no γ is present in our data when indeed it was really there. If we have good physical reasons for believing this non-degenerate model to be a correct one, we should probably decide to omit (or ignore) a test for the "significant" presence of σ_γ^2 but rather estimate its size instead. The estimation technique is already nearly obvious, but we shall discuss it later, with examples, under *components of variance*. Here we merely note that our balloon data give

$$\frac{11,310.167B^2 - 2B(11,156.200) + 11,009.900}{11.35B^2 - 2B(6.897) + 8.622} \leqslant 2.83 = F_{3, 36}(0.05)$$

which may be rewritten as

$$(11,278.046)B^2 - 2B(11,136.681) + 10,985.500 \leqslant 0. \tag{28}$$

The solutions of this quadratic consist of all B's between

$$B = \frac{11,136.681}{11,278.046} \pm \sqrt{\left(\frac{11,136.681}{11,278.046}\right)^2 - \left(\frac{10,985.500}{11,278.046}\right)}$$

$$B = \begin{Bmatrix} 0.955404 \\ 1.019526 \end{Bmatrix}.$$

Unless we have other evidence to the contrary, we may therefore conclude that no γ variations are plaguing us. [If equation (28) had had no real solutions, we would have concluded that a considerable γ disturbance was present in our y group means.]   These limiting values of B may bracket the plausible values for the structural slope, but—because of possible γ contamination—we do not care for this method of finding our slope confidence limits.

The corresponding data for the zinc experiment show possible degeneration along a line with a slope between 0.6276 and 1.4555.   In point of fact, these artificial data were constructed with a normally distributed γ with unit variance.   The sampling fluctuations of ϵ (which had a variance of *four*) happen to have quite obliterated the effect of γ, and the degeneration of our data is unaffected.   When γ is doubled, however, it stands out strongly enough so that the data no longer degenerate.

Having found b from (27), we must then attempt to set confidence limits on β.   One general technique is to estimate the variance of our slope estimate, b, and then use a t test.   Here

$$(b - B)^2/(\text{our estimate of } \sigma_b{}^2) \leqslant F_{1,\,m} = t_m{}^2, \tag{29}$$

where m is the equivalent number of degrees of freedom possessed by the estimate of $\sigma_b{}^2$.   Since, in general, the denominator of (29) will be a quadratic in B, we shall get a general quadratic equation to solve for our limits, B, instead of merely a simple square root of both sides.

Another possibility is to split out a single degree of freedom for regression and to test this against the rest of the Sum of Squares Between.   Since this is a risky business if the extraction is not skillfully performed (the two sums are not independent if the extraction is incomplete), it should only be attempted in a 99.44 per cent coordinate system.   In that system, the single degree could be split out by regarding the u_i. as accurately known and regressing the v_i. on them. Computationally, this alternative is unpleasant, as the transformation to the (u, v) plane involves the slope B, necessitating either an iterative calculation or the solution of a quartic.

Returning to the first proposal, we desire to estimate β by (27) and we also need the variance of this estimate for use in (29).   Clearly, a satisfactory estimate of β is

$$b = \frac{\text{CMPB}xy}{\text{CMSB}xx} = \frac{\text{MPB}xy - \text{MPW}xy}{\text{MSB}xx - \text{MSW}xx}, \tag{30}$$

where the MPB and MPW refer to the off-diagonal or cross terms (Product).   Tukey [33] proposes to estimate $\sigma_b{}^2$ by a quadratic in B:

$$s_b{}^2 = c_0 - 2c_1 B + c_2 B^2$$

$$= \frac{\dfrac{\text{MSB}x\text{MSB}(y - Bx)}{\text{DFB}} + \dfrac{\text{MSW}x\text{MSW}(y - Bx)}{\text{DFW}}}{(\text{MSB}x - \text{MSW}x)^2}. \tag{31}$$

This is the estimate to be used in (29) in an F test with $(1, m)$ degrees of freedom where m is equal to the number of Degrees of Freedom Between —and the test is restricted to cases in which DFB are greater than or equal to *two*. These procedures are the same whether we consider the finite population of deviations, γ_i, to have been completely or only partially sampled.

The balloon data again

To demonstrate the arithmetic we return briefly to our balloon data. In that experiment, non-degeneracy might arise from uncompensated fluctuations in the barometric pressure. At each tethering of the balloon these slow fluctuations could produce groups of readings which deviate from a structural line but which leave the Within-group variability reflecting solely the balloon bobbing and the instrumental errors. Our data actually display no such phenomenon, but if they had, our task would have been to estimate the structural slope and to decide how far from this estimate the true slope could actually have been—knowing that we had these Between-group disturbances in our y data. Clearly our slope confidence limits must invoke primarily the MSB rather than the MSW in coping with such perturbations. (If we were interested in the probable range of the structural slope in a new experiment where the barometric fluctuations have been skillfully eliminated by more careful instrumentation, it might just be plausible to use the MSW alone to get the slope limits. In general, however, the MSW will avail us little for answers about structural slopes with non-degenerate data.)

The slope estimate causes no trouble since

$$\text{CMSB} = \frac{1}{10}(\text{MSB} - \text{MSW}) = \left\| \begin{matrix} 1{,}129.88 \\ \\ 1{,}100.13 \end{matrix} \quad 1{,}114.93 \quad \right\| \quad \text{with 3 DF}$$

and thus

$$b = \frac{1{,}114.93}{1{,}129.88} = 0.986768.$$

(The other ratio gives $1{,}100.13/1{,}114.93$ or 0.986726.) The variance of b depends upon b itself. According to (31) we find that

$$s_b{}^2 = \frac{\frac{1}{3}(11{,}310.167)[11{,}009.9 - 2B(11{,}156.2) + B^2(11{,}310.167)]}{+ \frac{1}{36}(11.35)[8.622 - 2B(6.897) + B^2(11.35)]}{(11{,}298.817)^2}$$

which becomes

$$s_b{}^2 = 0.325136 - 2B(0.329456) + B^2(0.334003).$$

For our particular value of b,

$$s_b{}^2 = 0.000164 \quad \text{and} \quad s_b = 0.012806.$$

When we turn to find confidence limits for our slope, we encounter trouble—not because we are using non-degenerative methods on a probably degenerate example (they should still work, if with slightly reduced power) but rather because of a paucity of Degrees of Freedom Between. Our test is

$$(B - 0.9867)^2 \leqslant F_{1,3}\,s_b{}^2 = (10.13)[(0.325136) - 2B(0.329456) \\ + B^2(0.334003)] \quad (28')$$

which has no solution.

Geometrically equation $(28')$ may be shown as two parabolas, the closed region bounded between them normally demarking those values of B that are plausible. In Figure 43 we see that the left side of $(28')$ gives a simple parabola tangent to the B axis at b with the quadratic coefficient of *one*. The right side gives a more curved parabola (coefficient of 3.38) which has its minimum at nearly the same value (0.9864) but slightly *above* the axis (at 0.0005). Thus the locations of the minima and the curvature prevent these two parabolas from intersecting. If we consider the way such terms will usually arise from straight-line data, we see that the $s_b{}^2$ parabola will frequently have its minimum near b,

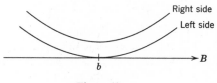

Figure 43

that it will—in fact—often be very close to $C(B - b)^2 + D$ in analytic form, so the question of intersection with the $(B - b)^2$ parabola depends critically on the constant C being less than *one*. In many examples C will be nearly $F_{1,\mathrm{DFB}}/\mathrm{DFB}$, and—for the 0.05 error rate level—this becomes less than one only for a **DFB** of *six* or more. Thus the restriction of (31) to DFB of *two* or more may frequently have to be strengthened—thereby reducing materially the usefulness of the technique.

Non-degenerate models—mean

When we turn to the question of where the centroid of the structural line might reasonably be, we must differentiate between Models 1 and 2. In *Model* 1, the AMSM for y becomes

$$nk\mu^2 + \sigma_\epsilon{}^2. \tag{32}$$

An appropiate test for limits on μ would therefore seem to be

$$\frac{nk(M - m)^2}{\text{MSW}yy} \leqslant F_{1,\ N-n}, \tag{33}$$

where

$$m = y.., $$

and the entire test concerns only vertical displacements at the centroid of the x values, so that no projection along the line is necessary.

In our balloon experiment, Model 1 would imply that we believed the barometric variations to have been exhaustively sampled, that we were interested in predicting future experiments which contain only those particular variations we have already experienced—either because there are no more, or there are no others we believe to be pertinent. Clearly this attitude is physical nonsense for barometric fluctuations in the balloon data, but the formal use of (33) gives

$$92.41 \leqslant 93.35 = m \leqslant 94.29$$

for the best value of μ and its plausible range.

We have already discussed rational reasons for analyzing our zinc data according to Model 1. The numbers are

$$15.542 \leqslant 16.093 \leqslant 16.644$$

for the mean of the magnigage (y) readings.

Under *Model* 2, the AMS mean is the same as (32), except for an additional term of $k\sigma_y{}^2$. The only appropriate Mean Square against which to test this is MSB, but the MSByy contains the obstructing term $S\eta\eta$. To circumvent this difficulty, we need only project down the contemplated slope, B, and test

$$\frac{nk(M_0 - m)^2}{\text{MSB}(y - Bx)} \leqslant F_{1,\ n-1}, \tag{34}$$

where, as before,

$$m = y.., $$

and the appropriate degrees of freedom are used in the F test.

For the balloon data, Model 2 implies that we are interested in the future behavior of our instruments under an infinite set of barometric fluctuations which we believe to have already been randomly sampled in this experiment. This philosophy might be quite sensible for our experiment if it were carefully conducted so as to avoid correlation in the barometric fluctuations between readings at successive tetherings. The fact that the num-

bers here turn out to be quite similar to the Model 1 limits merely emphasizes that the barometric fluctuations were small and unimportant. We
find

$$92.17 \leqslant 93.35 \leqslant 94.53$$

for the Model 2 limits on the y (altimeter) mean for the balloon. The
theodolite gave 94.15, which is within our limits, and we therefore conclude
that—within the ability of this experiment to discriminate—there is no
bias between the two measurement methods.

The magnigage readings permit a somewhat wider spread for the mean
under Model 2 because of the rather larger variance Between (3.14 as
opposed to 2.13 Within) and, of course, because of the larger F value
caused by the reduction in the pertinent degrees of freedom. We find

$$15.194 \leqslant 16.093 \leqslant 16.992$$

for the Model 2 limits on μ. The stripping readings have their mean at
13.927, so we must conclude that some bias is present between these two
methods—presumably close to

$$16.093 - 13.927 = 2.166$$

units. (These data were in fact constructed to have a bias of 2.00 units
between them.)

Instrumental variates

In all the preceding sections of this chapter, we have assumed that we
could separate the data points into distinct populations. In the example,
each sheet of metal was a separate population, and the distinction is a
natural one. The means of these populations, or their order ranks, were
used as *instrumental variates* for the purpose of isolating degrees of freedom for a mean and regression, thus splitting out the smallest category of
error. The instrumental variate—knowledge about which data points
belonged together—was essential to the entire computational scheme.
Often, however, even though natural populations exist and we postulate
a structural model on these assumptions, the data are not collected in a
way that preserves these sharp demarcations. That this is unfortunate is
an understatement, for the ability to separate the data into populations is
the power to analyze the model. If this power is denied to us in exact
form, we must seek it by proxy.

Sometimes a plot of the data will disclose natural gaps and groupings.
Lacking a definitive criterion, we may take the rank order of these groups
as our instrumental variate. A loss of power is inevitable, as the groupings may be incorrect, but if the data are spread out enough to suggest a

probable structural line to the eye, clearly the essential information is present and must be extractable—and under such circumstances any reasonable criterion cannot be too sensitive to errors of grouping.   Perhaps such a remark ought not to be made in print, for it lays us open to being cited as an authority for someone else's faulty judgment, but we feel that if our purpose is to analyze data realistically, we must face these anomalous situations which all too frequently occur rather than pretend that they do not exist.   If the information is not precise, it is usually necessary to make some subjective judgments, and the best place to make them is where they have the least influence on the information extracted. If the assumptions turn out to be wildly different from the physical facts, the conclusions will be bad too, but the fault will be with the person who made the assumptions—not with the method of analysis.   With this we rest our general case.

In the model at hand, the grouping may depend on some third quantity which then becomes our instrumental variate.   Natural gaps in this variable, z, may provide the basis for division into populations.   If the errors in z are uncorrelated with the population deviations, γ, this is better than using gaps in x or y, as the latter will certainly be correlated with the errors of measurement in x and y—a complication that violates our assumption of independence of γ and the (δ, ϵ) combination.

It is even possible, in extreme cases, to break up the data into arbitrary groups—say thirds or fifths—on the rank order of the raw x data.   This introduces some errors due to misclassification at the borders between these artificial populations (an excessively large error of measurement here will cause a datum to join the wrong family) and still further loss of power in that the populations thus formed have no direct structural basis, but the possible structural slopes can be found with approximately 90 per cent of the efficiency of the complete normal theory in examples where that normal theory actually applies but is not used.   The efficiency might well be lower if some other model were correct, but we quote this figure to stress the point that in spite of the apparent arbitrariness inherent in the division, the process is not at all bad for this rather common structure.

Quantitative instrumental variates

The previous instrumental variates have been qualitative: the rank order of populations; the assignation of a pair of (x, y) data to a particular population; the division into groups based on gaps or artificial lines.   If we do not have any clear populations, we may still avoid being so arbitrary as to divide the data on their x ranking if we possess the proper additional information in the form of a third variable, z, and if this variable has pleasant properties. For example, let us suppose that all three variables are measured erroneously, but that y has an additional source of error not vouchsafed to the other two, and further that this peculiar error is uncorrelated with *any* of the other errors. Then

$$x_i = \xi_i + \delta_i$$
$$y_i = \eta_i + \epsilon_i + \omega_i \qquad i = 1, ..., n \qquad (35)$$
$$z_i = \zeta_i + \gamma_i$$

where γ, δ, and ϵ represent error measurements from an infinite trivariate normal population with zero means, and ω is from an error population of size N and mean zero. If, in addition, we are willing to assume that there are *two* structural lines

$$\eta_i = \alpha_1 + \beta_1 \xi_i$$
$$\eta_i = \alpha_2 + \beta_2 \zeta_i \qquad (36)$$

hidden under these measurements, we can deal with the problem fairly well.

The only sums of squares possible in the model above are the *mean* and the residuals from that mean:

$$nx.^2 \qquad \text{and} \qquad \sum_i (x_i - x.)^2,$$

and similarly for (yy) and (xy). We note that, for $\beta_1 \neq 0$, equations (36) imply a third equation

$$\xi_i = \alpha_3 + \beta_3 \zeta_i$$

where

$$\beta_3 = \beta_2/\beta_1,$$

so that a regression of x on z will extract from Sxx the information concerning the influence of ξ_i, and a regression of y on z will similarly isolate the effect of η_i in a single degree of freedom from the Syy. Symbolically,

$$
\text{MSR} = \begin{Vmatrix}
\dfrac{S\xi\xi}{n-1} + \sigma_\delta^2 & & \\
& \dfrac{S\xi\eta}{n-1} + \rho\sigma_\delta\sigma_\epsilon & \\
\dfrac{S\eta\eta}{n-1} + \sigma_\omega^2 + \sigma_\epsilon^2 & & \dfrac{S\xi\zeta}{n-1} + \rho\sigma_\delta\sigma_\gamma \\
& \dfrac{S\eta\zeta}{n-1} + \rho\sigma_\epsilon\sigma_\gamma & \\
\dfrac{S\zeta\zeta}{n-1} + \sigma_\gamma^2 & &
\end{Vmatrix}.
$$

The extraction of the information by regression on z may be done crudely, using the raw data with no attempt to allow for the $\sigma_y{}^2$ and similar terms in the last column, or it may be performed in a more sophisticated way by division of the data, on z, into groups. These groups are then used to get an MSW and MSB—thence to Components of the Mean Square Between for (xz), (yz), and (zz). These components may be quite inaccurate in themselves, but they are used only to uncover the $S\xi\zeta$, $S\eta\zeta$, and $S\zeta\xi$ which lead to estimates of β_2 and β_3 by

$$b_2 = S\eta\zeta/S\zeta\zeta$$
$$b_3 = S\xi\zeta/S\zeta\zeta.$$

Having these numbers, we can split out a single degree of freedom for regression from the privileged (xy) Sum of Squares, leaving

$$\text{SSR} = \begin{Vmatrix} Sxx - \dfrac{S\xi\zeta^2}{S\zeta\zeta} & & Sxy - \dfrac{S\xi\zeta S\eta\zeta}{S\zeta\zeta} \\ & & \\ Syy - \dfrac{S\eta\zeta^2}{S\zeta\zeta} & & \end{Vmatrix}$$

as the error term with $n-2$ degrees of freedom and giving

$$\text{SSReg} = \begin{Vmatrix} \dfrac{S\xi\zeta^2}{S\zeta\zeta} & & \dfrac{S\xi\zeta S\eta\zeta}{S\zeta\zeta} \\ & & \\ \dfrac{S\eta\zeta^2}{S\zeta\zeta} & & \end{Vmatrix}$$

with one degree of freedom. Since the information about the line is presumably concentrated in the SSReg, we may determine its slope from the appropriate ratio

$$b_2/b_3 = b_1 = S\eta\zeta/S\xi\zeta$$

and set limits for this slope by testing the ratio of

$$\left(\frac{\text{MSReg}}{\text{MSD}}\right)_{y-Bx} \leqslant F_{1,\,n-2}$$

as before (i.e., by projection down a line of contemplated slope, B).

Here we have used regression on a quantitative variate to isolate the essential information from the conglomerate of errors. The effect of the

ω was left behind with the SSD, as it was not correlated with anything else. We cannot reliably estimate its magnitude because it is masked by other errors, and we have no way to get hold of it except by peeling away the other terms —a process that leaves the last term subject to considerable doubts unless done very carefully.

If we have at least two (x, y) pairs for each z, however, we can then break up the SS for (x, y) into

$$\|SSB\| + \|SSW\|.$$

Then a regression on z will further reliably separate the SSB into

$$\|SSReg\| + \|SSD\|.$$

We achieved this type of breakdown in our detailed discussion of the *qualitative* instrumental variate, which indeed in this latest model z has now become, for it really is just a name and rank order for a population of (x, y) values.

Components of variance

Thus far in this chapter we have been concerned chiefly with finding the structural line under varying degrees of handicaps in the form of miscellaneous errors. We now turn our attention briefly to the estimation of those errors themselves. In the simplest case the $\|MSW\|$ give direct estimates of what we have regarded as measurement errors—those errors but for which our points would have lain on a structural line under *Model* 0. In *Models* 1 and 2, however, there was an additional term, γ, which measured the departures from the line of the various population means. These γ_i were assumed to be a sample of n from a population of size N with zero mean and variance σ_γ^2. It is for this σ_γ^2 that we now wish an estimate and confidence limits. If we examine the components of the Mean Square Between (26), we see that an estimator for σ_γ^2 is

$$s_\gamma^2 = \text{CMSB}[(yy) - 2b(xy) + b^2(xx)] = \text{CMSB}(y - bx). \quad (37)$$

This estimator is *biased*, having the unpleasant property that it always *underestimates* σ_γ^2—a fact which becomes plausible when we note that s_γ^2 is that value of $\text{CMSB}(y - Bx)$ which is minimal with respect to variations in B—the minimization causing the quadratic estimator to go too low. An exact compensation for this bias is not available, but *most of it may be removed by evaluating* $\text{CMSB}(y - Bx)$ *for B equal to* $b + \sigma_b$ *and* $b - \sigma_b$ *and then averaging these two values.* Our difficulties arise from the fact that the estimator, $s_\gamma^2(b)$, is a quadratic function of a random variable, b. If it were a linear function, the expected value of $s^2(b)$ would be given by substituting the expected value of b in formula (31). This procedure does not succeed for quadratic functions, but rather the expected value is found by averaging the two values of the functions evaluated at $\beta \pm \sigma_b$, i.e., at the expected value of b increased and decreased by one standard deviation. If b were the only random variable here, this averaging procedure would give an unbiased result, but other terms in (31) are also subject to statistical fluctuations which thus far prevent discovery of the exact distributions. Since, however, the bias comes primarily from the quadratic dependence on b, we feel that the $\pm \sigma$ correction—as Tukey [33] terms it—should give an estimate which is quite satisfactory.

If we were convinced by ancillary information that barometric fluctuations were indeed present in the y values of our balloon data, we would certainly wish to estimate the variability they contributed. We have already computed b at 0.9867685 and s_b at 0.012806, so we merely have to evaluate $CMSB(y - Bx)$ for B equal to $(b \pm s_b)$ and average. Since

$$s_\gamma{}^2 = [1,100.13 - 2B(1,114.93) + B^2(1,129.88)],$$

we find

$$s_\gamma{}^2 = 0.138,$$

which is just another way of saying that γ is probably not important in our experiment. (Straightforward evaluation of $s_\gamma{}^2$ for the fitted value b gives the downward biased estimate of -0.048—a result we are glad to be able to explain away by bias, although statistical fluctuation would probably serve as well.)

The zinc data give less pleasing figures: The slopes at which $s_\gamma{}^2$ must be evaluated seem to be 0.8588 and 1.0977, yielding

$$s_\gamma{}^2 = -0.0803,$$

a result which must be laid to sampling fluctuation. The inevitable estimate of *zero* is the more distressing since a σ_y of *one* unit was incorporated in the data at their construction but apparently has been swallowed by the random ϵ variable having a σ_ϵ of *two*. (The minimum value of $s_\gamma{}^2$ is -0.215, mostly bias!)

In order to test these methods further, the SSB for the zinc data were inflated by doubling the size of the γ perturbations. The MSW were, of course, unaffected, but all the non-degenerate analyses changed. In particular, the test for degeneracy now indicates that an essential perturbing influence is present, b becomes 1.12218, and the $b \pm s_b$ estimate of $s_\gamma{}^2$ becomes 5.578 (the theoretical value is 4.0). Confidence limits for the slope are still not obtainable because of the small number of DFB (an effect we discussed at length in the section on slope limits).

A more complicated model

Let us consider briefly an experimental model in which we have physical reason to expect displacements of the population means from a theoretical line in both dimensions instead of merely in the y variable as before.   Now

$$x_{ij} = \xi_i + \omega_i + \delta_{ij}$$

$$\begin{aligned} i &= 1, ..., n \\ j &= 1, ..., k \end{aligned} \tag{38}$$

$$y_{ij} = \eta_i + \gamma_i + \epsilon_{ij}$$

where the (δ, ϵ) are assumed to be bivariate normally distributed with zero mean, and ω and γ are from independent finite populations of size M and N with zero means and are uncorrelated with δ, ϵ, and each other. We further assume that the structural line is

$$\eta_i = \mu + \beta(\xi_i - \xi.) \tag{39}$$

as before.   This model differs from our previous one only by the addition of ω, but this complication is crucial.   We are assuming the knowledge of a qualitative instrumental variate, the name of the population (i.e., we know that x_{ij} belongs to the jth population rather than the $j + 1$st). Thus we may isolate the (δ, ϵ) effects in the MSW and MSB and remove them from the MSB, giving the CMSB.   Here

$$\text{CMSB} = \left\| \begin{array}{cc} \dfrac{S\xi\xi}{n-1} + \sigma_\omega^2 & \\ & \dfrac{S\xi\eta}{n-1} \\ \dfrac{S\eta\eta}{n-1} + \sigma_\gamma^2 & \end{array} \right\| ,$$

and we see that we have no way of prying loose the $S\xi\xi$ from its annoying brother, σ_ω^2, in order to find the usual estimate of β, i.e., $S\xi\eta/S\xi\xi$. It is only if we have still another variable correlated with either ξ_i or ω_i—but not with both—that we can separate these terms.   Once we know β we can work back through $S\eta\eta$ to find σ_γ^2.   Lacking a concrete example, we feel this problem to be too complicated for further profitable discussion.

CHAPTER 6

Several Lines;
the Analysis of Variance

The Hottentots, we are told, distinguish between *one*, *two*, and *three* but then lump all further integers into the single category of *many*. The straight-line analyst is one step less sophisticated; he recognizes only one or two sets of data as peculiarly identifiable and lumps three or more together into a simple *many*, to be handled more or less uniformly regardless of the exact number. The amount of computational labor and the interpretational complexities will both usually increase with the amount of data, but the general approach, the philosophy of what to look for and how to do it, remains unaltered. In this chapter we shall illustrate these general techniques on two sets of lines, these being the simplest members of the large class. If the reader understands these examples, he should have little difficulty in analyzing more complicated sets of data should he be fortunate enough to obtain them.

Our major effort will be expended on a set of titrations for desoxy-

TABLE 1

x	y_1	y_2	y_3	$y.$
17	15	18	9	14.00
21	15	16	11	14.00
24	22	25	20	22.33
32	30	34	21	28.33
36	34	33	31	32.67
44	39	40	27	35.33
49	44	43	25	37.33
60	56	57	40	51.00
71	66	64	45	58.34
82	75	80	58	71.00
43.6	39.6	41.0	28.7	36.433

172

ribonucleic acid using three different indicators. The exact amount present, x, was determined by still another technique which we shall temporarily presume accurate. Ten different samples were each split into three parts and each part analyzed by one of the three methods, the results being the y values. The data are given in Table 1. Note that each of the three methods was used at each of the concentrations. This simultaneity of the y data is most important, as it allows much closer examination of the underlying structure than would the same quantity of y numbers taken at *different* values of x. Since it keeps occurring and cannot be ignored, the less satisfactory model will be treated later in the chapter. We hasten to point out, however, that the analyst can more profitably treat sets of data which are *balanced*, and all experimental men may take this as a strong plea to strive for such balanced sets of data when they design their experiments. A little effort here will put extractable information into the data which would otherwise be thoroughly obscured, if not completely absent.

Even a casual glance at our data suggests that the first two columns may well be equivalent but that the third is clearly different. Since the data are not evenly spaced in x, it is not easy to judge the linearity of the data without plotting them, so a graph is the next step. Although we omit printing the graph here to save space, we hasten to assure the reader that we did *not* omit it when analyzing these data. We do not omit it even when the data are *evenly* spaced. The ability of the human eye to pick out linear and even quadratic trends from properly plotted data is probably as powerful a discriminator as any of the quantitative algebraical techniques illustrated in this chapter. The advantage of the algebraic methods lies in their utter indifference to the temporary foibles of their user. Thus they should be employed in conjunction with graphical display to confirm or caution against the qualitative diagnoses of the experimenter. In their specialized expositional eagerness many statistics texts give the impression that their arithmetical jugglings are sufficient unto themselves without recourse to other sensible methods of examining the numbers. We hasten to assure the reader that we do not believe this to be the intent of most of these texts and it most certainly is not ours. All reasonable techniques should be tried, graphical display and differencing of equally spaced data being two of the most important.

Simple analysis of variance

Before fitting any straight lines to the data of Table 1, we shall examine the total variability of the numbers. We assume that each y value has something in common with the others in the same row and something in common with the others in the same column. Algebraically, we are assuming that each y entry is made up of at least four parts:

$$y_{ij} = \mu + \xi_i + \eta_j + \epsilon_{ij}$$

where μ = a mean value common to all entries,

ξ_i = a value common to every entry in one row, but probably different for each row,

η_j = a value common to every entry in one column,

ϵ_{ij} = a random perturbation applied to each entry, with zero mean and unknown variance, σ^2.

This simple model contains no lines explicitly, but it has room for growth. For instance, we have not said much about ξ_i except that it varies from row to row. If we make ξ_i a linear function of x, we have introduced a line where it is most needed, and other more complicated extensions of our model are also possible. For the moment, however, we shall perform some arithmetic based on this simple model.

First we append the row and columns averages (or sums) to our table as shown. We then compute the sums of squared deviations from the grand mean of all the y entries. This number represents the total amount of fluctuation of the y data about their mean. It is to be explained by breaking it up into *components of variability* whose sources may be more easily identified. We now calculate the sums of squared deviations of the row means from the grand mean; likewise for the column means. In order to put these three numbers on the same basis for comparison, it is necessary to multiply each sum of squares by the number of y entries that went into the means from which the sum was computed. Thus, since the row averages contain three y values, the squared deviations of these row averages must be multiplied by three. The formulae are

$$\text{Total SS} = \sum_{ij} (y_{ij} - y_{..})^2 \equiv \left[\sum_{ij} y_{ij}{}^2 - \left(\sum_{ij} y_{ij}\right)^2 \Big/ (r \cdot c)\right] = 10{,}733.4$$

$$\text{SS rows} = c \sum_i (y_{i.} - y_{..})^2 \equiv c\left[\sum_i y_{i.}{}^2 - \left(\sum_i y_{i.}\right)^2 \Big/ r\right] = \quad 9{,}522.6$$

$$\text{SS columns} = r \sum_j (y_{.j} - y_{..})^2 \equiv r\left[\sum_i y_{.j}{}^2 - \left(\sum_j y_{.j}\right)^2 \Big/ c\right] = \quad 906.9.$$

Although we see that the SS rows and SS columns account for most of the total variability, by subtraction we find that there is a noticeable piece left over. This residual, usually called SS(row by column), can also be computed directly from the formula

$$\text{SS}(r \times c) = \sum(y_{ij} - y_{i.} - y_{.j} + y_{..})^2$$

but is invariably obtained by the much easier process of subtraction. It *measures the variability of the data not accounted for by the row means and the column means.* Sometimes it is called the *interaction of rows and columns.*

We summarize these computations in the analysis of variance (anova) table (Table 2) by displaying the SS together with their appropriate degrees of freedom. Note that the bottom line is the sum of those above, both

TABLE 2

	SS	DF	DF (symbolically)	MS
Columns	906.9	2	$c - 1$	453.5
Rows	9,522.6	9	$r - 1$	1,058.1
Interaction	303.9	18	$(r - 1)(c - 1)$	16.88
Total	10,733.4	29	$rc - 1$	

in the SS and DF columns. We postpone discussion of the row effects until we put a straight line or two into our model, as most of this variability is obviously ascribable to the linear trend; but the column effect can be looked at immediately. The SS column measures the discrepancies between the column means, and in this example it says that these discrepancies are rather large compared with the unexplained residual (interaction) variability. An F test of MS columns/MS interaction is highly significant with 2 and 18 degrees of freedom, thus confirming part of our original statement that the three columns are not all alike.

Adding one line

If we now decide to fit all these data with a single line (which is equivalent to fitting a single line to the row means), we gain an additional line of entries in our anova table. We compute

$$Sxx = 4,318.4 \qquad b_0 = Sxy./Sxx = 0.85069$$
$$Sxy. = 3,673.64 \qquad SSReg_0 = b_0 Sxy. = 3,125.129$$
$$Sy.y. = 3,174.205 \qquad SSR_0 = Sy.y. - b_0 Sxy. = 49.076$$

where $Suv = \sum(u - u.)(v - v.) = \sum uv - (\sum u)(\sum v)/n$ and
n is the number of (u, v) pairs in the summation.

Since the line was fitted with row means (of three data each), the $SSReg_0$ must be multiplied by three in order to assume its rightful place in the anova table (Table 3). Since a general mean has been removed in all SS calculations, the line amounts to only *one* additional parameter fitted

TABLE 3

	SS	DF	MS
Columns	906.9	2	453.5
Average Regression	9,375.387	1	9,375.387
Other Row Effects	147.213	8	18.402
Interaction	303.9	18	16.88
Total	10,733.4	29	

and hence carries only *one* degree of freedom. We have thus "explained" a very large hunk of our row variability by this one line.

The row variability left unexplained by the line removal (Other Row Effects)* is perhaps the first interesting item uncovered by our arithmetic. It says that a substantial amount of the deviations from the fitted line are shared in common by the three data; i.e., when y_1 is above the fitted line, then—in general—y_2 and y_3 are also. This phenomenon is forced on the data merely by fitting a line to mean values, but perhaps the size of the effect suggests that some physical forces may be operating in addition to the algebraical ones. Certainly at this stage no decision is possible.

Three more lines

If one line did so much toward explaining away the variability of our data, we might be excused for getting excited enough to fit three more, one for each of the three experiments—three calibration lines, if you will. We should like to know whether these three are necessary, or has our one average calibration already explained the data with all the precision warranted by their inherent variability? This question is probably the most interesting physically and is the one that would motivate any general treatment of these data.

In order to fit three calibration lines we need to compute the various Sxy and Syy values set forth below:

$$Sxy_1 = 4,084.4 \qquad b_1 = 0.94581$$
$$Sy_1y_1 = 3,882.4 \qquad SSReg_1 = 3,863.1 \qquad SSR_1 = 19.3$$

$$Sxy_2 = 4,033.0 \qquad b_2 = 0.93391$$
$$Sy_2y_2 = 3,834.0 \qquad SSReg_2 = 3,766.5 \qquad SSR_2 = 67.5$$

$$Sxy_3 = 2,902.8 \qquad b_3 = 0.67219$$
$$Sy_3y_3 = 2,110.1 \qquad SSReg_3 = 1,951.2 \qquad SSR_3 = 158.9.$$

* This value may be obtained as 3 SSR_0 or, identically, by the subtraction (SS rows − 3 $SSReg_0$).

From these sums of squares and *Sxx* we get the three slopes *b*, the three SSReg which show how much variability is accounted for by each line, and the three SSR showing the amount left unexplained. The total (three line) regression variability exceeds that of the one average line by 205.413, as seen from

Total SSReg (3 lines) = 9,580.8	3 DF
SSReg$_0$ (1 line) = 9,375.387	1 DF
SS slope = 205.413	2 DF

If we once again turn to our anova table, the new entry is this *additional variability ascribable to fitting three slopes instead of one* (Table 4). Since

TABLE 4

	SS	DF	MS
Differences Between Means	906.9	2	453.5
Average Regression	9,375.387	1	9,375.387
Differences Between Slopes	205.413	2	102.707
Other Row Effects	147.213	8	18.402
Residual Variability	98.487	16	6.155
Total	10,733.4	29	

this is a row by column effect (different slopes in each column), it was contained in our previous interaction term. The column effects may now be properly identified as the variability ascribable to differences between *y* values, i.e., different levels between three more or less parallel lines. The other terms remain the same.

The variability ascribable to fitting three slopes instead of just one is certainly large enough to justify some such move, although there still remains our original hypothesis that the really important part of this improvement comes from the third line's being different from the other two. Thus our present step might have been to fit only two lines, one to the average of y_1 and y_2 and the other to y_3. We shall carry out this analysis next, but first we should examine the last two detail lines of our anova table.

Other Row Effects measures how much the average *y* values wobble about their common (average) fitted line. It could be the *Common Snakiness*, if a term is needed to describe a more or less random wiggle

about a line.   Or this term could be measuring deviations from the line
caused largely by a quadratic trend in the data, deviations that are quite
systematic.   It is possible to fit and remove a quadratic or other systematic
function by arithmetical procedures analogous to the ones we used for the
straight line, but unless the x data are evenly spaced they are sufficiently
tedious that a graphical exploration is preferable.   If a plot of the deviations of y. from the fitted line exhibits a strong suspicion of curvilinearity,
then the analytical procedures should be invoked for the quantitative
information they will give, but otherwise time will be saved by omitting
them.   Our plot disclosed no such quadratic shape, so we conclude that
147.213 represents a measure of the Common Snakiness of our data about
the average line.

The Residual Variability measures the degree of wobble of the individual
y data about their three respective calibration lines.   It is perhaps the
smallest meaningful measure of irreducible variability.   It says that an
individual y reading tends to have a standard error about its appropriate
calibration line of $\sqrt{6.155}$ or 2.48 units.   A quick look at the residuals for
the separate lines (SSR) suggests that these three sets of data may not be
equally precise—that the first set is quite good, the third rather poor.   If
these variances are really inhomogeneous, it may be unwise to pool them
for a common measure of variability—as the anova table has done for us.
In this unhappy but common situation, we can perhaps gain our most
legitimate picture of the equivalence of these three sets of data by plotting
each of the lines together with its confidence limits for the location of the
true line.   The degree of overlap between these confidence regions will
show rather directly whether or not a common true line is plausible.   Even
if it should be plausible, however, we would be wary about equating the
two or three processes producing these data.   A difference in variability,
although unlike a difference in mean or slope, is still a difference—it can
have serious economic consequences in a control laboratory and even in
the efficiency of a research program.

We can test for homogeneity of variance as described in Chapter 3, the
ratio 158.9/19.3 here suggesting that the three sets of data are indeed *not*
homogeneous (the 5 per cent critical value of this ratio for three variances
of eight degrees of freedom each is 5.90).   The cautious person will therefore be unhappy about analyses based on pooled residuals—using them
more as guides to his intuition than as dicta from Above.   For expository
purposes, however, we are going to proceed with these analyses to show
the type of information that may be extracted when the variances may
legitimately be pooled.

If we are willing to take the observed data as samples from a homogeneous error population, the Common Snakiness stands out strong and

significant against the critical measure of Residual Variability. It says that we should seek a reason why the three different analyses tended to depart from their common line in a common way *more violently* than would have been expected on the basis of their inherent variability. Two possibilities occur immediately: The samples suffered some perturbing phenomenon such as different temperatures or amounts of evaporation *before* being separated into three aliquots, or the common "accurate" analysis (x) may itself be erroneous. Doubtless persons familiar with the chemical techniques involved can suggest several more, but the statistician has here done the most he can by pointing a suspicious finger. Henceforth the chemist must carry the ball.

One final model: Our original hypothesis

We now choose to invoke the model we first suggested: a calibration line for the y_3 data and a joint calibration line for the y_1 and y_2 data. Although the complexities of this analysis are not great, we felt that enough strange territory was being covered to warrant a gradual introduction to this model. We now augment our original table by a column y_{12} which is the arithmetic average of y_1 and y_2. We also compute

$$Sxy_{12} = 4,058.7 \qquad b_{12} = 0.93986$$
$$Sy_{12}y_{12} = 3,846.1 \qquad SSReg_{12} = 3,814.618 \qquad SSR_{12} = 31.482$$

by the usual formulae. The column effects may now be separated into one degree of freedom for differences between the two calibration means (for y_{12} and y_3),

$$20(40.30 - 36.433)^2 + 10(28.7 - 36.433)^2 = 897.1,$$

and one degree of freedom for fluctuations of the y_1 and y_2 means about the y_{12} mean,

$$10[39.6 - 40.30)^2 + (41.0 - 40.30)^2] = 9.8,$$

the sum of which is, of course, our original column value of 906.9.

The slope effects may be similarly separated, remembering that $SSReg_{12}$ must be multiplied by two before it can assume its rightful parity among the assembled squares:

$2\,SSReg_{12} + SSReg_3$	$= 9,580.436$	2 DF
$SSReg_0$	$= 9,375.387$	1 DF
Differences between one slope and two	$= 205.049$	1 DF

The effect of using a single slope for y_1 and y_2 instead of two is found by

$SSReg_1 + SSReg_2$	=	7,629.600	2 DF
$SSReg_{12}$	=	7,629.236	1 DF

Difference between one and two			
calibration slopes for y_1 and y_2 =		0.364	1 DF

This quantity is negligible no matter how it is measured!

A further breakdown of our Residual Variability term is possible, although the type of information that the breakdown affords is not very interesting, and it is carried out here primarily for completeness. The residuals about the lines for y_3 and y_{12} may be compared with those about the common line y. and are found to be

$2\,SSR_{12} + SSR_3$	=	221.864	16 DF
$3\,SSR_0$	=	147.213	8 DF

Difference between residuals			
(12 + 3) and 0	=	74.651	8 DF

In an analogous manner we may look at the residual around the lines for y_1 and y_2 versus y_{12}. Here we find

$SSR_1 + SSR_2$	=	86.8	16 DF
$2\,SSR_{12}$	=	62.964	8 DF

Difference between residuals			
(1 + 2) and 12	=	23.836	8 DF

Collecting these items into our anova table, we obtain Table 5.

In résumé we see that after removing a common grand mean (the 30th degree of freedom which is missing in our table) and a common slope, the largest effect is that of fitting two lines—one to the y_3 data and the other to the average of y_1 and y_2. This removes sizable chunks of variability both through the mean and the slope differences. The further reductions in both mean and slope by fitting y_1 and y_2 separately are not justified, although the 9.8 reduction due to the mean would not have to be much larger before some doubts would arise about whether or not a real effect was to be found here.

Finally, we should actually compute, graph, and examine the deviations from our fitted lines, especially since the numbers have suggested a tendency for these residuals to share a large common part that could point to a

TABLE 5

Variability Ascribable to	SS	DF	MS
Means: Difference between y_{12} and y_3	897.1	1	897.1
Additional difference between y_1 and y_2	9.8	1	9.8
Slopes: Common slope for all three	9,375.387	1	9,375.387
Separate slopes for y_{12} and y_3	205.049	1	205.049
Separate slopes for y_1 and y_2	0.364	1	0.364
Residuals: Common snakiness about y. line	147.213	8	18.402
Separate lines for y_{12} and y_3	74.651	8	9.331
Separate lines for y_1 and y_2	23.836	8	2.979
Total	10,733.4	29	

weakness in the experimental techniques. Accordingly, we show values of $y_{12} - \zeta_{12}$ and $y_3 - \zeta_3$ versus x—where ζ_{12} and ζ_3 are the fitted lines:

$$\zeta_{12} = 40.3 + 0.93986(x - 43.6) = -0.67787 + 0.93986x$$
$$\zeta_3 = 28.7 + 0.67219(x - 43.6) = -0.60748 + 0.67219x.$$

These discrepancies are listed in Table 6 and graphed in Figure 44. The

TABLE 6

x	$y_{12} - \zeta_{12}$	$y_3 - \zeta_3$	$y_1 - \zeta_1$	$y_2 - \zeta_2$
17	+1.2	−1.8	+0.6	+1.8
21	−3.6	+2.5	−3.2	−3.9
24	+1.6	+4.5	+0.9	+2.3
32	+2.6	+0.1	+1.4	+3.8
36	+0.3	+7.4	+1.6	−0.9
44	−1.2	−2.0	−1.0	−1.4
49	−1.9	−7.3	−0.7	−3.0
60	+0.8	+0.3	+0.9	+0.7
71	−1.1	−2.1	+0.5	−2.6
82	+1.1	+3.5	−0.9	+3.1

tendency of these deviations to fluctuate together is clearly visible if we note their signs at each point. The quantitative agreement is less decisive because of the two distressingly discrepant readings in y_3. The deviations from ζ_{12} ($\bigcirc$) certainly do not have any serious quadratic component, but all that can be said about the ζ_3 deviations is that the discrepant readings

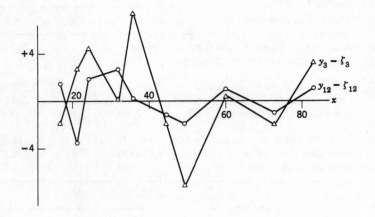

Figure 44

effectively mask what otherwise might well be a weak quadratic term (a parabola opening upward).

The graphs of deviations from the ζ_1 and ζ_2 lines show similar correlations, quadratic components being entirely absent. The fitted lines for ζ_1 and ζ_2 are

$$\zeta_1 = 39.6 + 0.94581(x - 43.6) = -1.63732 + 0.94581x$$
$$\zeta_2 = 41.0 + 0.93391(x - 43.6) = +0.28152 + 0.93391x.$$

The discrepancies of the observed data from the fitted lines are listed in Table 6 and are plotted in Figure 45.

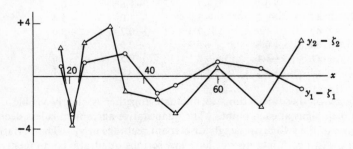

Figure 45

The hindsight heresy

The time has come to confess that we committed a classical statistical sin while analyzing the desoxyribonucleic data. We constructed our hypothesis after looking at the data and then applied significance tests which presumed the formulation of this hypothesis before the experimental numbers were known to us. We may plead that indeed we could do naught else since we neither designed the experiment nor inherited any *a priori* hypothesis with these data. What then, we may ask, could we have done except construct an hypothesis *a posteriori*? This is, of course, not quite the point.

The sin consists not in constructing hypotheses in the full light of the data—which is frequently inevitable—but rather in failing to allow for that fact when deciding whether or not the data support these hypotheses. The dangers encountered in *a posteriori* hypotheses are twofold:

1. The analyst will usually be drawn to test extreme deviations of the data but will use techniques that do not presume any such selection.

2. The analyst will mentally apply and reject *many* hypotheses before settling on the ones to be tested but will not adjust his error rate to correspond to his behavior.

The first of these dangers may be avoided by using tests based on the extreme properties involved (the distribution of the *range* is the convenient statistic here). The second danger is much more important—and correspondingly more difficult to circumvent. It depends essentially on the personality of the individual examining the data and thus allows no simple cure or even any hope for reproducibility. Its effect can be materially reduced, however, by providing a whole set of hypotheses—broad enough to include most of those that reasonable people will care to invoke—and by further providing a mechanism by which the analyst can consider and test any or all of these hypotheses at a known fixed error rate. Until recently such desirable statistical techniques did not exist, but now most of the commoner balanced sets of data can be examined by methods known as *multiple-comparison tests*. The statistical derivation of these tests is not attempted here. We merely treat the present example from the multiple-comparison point of view—the simplest in a family of techniques—and refer the interested reader to a book by Tukey* in which one view on the present state of this rapidly developing branch of statistics will be set forth in some detail.

* J. W. Tukey, *The Problem of Multiple Comparisons*, in preparation.

The multiple-comparison approach

We shall now re-examine our three separate lines—already fitted—and ask whether the data warrant all of them. Could, for instance, the first two sets of data be summarized adequately by one line? Or could all three? We ask these questions *because* the data suggest them, and there is no need for regret.

The three lines have the three means, slopes, and residuals:

Line	m	b	SSR
1	39.6	0.9458	19.3
2	41.0	0.9339	67.5
3	28.7	0.6722	158.9

As before, we shall make the dubious assumption that the data are from a population with homogeneous variability about their true values and hence the SSR have been pooled for a common estimate of this variance 245.7/24. This gives

$$s^2 = 245.7/24 = 10.238$$

and the estimated variance of each m value is then

$$s_m{}^2 = s^2/10 = 1.024$$

and

$$s_m = 1.012,$$

and that of each b is

$$s_b{}^2 = s^2/Sxx = 10.238/4318.4 = 0.00237$$

so that

$$s_b = 0.0487.$$

In the light of these variances we want to know whether the spread in the means is so large that it probably does not arise from random fluctuations. We want to know whether $(m_1 - m_2)$ is perhaps really trying to be zero, whether $(m_1 - m_3)$ could reasonably have been zero, whether $(0.5m_1 + 0.5m_2 - m_3)$ could have been zero. These are the most likely questions, but there are others such as what true values of μ_3 could reasonably have given birth to m_3—and similarly for the other means. The same sorts of questions may be posed for the slopes.

Clearly these questions are not all independent of one another. The answer to one will depend—often strongly and sometimes completely—on the answers to some of the others. Classical procedures run the risk of making erroneous statements, say 5 per cent of the time, if the comparisons are independent, but if ten independent comparisons are made, the chance of at least one erroneous statement is $1 - (0.95)^{10}$ or 30 per cent. If these ten statements are completely *dependent*, the chance of at least one erroneous statement subsides to only 5 per cent again (but actually all ten will then be wrong in those unfortunate 5 per cent situations).

Another and more serious trouble arises from the fact that our ten interesting comparisons are chosen after looking at the data—thereby implying that we have mentally made a host of other comparisons and discarded them as being uninteresting. These discarded comparisons could also, however, have been erroneous—and the chance that they were erroneous has to be allowed for in our error rate. If, for instance, we implicitly made 15 dull comparisons and if these were independent (which they fortunately are not), the total error rate is $1 - (0.95)^{25}$ or a 59 per cent chance of at least one comparison being in error (actually, because of dependence it is between 59 per cent and 5 per cent—though exactly where is almost impossible to specify). To avoid this unpleasant state of affairs, Tukey has devised a procedure that we now use.

Since our standard deviations, s, each bear 24 degrees of freedom, we enter Table 7 to find the Least Significant Difference, LSD,

$$\frac{\text{LSD}}{s} = 2.92,$$

and since there are three items we are interested in comparing, we find from Table 8 that

$$\frac{\text{WSD}}{\text{LSD}} = 1.20 + 0.4/\text{DDF} = 1.20 + 0.4/24 = 1.22.$$

Multiplying, we get

$$\frac{\text{WSD}}{s} = (2.92)(1.22) = 3.57,$$

which says that the Wholly Significant Difference is $3.57s$.

We are then entitled to make any and all linear comparisons between the three means, provided only that the coefficients of these comparisons add to zero. To make these comparisons we multiply the WSD by the *norm* of the linear combination in question—this *norm* simply being the sum of the positive coefficients. For example,

$$\mu_1 - \mu_2 = m_1 - m_2 \pm (\text{WSD})(1)(s_m)$$
$$= 39.6 - 41.0 \pm (3.57)(1)(1.012) = -1.4 \pm 3.6$$

so that the difference between the true means lies between 2.2 and -5.0.

| TABLE 7 | | | TABLE 8 | | | |
| Factor Required to Find LSD | | | Factor Required to Find WSD | | | |

DDF	60/DDF	LSD/s^a	m	WSD/LSD	m	WSD/LSD^a
1		18.0	2^b	1.00 + 0.0/DDF	21	1.82 + 2.5/DDF
2		6.10	2	1.02 + 0.2/DDF	22	1.83 + 2.6/DDF
3		4.50	3	1.20 + 0.4/DDF	23	1.85 + 2.7/DDF
4		3.92	4	1.32 + 0.6/DDF	24	1.86 + 2.8/DDF
5		3.64	5	1.40 + 0.8/DDF	25	1.87 + 2.8/DDF
6		3.46	6	1.46 + 1.0/DDF	26	1.88 + 2.9/DDF
7		3.34	7	1.51 + 1.2/DDF	27	1.89 + 3.0/DDF
8		3.26	8	1.55 + 1.4/DDF	28	1.90 + 3.1/DDF
9		3.20	9	1.59 + 1.5/DDF	29	1.91 + 3.1/DDF
10	6	3.15	10	1.62 + 1.6/DDF	30	1.91 + 3.2/DDF
	5	3.08	11	1.65 + 1.7/DDF	35	1.95 + 3.4/DDF
	4	3.01	12	1.67 + 1.8/DDF	40	1.99 + 3.7/DDF
	3	2.95	13	1.70 + 1.9/DDF	45	2.01 + 3.9/DDF
	·2	2.89	14	1.72 + 2.0/DDF	50	2.04 + 4.1/DDF
	1	2.83	15	1.74 + 2.1/DDF	60	2.08 + 4.4/DDF
	0	2.77	16	1.75 + 2.2/DDF	80	2.15 + 5.0/DDF
			17	1.77 + 2.3/DDF	100	2.19 + 5.4/DDF
			18	1.78 + 2.4/DDF	200	2.37 + 6.9/DDF
			19	1.80 + 2.4/DDF	500	2.61 + 9.1/DDF
			20	1.81 + 2.5/DDF	∞	∞ + ∞ DDF

^{a} Values of LSD/s are $\sqrt{2}$ times upper 5 per cent points of Student's $|t|$.

^{a} Values of WSD/s are upper 5 per cent points of the Studentized range. DDF are the Denominator Degrees of Freedom.

^{b} For comparison of the 2 determinations only.

In particular, zero is a quite plausible value. The norm is *one*, this being the sum of the positive coefficients in this almost trivial linear combination of the means.

A more complicated comparison is

$$(\mu_1 + \mu_2)/2 - \mu_3 = (m_1 + m_2)/2 - m_3 \pm (WSD)(1)(s_m)$$
$$= 40.3 - 28.7 \pm 3.6 = 11.6 \pm 3.6,$$

so that the difference between the third mean and the average of the other two lies between 8 and 15.2 (in particular zero is *not* a credible value). Here the norm is still *one*, being $\frac{1}{2} + \frac{1}{2}$. Finally we might wish, for reasons entirely unknown to this writer, to compare

$$\mu_1 - 2\mu_2 + \mu_3 = m_1 - 2m_2 + m_3 \pm (WSD)(2)(s_m)$$
$$= -13.7 \pm 7.2,$$

and we would conclude that this linear combination of true values lay between -20.9 and -6.5. Here the norm is 2. Tukey gives procedures that allow linear comparisons whose sums of coefficients are not zero, but most of the usual questions fall in the framework given here.

Comparisons between the slopes require a Wholly Significant Difference of $(3.57)(0.0487)$ or 0.174 units. Against this yardstick, the first two lines are indistinguishable but the third belongs to another family entirely.

This procedure guarantees that if *all* possible linear comparisons are made, then the probability that one or more false statements will have been made about this set of data is 5 per cent. In particular, since we made less than the whole set of comparisons, we are being conservative—but at the same time, since our look at the data did not lead us outside the realm of linear combinations for our comparisons, we are safeguarded against fallacies to which classical procedures have been woefully susceptible.

These data are so thoroughly separated that the visual evidence from graphs is overwhelming, and the safeguards of multiple comparisons are quite as unnecessary as any other statistical techniques (unless our interest devolves to the fine structure of the deviations). But let not the self-sufficient scoff at these mild mechanisms, for they are most useful in refuting unjustifiably complicated hypotheses. They are designed to help the experimental man from giving in too often to his admittedly good physical intuition, when his variable data might allow it too free reign. These formalisms, like Blackwood, aim to keep us from unwarranted flights of fancy.

More acid analyses

For our second example we turn to data which were taken in pairs—*duplicate samples* is the usual chemical phrase. We might hope the variation exhibited by duplicates would measure that smallest degree of indeterminacy which must be endured in the experimental process—and indeed it may. All too often, however, this smallest variability is not the pertinent yardstick against which to measure the adequacy of calibrations or the accuracy of analytical results. Since the duplicates are usually taken together, processed at the same time, and finally measured side by side by the same instrument and observer, they share common values of many variables which were, in fact, uncontrolled. The temperature and humidity of the room, the observer's sense of a colorimetric end point, the length of time in a sintering oven—all these and a host of other possibly important variables have been balanced out by the usual technique of running duplicate samples. Such balancing is desirable if some absolute standard material has been included among the samples so that only departures from this accepted norm are being measured. But the balancing hides the effects of the uncontrolled variables, and if absolute answers are needed, duplicate samples—by their apparent precision—give a false sense of security. Although we hesitate to assert that these phthalic anhydride data of Shreve and Heether suffer from the specific malady of "duplicity," the evidence strongly suggests that conclusion.

As with most Per Cent Found versus Per Cent Taken data, a trivial straight line should be removed first. We have therefore also recorded in Table 9 the difference between Per Cent Found and Per Cent Taken, multiplied by 100 to avoid decimals. The analyses were confused by the presence of four organic acids, and the levels of phthalic anhydride were approximately, but not exactly, the same with each of these acids. The sums and differences of the data are also included.

TABLE 9

Analyses of Phthalic Anhydride

With	Per Cent Taken	Per Cent Found		$100(F - T)$		S	D
	5.74	5.80	5.90	6	16	22	10
	25.82	25.83	25.75	1	−7	−6	−8
Succinic acid	51.47	51.55	51.63	8	16	24	8
	75.91	76.10	76.04	19	13	32	−6
	95.60	95.38	95.46	−22	−14	−36	8
	5.12	5.22	5.36	10	24	34	14
	27.49	27.29	27.33	−20	−16	−36	4
Adipic acid	50.21	50.29	50.19	8	−2	6	−10
	75.46	75.17	75.27	−29	−19	−48	10
	94.72	94.44	94.60	−28	−12	−40	16
	6.43	6.65	6.53	22	10	32	−12
	26.14	26.40	26.22	26	8	34	−18
Sebacic acid	50.56	50.27	50.35	−29	−21	−50	8
	74.92	74.65	74.69	−27	−23	−50	4
	96.47	96.28	96.12	−19	−35	−54	−16
	5.79	5.63	5.67	−16	−12	−28	4
	25.33	25.44	25.53	11	23	34	12
Itaconic acid	52.66	52.66	52.76	0	10	10	10
	75.10	75.00	74.90	−10	−20	−30	−10
	95.28	95.07	95.03	−21	−25	−46	−4

A brief glance at the Sum column will disclose that the variability of these data is rather large—certainly no clear-cut parabola is immediately evident nor is even a straight line.   This variability is neither surprising nor disturbing, since the main effect has been subtracted and the scale has been blown up a hundredfold.   Any curve found here is merely a correction to the 45° linear calibration the chemist expects.   Since small horizontal shifts of these points will make no material change in our conclusions, we choose to regard all approximately 5 Per Cent Phthalic Anhydride Taken concentrations to be the same, and similarly for the other four levels. Furthermore, in the interests of more expedient analysis we feel no particular qualms about shifting these common x levels the small amounts necessary to have them *equally spaced* on the Per Cent Taken scale (at 4, 27, 50, 73, 96).

If we now concentrate our attention on the sums of the two duplicates, they may be conveniently displayed as in Table 10, in which each column

TABLE 10

x	Succinic	Adipic	Sebacic	Itaconic	Totals	Squares
−2	22	34	32	−28	60	3,448
−1	−6	−36	34	34	26	3,644
0	24	6	−50	10	−10	3,121
1	32	−48	−50	−30	−96	6,728
2	−36	−40	−54	−46	−176	7,928
Totals	36	−84	−88	−60	−196 √	19,696
Squares	3,416	6,392	10,096	5,056	44,568	24,960 √

and row contains its sum and sum of squares (the check marks indicate the two totals that are found by two separate computations, providing a useful check).   The equally spaced independent variates, x, may be taken as −2, −1, 0, 1, and 2.

Now that we have cavalierly squeezed our incremental data into the standard analysis of variance form, the total Sum of Squares may be broken down into parts ascribable to the general Mean, the Column Means, the Row Means, and the Row-by-Column Interaction as shown in the usual anova table (Table 11).   The term for the general Mean, often subtracted immediately from the total, does not usually appear explicitly, but its geometric significance makes it worth recording here in line-fitting problems.

TABLE 11

	SS	DF	MS
Mean	1,920.8	1	1,920.8
Columns	2,018.4	3	672.8
Rows	9,221.2	4	2,305.3
Row × Column	11,799.6	12	983.3
Total	24,960.0	20	

Our problem is to decide whether any additional calibration information is contained in these data, or whether all the fluctuation here is merely that residual uncontrolled variation which must be endured.   In particular, is the Mean big enough to warrant notice and to be subtracted out? Should different means be used for the four acids?   Is perhaps a common line justified, or are even four lines needed?   What about parabolas, cubics?   Lest our fancy run away with us, we note that very few physical experimenters would condone fitting even a cubic to five points—nor would many statisticians.   It uses up four degrees of freedom, and the one degree of freedom remaining is scarcely a comfortable base for estimating variability.   The question about lines and parabolas can perhaps best be postponed until the middle of Chapter 7, so that orthogonal polynomials may be invoked, but the efficacy of one or several means will be considered now.

If the only data available were those of Table 10, we would conclude immediately that although the general Mean was just possibly a real effect (rather than a statistical accident in this set of data), almost certainly the additional contribution of four means—one for each acid—is not real. The additional reduction in the SS averages to only 672.8 per fitted constant, and this is considerably smaller than the Row-by-Column Mean Square term which measures the general inconsistency of the data.   Even if the columns had *no* effect whatsoever, we would expect the Column MS to be about the same size as the $R \times C$ MS.   Hence when it is smaller we quickly disclaim any suspicion of an effect.

Another estimate of variability

Unfortunately for our peace of mind, the chemists have furnished us another estimate of their data variability.   The duplicate samples allow a direct estimate quite independently of the arithmetic in the preceding paragraphs. We need only compute the sum of the squared deviations of each datum from the mean value of the appropriate pair. Thus

$$20s^2 = \sum_i (y_{i1} - y_{i\cdot})^2 + \sum_i (y_{i2} - y_{i\cdot})^2 \tag{1}$$

where

$$2y_{i\cdot} = y_{i1} + y_{i2}$$

gives an estimate, s^2, of the variability of a single datum based on 20 degrees of freedom. Algebraic identities allow the expression of (1) in terms of the difference, D_i, between the data pairs—a computational shortcut. We find

$$20s^2 = \sum D_i^2/2 \tag{2}$$

where

$$D_i = y_{i1} - y_{i2},$$

and in the example at hand s^2 becomes 55.2. Since the previous anova is based on sums of *two* data, the new variance estimate should be doubled before comparing it to the anova table. Thus the new measure of irreducible variability is 110.3 on 20 degrees of freedom as compared with 983.3 on 12 degrees of freedom. Clearly, something is fishy in Halifax.

If we reappraise our anova table by this new yardstick, we conclude that a separate mean for each acid is indeed justified—and that the R × C term clearly shows the differences between the acids to be different at each level of concentration, i.e., there is a real interaction of acid and concentration.

Resolution of the quandary

What then are we to believe? Are the data rather precise but the four acids sufficiently different, requiring separate and generically different calibrations, as the duplicates would imply? Or is our earlier picture correct, with rather variable data so that a common calibration suffices—the duplicate variance estimate being too small and misleading?

Your author votes strongly in favor of the proposition that the duplicate variance is small and misleading—but his arguments are not strictly statistical. They will be developed further in Chapter 7, but in essence they consist of a strong faith that calibration curves of chemically similar substances will exhibit similar analytic behavior. To believe the precise variance estimate would imply that itaconic and succinic acids need cubic corrections whereas sebacic needs only a straight line and adipic requires at least a quartic. Men who seek order in our universe will probably prefer the alternative explanation that crucial variables were uncontrolled during these experiments but that the duplicates shared these common, if variable, conditions. The resulting agreement between duplicates is therefore an overly optimistic estimate of the reproducibility of this chemical analytical technique.

The statistician would stress the importance of including all pertinent sources of variability in the design of the initial experiment. He feels sufficiently strongly about this point to shun the term *duplicate* experiment, preferring the more general term *replicate*. These duplicates were probably *not* replicates. They were probably not carried out so as to give an honest estimate of the variation to be expected when identical samples are analyzed on different days, using different standard solutions, under different lighting conditions, and perhaps even by different people. We conjecture that some of these changes did occur, but that they occurred only between acids and not between duplicates and hence that some of the apparent differences between acids are, in fact, due to uncontrolled experimental variation which the duplicates do not measure.

If our conjecture is correct, the interesting questions about the intrinsic accuracy of this analytical procedure are answered more nearly by the values from the anova table than from the duplicates. In units of the original data, then, we feel the standard deviation of a single analysis to be

$$(983.3/2)^{1/2}/100 = 0.22$$

rather than

$$(2{,}206/40)^{1/2}/100 = 0.07$$

as the duplicates suggest.

CHAPTER 7

The Exposure of Curvature: Orthogonal Polynomials

Although it is far from certain that our Creator cast this universe in a linear mold, it is quite apparent that we strive continually to force it back into one. Our arithmetic becomes so much easier! Sometimes our data are already adequately linear. Often we are successful. Occasionally we can find new variables to straighten out the curved lines into which our data seem to have contorted themselves. But to hope for linearity in all our experiments is sheer folly, and statistical methods must be provided if they are to serve the world in which we live rather than that ivory tower wherein all lines are straight and fluctuations normal.

In this chapter we examine the commonest technique for dealing with curvilinear relations—fitting by polynomials. We hasten to point out that transformations of variables are very useful: Exponential curves straighten out beautifully when logarithms are plotted, and the arch of a sine curve is not beyond the analytical pale for persuading reluctant periodic data to adopt a more tractable form. We only add that even when the known physical laws suggest these changes of variable they are preferably invoked to give a uniform *variability* to our data, and we may still not receive the added convenience of straight lines. [When faced with a mutually exclusive choice between a transformation for uniform variance (homoscedasticity) and one for a linear relationship, this writer must almost always decide in favor of the former. A scale in which the variability is constant allows greater intuitive insight than one—however convenient for mental arithmetic—that stresses a linear dependence.]

We therefore assume in the sequel of this chapter that such transformations as may have been necessary for uniform variance have been applied, and that we are now faced with data which at least suggest that they are not adequately represented by a straight line. If theory specifies a particular form of non-linearity, we shall do well to use it in our investigations. Often, however, no such suggestion is available and we then choose our forms for their computational expediency—and invariably we must then invoke polynomials. Our primary purpose is to remove the obscuring curvature from our data. If the scatter in our data is large, polynomials will suffice just as well as less arithmetically tractable functions; if they are small, we may have to consider more physically sophisticated models.

A sodium titration

In studying a titrimetric method for determining sodium in biological fluids, Trinder [32] obtained the data of Table 1 on standard sodium chloride solutions. He concluded that the method was unreliable above 400 mg. of sodium per 100 ml. Since casual examination reveals a curvature to these data, we shall remove it to see whether we can uncover evidence of systematic fluctuations pointing toward some lack of control in his procedure whose removal would add precision to the method. Although nothing is said about the order in which the data were taken, we shall keep in mind the possibility that each column of Table 1 was obtained on a different day and hence contains a measure of the day-to-day variability. (Most analytical chemists shrink from such a procedure, preferring the false sense of security gained from "reproducibility" measurements made as close together in time as possible. One wag has appropriately referred to the error measured from such duplicate samples as *duplicity*.) Another more likely hypothesis is that all the samples at one concentration were run simultaneously, thus confounding the effects of day-to-day variation with those of concentration. And, again, it is possible that all the measurements were made on one grand occasion. In order to avoid the arithmetic unpleasantness of an unbalanced analysis, Table 1 includes two quite fictitious data, added by the author and indicated by asterisks.

TABLE 1

Na, mg./100 ml.

Present	Found						Totals
100	103	100	100	103	103	98	607
200	202	201	201	203	201	200	1,208
300	305	298	296	304	304	299	1,806
400	394	399	402	397	406	396	2,394
500	489	487	480	502	491*	494*	2,943
1,500	1,493	1,485	1,479	1,509	1,505	1,487	8,958

They contribute nothing to the conclusions and make the present exposition much simpler. We do not, however, recommend such shenanigans with a paying customer's data unless you are prepared to give a carefully worded defense in doubletalk. (Replacing an occasional missing datum in a balanced design by fitting a constant is, of course, a quite legitimate operation—but that is *not* what the author did here.)

In order to simplify the arithmetic we first rewrite Table 1 by subtracting off the Present column from each of the Found columns. This removes the obvious "perfect" calibration line which any chemist would prefer to obtain. We shall then examine the residuals from this perfect calibration line to see whether the actual curve still has a linear component (i.e., it was not the 45° line after all), as well as quadratic and higher terms. To our reduced data (Table 2) we append row and column sums and sums of squares, and—on the right—the first three orthogonal polynomials [4].

TABLE 2

P	$F - P$						$\sum y$	$\sum y^2$	ξ_1	ξ_2	ξ_3
100	3	0	0	3	3	-2	7	31	-2	2	-1
200	2	1	1	3	1	0	8	16	-1	-1	2
300	5	-2	-4	4	4	-1	6	78	0	-2	0
400	6	-1	2	-3	6	-4	-6	102	1	-1	-2
500	-11	-13	-20	2	-9^*	-6^*	-57	811	2	2	1
$\sum y$	-7	-15	-21	9	5	-13	-42	990	10	14	10
$\sum y^2$	195	175	421	47	143	57	3,434	1,038			

The total variability of our data is measured by the sum of the squared deviations of each datum from the grand mean. We calculate this expediently by the usual formula

$$\sum_{ij} (y_{ij})^2 - \frac{(\sum y_{ij})^2}{rc} = 1,038 - \frac{(42)^2}{30} = 979.2,$$

a measure based on 30-minus-1 data, or 29 *degrees of freedom*. The tendency of the various columns to be alike is measured by the squared deviations of their sums from the grand mean—all divided by 5 since these are 5 data entering into each column sum. Thus:

$$\tfrac{1}{5} [990 - (42)^2/6] = 139.2,$$

based on 6-minus-1 data or 5 degrees of freedom, being 6 column sums
that were squared to give the 990.   The row variability, which we tentatively ascribe to concentration effects, is found analogously,

$$\tfrac{1}{6} [3,434 - (42)^2/5] = 513.533,$$

on 4 degrees of freedom.

We summarize our findings in the usual anova table, Table 3, and we

TABLE 3

	SS	DF	MS
Rows (concentrations)	513.533	4	128.384
Columns	139.200	5	27.840
Row × Column (by subtraction)	326.467	20	16.323
Total	979.200	29	

quickly note that the columns do not appear to contain much more
variability than would be expected from the internal variability as measured
by the Row by Column interaction mean square.   In fact, a formal F test
is quite insignificant.

We shall now subdivide the concentration (row) variability into components ascribable to linear, quadratic, and cubic trends.   We could do
this by making classic least-squares fits of a straight line, a parabola, and
a cubic separately to the row totals versus the Na Present values.   Then
for each curve we could compute the sums of the squared residuals.

Orthogonal polynomials

The major waste in these classic computations lies in the fact that the
coefficients of the best-fitting line bear no simple relation to those of the
parabola, which in turn seem quite aloof from the cubic.   Thus a higher-
degree curve requires the repetition of all the work already expended for
its more lowly brethren, rather than merely requiring some increment of
effort to raise the degree by one from those already computed.   Since our
x data (Na Present) are evenly spaced, however, these extensive computations may be drastically curtailed—almost to the vanishing point—by the
use of *orthogonal polynomials*.   Such polynomials allow the computation
of the least-squares fitted curve of any degree, each one merely being an
additional increment to the next lower one, and the additional reduction
in the residual sum of squares may also be found immediately rather than

by differences. A fuller explanation of orthogonal polynomials is offered in the Supplement to this chapter, but for the example at hand the numerical procedure is quite clear.

We find the slope of the line best fitting the row sums by adding up the cross products of these numbers and the corresponding elements of ξ_1 and then dividing by the sum of the $\xi_1{}^2$ (which is given at the foot of the ξ_1 column). Thus

$$[(7)(-2) + (8)(-1) + (6)(0) + (-6)(1) + (-57)(2)]/10 = -14.2$$

is the regression coefficient (slope) of the *row sums against the standardized variable*

$$\text{(Na Present} - 300)/100 = \xi_1.$$

The reduction in row variability ascribable to fitting this line is found from

$$\tfrac{1}{6}[(-142)^2/10] = 336.067,$$

where the division by 6 is to reduce the squares to the parity of an individual datum—the 142 having been based on sums of 6 data.

In like manner, the reduction achieved by fitting the parabola is

$$\tfrac{1}{6}[(-114)^2/14] = 154.714,$$

where the 114 is the sum of the cross products of ξ_2 and the row sums. The parabolic regression coefficient is $-114/14 = -8.143$ for the row sums. The cubic yields

$$\tfrac{1}{6}[(36)^2/10] = 21.600.$$

If we add these contributions and subtract from the known total of 513.533, we obtain an "unexplained" row variability of only 1.152, which would be

TABLE 4

	SS	DF	MS
Concentration Components	(513.533)	(4)	
Average Linear	336.067	1	336.067
Average Quadratic	154.714	1	154.714
Average Cubic	21.600	1	21.600
Other Row Effects	1.152	1	1.152
Column Effects (extra means)	139.2	5	27.840
Row × Column	326.467	20	16.323
Total	979.200	29	

precisely the additional contribution of a quartic—a fact that is obvious if we note that since we have only five data points, a quartic must fit them exactly.

In our summary anova table, Table 4, we have not changed the Interaction or Column terms, but the Concentration effects are now seen to reside almost entirely in the linear and quadratic components.

Separate calibrations

Finally we shall examine the effect of fitting *separate* calibration curves to each of the columns (a plausible operation if they represent different days). Each regression coefficient and its contribution to the variability are found as before, except that since we are now working directly with the individual data rather than a sum, no divisor of six is needed. For expediency we examine the sums of squares first without recording the individual regression coefficients—thereby temporarily bypassing a little labor and avoiding it altogether should the contributions prove to be negligible.

The effect of fitting six separate *slopes* is given by

$$[(-36)^2 + (-28)^2 + (-39)^2 + (-8)^2 + (-19)^2 + (-12)^2]/10 = 417.0$$

so that the *additional contribution* of six slopes over one average slope is

$$417.0 - 336.067 = 80.933$$

with five degrees of freedom. Similarly, the separate quadratic contributions are

$$[(-22)^2 + (-22)^2 + (-35)^2 + (+2)^2 + (-27)^2 + (-10)^2]/14 = 216.143,$$

which accounts for an excess of 61.429 over the average parabola. The six cubics give

$$[(+2)^2 + (-9)^2 + (-22)^2 + (+11)^2 + (-22)^2 + (+4)^2]/10 = 119.000.$$

We could also fit individual quartics, thereby exhausting the changes that can be rung (wrung?) on these data, but our previous anova table confirmed our common-sense feeling that quartics can have no meaning here—and cubics are certainly suspect.

We summarize our data with a final anova table, Table 5. There can be little doubt that all the effects separated out here are measures of the same common experimental variability except for the Average Line and the Average Parabola. All other rows in the anova table can be pooled

TABLE 5

Components	SS	DF	MS
Average Linear	336.067	1	336.067
Quadratic	154.714	1	154.714
Cubic	21.600	1	21.600
Quartic	1.152	1	1.152
Extra Means (columns)	139.200	5	27.840
Lines	80.933	5	16.187
Parabolas	61.429	5	12.286
Cubics	97.400	5	19.480
Other Row × Column Effects (by subtraction)	86.705	5	17.341
Total	979.200	29	

for a single estimate of variability based on 27 degrees of freedom. This is

$$488.419/27 = 18.1 = s^2$$

so that the standard deviation of each experimental datum is about 4.3 of the original units.

A look at the residuals

Having decided on our calibration curve, we now return to the data to apply it, recording deviations from the fitted curve. The fitted points may be easily found by multiplying the regression coefficients for the linear and quadratic components by the corresponding elements of the ξ_1 and ξ_2 columns and then adding them together with the mean value of the row sums. Thus the fitted point for the 400 mg. Na Present is given by

$$-42/5 + (-14.2)(1) + (-8.143)(-1) = -14.457$$

whereas for 300 mg. it is

$$-42/5 + (-14.2)(0) + (-8.143)(-2) = +7.886.$$

The fitted points for the row sums and for the individual items are shown below

100	3.714	0.62
200	13.946	2.32
300	7.886	1.31
400	−14.457	−2.41
500	−53.092	−8.85

so we have the deviations shown in Table 6. When we compare these

TABLE 6

Present	Found − Predicted					
100	2.4	−0.6	−0.6	2.4	2.4	−2.6
200	−0.3	−1.3	−1.3	0.7	−1.3	−2.3
300	3.7	−3.3	−5.3	2.7	2.7	−2.3
400	−3.6	1.4	4.4	−0.6	8.4	−1.6
500	−2.1	−4.1	−11.1	11.9	−0.1*	2.9*

deviations with the estimated standard error of a measurement, we must concur with the analyst that the values for 500 mg. Na are not reassuring. Since it is these values that probably contribute the chief quadratic component, we recommend reanalyzing these data, omitting the last row, to see whether a straight line is then adequate for calibration.   We leave this analysis to the reader as an exercise, remarking only that the orthogonal polynomials are

ξ_1	ξ_2	ξ_3
−3	+1	−1
−1	−1	+3
+1	−1	−3
+3	+1	+1

and that a quadratic component will *not* be justified.   In fact, the linear one also disappears!

Unequally spaced data

In order for analyses with many lines or curves to be computationally practical, orthogonality is important. Our balanced designs invoke orthogonality to separate out row, column, and interaction effects by simple arithmetic.   Just as we would strive to design a balanced experiment for ease of analysis, so we prefer to secure to ourselves the advantages of those simple orthogonal polynomials by having our independent variables *equally spaced*. Often, however, we must deal with variables over which we have no satisfactory control, from which we cannot expect equal spacing.   Fortunately we can still obtain most of the advantages of orthogonal polynomials by constructing them for the values of the independent variable with which we happen to be stuck.   They will not turn out to be simple integers, nor will they be found by turning to a page of an accessible book, but we *can* compute them; in fact, it is desirable to compute them even if only two lines are to be fitted to the same values of the independent variable. The labor is no more, the aesthetic satisfaction is considerable, and they are then available should further fitting seem desirable later in the problem. In the following example we shall use orthogonal polynomials which are constructed in the Supplement to this chapter on a rather unorthodox set of intervals.

In some experiments designed to measure the concentration of calcium in the presence of lanthanum, Heidel and Fassel recorded the following data from which they propose to construct a calibration curve for use on subsequent samples. The known concentrations of calcium were presumably established gravimetrically, whereas the observed values, y, were obtained from less precise flame photometric values. These data were taken on three different days: when the solutions were new, then two days old, and finally when they were eight days old. The obvious question is whether sufficient stability exists in these solutions to warrant the use of a *single* calibration curve, or whether separate curves are required to extract the maximum precision from subsequent data.

The choice of concentrations approximately evenly spaced in a logarithmic scale suggests that the data might better be analyzed in their logarithms, but a glance at the errors fails to suggest that these are proportional to the size of the measurements—and this, after all, would be the real justification for such a transformation. Lacking any such good reason for using logarithms, we analyze the data in that form in which the authors were pleased to present them.

Table 7 displays not only the data of Heidel and Fassel but also column and row sums, sums of squares, and the first three orthogonal polynomials for this set of independent variables. The conventional analysis of variance manipulations give the variability ascribable to column means as only 0.000763 (computed from

$$\tfrac{1}{8} [225.166134 - (25.990)^2/3] = 0.000763$$

with two degrees of freedom), whereas the row sums yield 33.476454. The complete anova table suggests that although the columns are not quite the same, nevertheless we cannot safely conclude that these differences represent anything more than random fluctuations if these latter are measured by the Day by Concentration interaction (Table 8). By the same token, the variability we have labeled Day by Concentration may be far from random. It may represent the extent to which different curves are needed to summarize data from different days, and it is this possibility which we must explore further.

We first fit an average calibration curve, using the row sums and the orthogonal polynomials. Since the method is analogous to our previous

TABLE 7

x'	y_0	y_2	y_8	$3y.$	$\sum y^2$	ξ_1	ξ_2	ξ_3
0.025	0.066	0.054	0.060	0.180	0.010872	-0.27825914	0.32387185	-0.35344732
0.050	0.106	0.102	0.109	0.317	0.033521	-0.26712877	0.28409517	-0.26113967
0.125	0.259	0.260	0.256	0.775	0.200217	-0.23373767	0.16976608	-0.02077122
0.250	0.495	0.500	0.504	1.499	0.749041	-0.17808585	-0.00411252	0.26614980
0.375	0.727	0.708	0.734	2.169	1.568549	-0.12243402	-0.15715382	0.42567940
0.625	1.16	1.14	1.15	3.45	3.9677	-0.01113037	-0.40072442	0.43052555
1.250	2.18	2.17	2.17	6.52	14.1702	0.26712877	-0.64499768	-0.59738819
2.500	3.73	3.68	3.67	11.08	40.9242	0.82364704	0.42925534	0.11039164
5.200	8.723	8.614	8.653	25.990	225.116134	0	0	0
	20.867	20.383	20.374	184.864	61.624300	1	1	1

TABLE 8

	SS	DF	MS
Concentration (rows)	33.476454	7	4.7823
Days (columns)	0.000763	2	0.000382
Day by Concentration	0.002079	14	0.000149
Total	33.479296	23	

illustration, we show only one coefficient computation here. Three times the quadratic coefficient of the *average* calibration is found by multiplying the row sums with their corresponding ξ_2 elements and summing. Thus the coefficient itself is

$$\tfrac{1}{3}[(0.180)(0.32387185) + \ldots + (11.08)(0.42925534)] = -0.29961415.$$

The contribution of this quadratic term to the total variability is given by its square, multiplied by three to put it on a *per datum* basis. A summary of the various individual and average coefficients, together with their contributions, are given in Table 9, the average ones being the next-to-bottom

TABLE 9

Coefficients			Contributions		
Linear	Quadratic	Cubic	Linear	Quadratic	Cubic
3.357252	−0.290640	−0.006311	11.271142	0.084472	0.0000398
3.319231	−0.299526	−0.015959	11.017290	0.089716	0.0002547
3.304383	−0.308676	−0.004491	10.918937	0.095281	0.0000202
			33.207369	0.269469	0.0003147
3.326955	−0.299614	−0.008920	33.205881	0.269306	0.000239
			0.001488	0.000163	0.000076

line of the table. The bottom line shows the *additional* contributions from separate curves over those from an average curve. These additional contributions were previously included in the general interaction term but may now be displayed for the rather special interaction they measure, i.e., the differences between individual days' calibrations. Table 10 summarizes our present calculations.

TABLE 10

Assignable Cause	SS	DF	MS
Concentration Calibrations	(33.476454)	(7)	
Linear (average)	33.205881	1	33.205881
Quadratic (average)	0.269306	1	0.269306
Cubic (average)	0.000239	1	0.000239
Other (average)	0.001028	4	0.000257
Separate Means	0.000763	2	0.000382
Separate Linear Terms	0.001488	2	0.000744
Separate Quadratic Terms	0.000163	2	0.000082
Separate Cubic Terms	0.000076	2	0.000038
Interaction (by subtraction)	0.000352	8	0.000044
Total	33.479296	23	

Although the average Linear and Quadratic terms are clearly needed to represent these data, it seems that the Cubic term is signally unsuccessful in accounting for additional variability. When we compare the average Cubic Mean Square with the Mean Square called *Other* we see that these are ostensibly the same, the implication being that further fluctuation is largely random and that the linear and quadratic terms have already removed the systematic part. There is then a strong argument for recombining the Cubic and Other categories, as well as the Separate Cubic and the Interaction terms. Clearly the new Other and Interaction terms will have Mean Squares which are not substantially different from their values in Table 10, so we shall merely leave the table alone and look at it.

Our major conclusion must be that these three sets of data demand separate means and linear trends but that separate quadratic terms are probably not justified. Perhaps chemists who are familiar with these reactions and analytical procedures can explain why the general *slope* of the calibration curve should drift whereas the calibration *means* seem to be fluctuating just within the finest experimental measure of variability, the Interaction Mean Square, or even why the curvature should increase (albeit an insignificant amount)—but the statistician can only point to these phenomena with raised eyebrows. Are there perhaps good physical hypotheses to lend credence to mechanistic explanations, or should we merely stop here, using these estimates as adequate measures of the variability inherent in these procedures? Only the chemist can answer.

SUPPLEMENT ON ORTHOGONAL POLYNOMIALS FOR
UNEQUALLY SPACED POINTS

This is an expository supplement on some of the computational techniques for fitting general polynomials to discrete data. We take advantage of that orthogonality present in the standard routine for solving the normal equations which is usually ignored by the inexperienced computer, thereby preventing him from realizing the full information which is readily available.

If we are required to fit several sets of data with error in the y coordinate only, all taken at the same several values of x, the construction of a table of orthogonal polynomials for this set of abscissae should be considered. We propose to work an example by such a table, as well as by the intelligent use of the classical method using powers of x.

An inefficient method

A conventional explanation of the classical method follows:

1. *Linear fit*

$$y = m_0 + m_1 x$$

$$m_0 = \frac{\begin{vmatrix} \sum y & \sum x \\ \sum xy & \sum x^2 \end{vmatrix}}{\begin{vmatrix} n & \sum x \\ \sum x & \sum x^2 \end{vmatrix}}, \qquad m_1 = \frac{\begin{vmatrix} n & \sum y \\ \sum x & \sum xy \end{vmatrix}}{\begin{vmatrix} n & \sum x \\ \sum x & \sum x^2 \end{vmatrix}}.$$

The denominator may be precomputed, but the numerators must be evaluated for each set of observations. The minimized sum of squares of residuals is found from

$$SS_{min} = \sum y^2 - m_0 \sum y - m_1 \sum xy.$$

2. *Parabolic fit*

$$y = n_0 + n_1 x + n_2 x^2$$

$$n_0 = \frac{\begin{vmatrix} \sum y & \sum x & \sum x^2 \\ \sum xy & \sum x^2 & \sum x^3 \\ \sum x^2 y & \sum x^3 & \sum x^4 \end{vmatrix}}{\begin{vmatrix} n & \sum x & \sum x^2 \\ \sum x & \sum x^2 & \sum x^3 \\ \sum x^2 & \sum x^3 & \sum x^4 \end{vmatrix}}, \quad n_1 = \frac{\begin{vmatrix} n & \sum y & \sum x^2 \\ \sum x & \sum xy & \sum x^3 \\ \sum x^2 & \sum x^2 y & \sum x^4 \end{vmatrix}}{|D_3|}, \quad n_2 = \frac{\begin{vmatrix} n & \sum x & \sum y \\ \sum x & \sum x^2 & \sum xy \\ \sum x^2 & \sum x^3 & \sum x^2 y \end{vmatrix}}{|D_3|}.$$

Again, $|D_3|$ may be precomputed, but the numerators are new for each of the n's—*and all the* n's *are different from the* m's. The parabolic fit is measured by

$$\mathrm{SS}_{\min} = \sum y^2 - n_0 \sum y - n_1 \sum xy - n_2 \sum x^2 y.$$

If the linear fit is suspected of being insufficient, and thus a parabolic fit is computed to see whether additional reduction in the minimum sum of squares is significant, the computation required is that of five regression coefficients and two sums of squares.

Although this exposition is correct, it is misleading because the efficient computational version does *not* proceed as implied. It is true that the m's and n's are different, but many of the earlier steps used in evaluating the n's are identical with the steps already used for the m's, so that savings can be effected by using the *Crout method* for linear simultaneous algebraic equations. (See Milne [26, p. 17] or *Marchant Methods*, or any standard book on numerical methods.) It combines the features of orthogonalization with the format of linear equation solving—and either type of solution for the problem may be extracted from the fundamental Crout matrix—depending on one's point of view.

Discrete orthogonal polynomials

Before giving the Crout versions, expositional clarity suggests that the formal procedure for constructing orthogonal polynomials be set forth in much the same fashion as was done for the method using the powers of x. Our detailed example is chosen with simple numbers to make it easier to follow the arithmetic.

We wish to expand the tabulated function, y, in terms of a set of polynomials, $p_j(x_i)$ in x, giving:

$$y = A_0 p_0(x) + A_1 p_1(x) + \dots = \sum_j A_j p_j(x) \tag{1}$$

where the $p_j(x)$ are polynomials of degree j defined by the orthogonality relations

$$\sum_{i=1}^{n} p_k(x_i)\, p_j(x_i) = \begin{cases} 1 & \text{if } k = j \\ 0 & \text{if } k \neq j \end{cases} \tag{2}$$

$$p_0(x) \equiv 1.$$

If we consider $p_1 = a_0 + a_1 x$, then

$$\sum p_1^2 = a_0^2 n + 2a_0 a_1 \sum x + a_1^2 \sum x^2 = 1$$

$$\sum p_0 p_1 = a_0 n + a_1 \sum x = 0,$$

so that

$$a_0 a_1 n + a_1^2 \sum x = 0$$
$$a_0 a_1 \sum x + a_1^2 \sum x^2 = 1$$

and

$$a_1^2 = \frac{\begin{vmatrix} n & 0 \\ \sum x & 1 \end{vmatrix}}{\begin{vmatrix} n & \sum x \\ \sum x & \sum x^2 \end{vmatrix}}, \quad a_0 a_1 = \frac{\begin{vmatrix} 0 & \sum x \\ 1 & \sum x^2 \end{vmatrix}}{\begin{vmatrix} n & \sum x \\ \sum x & \sum x^2 \end{vmatrix}}.$$

Similar arguments for $p_2 = b_0 + b_1 x + b_2$ show

$$b_2^2 = \frac{\begin{vmatrix} n & \sum x & 0 \\ \sum x & \sum x^2 & 0 \\ \sum x^2 & \sum x^3 & 1 \end{vmatrix}}{|D_3|}; \quad b_2 b_1 = \frac{\begin{vmatrix} n & 0 & \sum x^2 \\ \sum x & 0 & \sum x^3 \\ \sum x^2 & 1 & \sum x^4 \end{vmatrix}}{|D_3|}; \quad b_2 b_0 = \frac{\begin{vmatrix} 0 & \sum x & \sum x^2 \\ 0 & \sum x^2 & \sum x^3 \\ 1 & \sum x^3 & \sum x^4 \end{vmatrix}}{|D_3|}.$$

The general law can easily be seen from these examples.

Just as the determinant form is not efficient in the case of the powers of x, so it is also inefficient in solving these linear equations for the coefficients of the orthogonal polynomials. In order to facilitate cross checking, however, we first worked out our numerical example via the determinantal scheme given in Table 11.

TABLE 11

x	y		$\lvert D \rvert$				
1	1	6	30	210	1,710	29	$\sum y$
2	1	30	210	1,710	14,994	212	$\sum xy$
4	3	210	1,710	14,994	136,950	1,754	$\sum x^2 y$
5	5	1,710	14,994	136,950	1,281,930	15,434	$\sum x^3 y$
8	9					217	$\sum y^2$
10	10						

We find

$$p_0 \equiv 1/\sqrt{6}$$

$$p_1 = \frac{1}{\sqrt{60}} (x - 5)$$

$$p_2 = \frac{1}{8\sqrt{6}} (x^2 - 11x + 20)$$

$$p_3 = \frac{1}{24\sqrt{20{,}810}} (80x^3 - 1{,}295x^2 + 5{,}653x - 5{,}740).$$

Evaluating these polynomials at the given points of x, we obtain Table 12.

TABLE 12

x	y	P_0	P_1	P_2	P_3
1	1	1	-4	10	$-1{,}302$
2	1	1	-3	2	$1{,}026$
4	3	1	-1	-8	$1{,}272$
5	5	1	0	-10	150
8	9	1	3	-4	$-2{,}436$
10	10	1	5	10	$1{,}290$
Normalization N_j		$\dfrac{1}{\sqrt{6}}$	$\dfrac{1}{\sqrt{60}}$	$\dfrac{1}{8\sqrt{6}}$	$\dfrac{1}{24\sqrt{20{,}810}}$
$\sum_i P_j{}^2(x_i) = N_j{}^{-2}$		6	60	384	11,986,560

$\sum y P_0 = 29$
$\sum y P_1 = 67$
$\sum y P_2 = 2$
$\sum y P_3 = -4{,}734$

Since we have the orthogonality properties (2), we can evaluate the coefficient A_j in equation (1) by multiplication and summation:

$$\sum_i^n p_j(x_i)\, y(x_i) = A_j \sum_i^n p_j{}^2(x_i) = A_j. \tag{3}$$

Note that this equation uses the $p_j(x)$, which are normalized so that the sum of their squares is *one*. If the abscissae are simple integers, as in this example, it is often more convenient to use the integral part of the orthogonal polynomials, i.e., the P_i of the last table—and compensate for the missing denominator where necessary. Thus, A_j may also be found from:

$$A_j = N_j \sum_i P_j(x_i)\, y(x_i) = B_j/N_j. \tag{4}$$

The smoothed (fitted) curves may now be written explicitly in terms of either the $p_j(x)$ or the $P_j(x)$, the latter invoking a second factor of N_j.

Often we wish to evaluate these fitted curves only at the points where we have observations. If this be true, the expressions using the $P_j(x)$ are the more useful ones and the coefficients become the B_j defined in (4). Thus

$$y(x) = \sum_j A_j N_j P_j(x) = \sum_j B_j P_j(x),$$

where

$$B_j = \sum P_j(x_i)\, y(x_i) / \sum P_j{}^2(x_i).$$

The coefficients for this example are

$$\text{either}\begin{cases} A_0 = \dfrac{29}{\sqrt{6}} & = 11.8392 \\[2mm] A_1 = \dfrac{67}{\sqrt{60}} & = 7.7460 \\[2mm] A_2 = \dfrac{2}{8\sqrt{6}} & = 0.10206 \\[2mm] A_3 = \dfrac{-4{,}734}{24\sqrt{20{,}810}} = -0.13674 \end{cases} \quad \text{or} \quad \begin{cases} B_0 = \dfrac{29}{6} & = 4.83333 \\[2mm] B_1 = \dfrac{67}{60} & = 1.11667 \\[2mm] B_2 = \dfrac{2}{384} & = 0.00521 \\[2mm] B_3 = \dfrac{-4{,}734}{11{,}986{,}560} = -0.00039 \end{cases}$$

One other calculation to be performed is the calculation of the sum of squares of residuals at each stage of fitting:

$$SS_{\min} = \sum y^2(x_i) - A_0{}^2 - A_1{}^2 - \dots$$

Reduction due
to removal of:

$SS_{\min} = 217.00000$

⟵140.16667 mean

$SS_0 \;=\; 76.83333$

74.81667 slope

$SS_1 \;=\; 2.01667$

0.01042 parabola

$SS_2 \;=\; 2.00625$

1.86963 cubic

$SS_3 \;=\; 0.13662$

An efficient method

Now let us solve the same problem by the Crout method, but writing out the intermediate steps which are usually omitted on the worksheet because they are carried by the machine. (We do this only temporarily, to disclose the inner structure of the algebra involved. After the process is understood, the calculational scheme may be restored to its well-known form without danger of further confusions.)

We head the columns in Table 13 by the symbols $x_0, x_1, x_2, \dots$ for $1, x, x^2, \dots$

The computations are the familiar ones: the first column is copied directly from the (symmetrical) matrix. Each element except the first is divided by the first element and placed in the first *row* (in parentheses). The remainder of the lower half of the matrix is copied verbatim. The numbers in the lower half of the second matrix are found by multiplying the

TABLE 13

	x_0	x_1	x_2	x_3	y
x_0	6	(5)	(35)	(285)	(4.83333)
x_1	30	210			
x_2	210	1,710	14,994		
x_3	1,710	14,994	136,950	1,281,930	
y	29	212	1,754	15,434	217

	$x_{1 \cdot 0}$	$x_{2 \cdot 0}$	$x_{3 \cdot 0}$	$y_{0 \cdot 0}$
$x_{1 \cdot 0}$	60	(11)	(107.4)	(1.11667)
$x_{2 \cdot 0}$	660	7,644		
$x_{3 \cdot 0}$	6,444	77,100	794,580	
$y_{0 \cdot 0}$	67	739	7,169	76.83333

	$x_{2 \cdot 01}$	$x_{3 \cdot 01}$	$y_{0 \cdot 01}$
$x_{2 \cdot 01}$	384	(16.1875)	(0.00520833)
$x_{3 \cdot 01}$	6,216	102,494.4	
$y_{0 \cdot 01}$	2	−26.8	2.01667

	$x_{3 \cdot 012}$	$y_{0 \cdot 012}$
$x_{3 \cdot 012}$	1,872.900	(−0.031595)
$y_{0 \cdot 012}$	−59.175	2.00625

	$y_{0 \cdot 0123}$
	0.13662

leading row and column elements of the first matrix and subtracting from the element at the intersection of that row and column. The first column of the second matrix is now divided by the leading element, the results being placed in the first row (in parentheses again). This continues to the bitter

TABLE 14[a]

6	(5)	(35)	(285)	(4.83333)
30	60	(11)	(107.4)	(1.11667)
210	660	384	(16.1875)	(0.00520833)
1,710	6,444	6,216	1,872.9	(−0.031595)
29	67	2	−59.175	0.13662

[a] All the numbers except those in the last column are exact in this example.

end. This is identically the Crout forward computation and, if we have no need of intermediate results, it is usually represented as in Table 14.

The first interesting fact to notice is that the *reductions* in the minimum sum of squares achieved by fitting first a mean, then a line, then a parabola, and finally a cubic are given by

$$(29)(4.83333) = 140.16667$$
$$(67)(1.11667) = 74.81667$$
$$(2)(0.005208) = 0.01042$$
$$(-59.175)(-0.031595) = 1.86963.$$

Thus, no matter in what form the answers may be desired, we have here an immediate test to tell us whether our fit is significantly close, for we can test the latest reduction against the ratio of the residual sum of squares to their degrees of freedom with the standard F test. Only after carrying this matrix out sufficiently far do we *then* worry about (*a*) finding the explicit form of the approximating polynomial, or (*b*) finding points on the approximating polynomial which represent a smoothed version of the curve.

Since the sums of squares come out so nicely, it is natural to suspect that the orthogonal polynomials are lying around somewhere also. That this is true will become evident if we state the algebraic relations which we intended to imply by our notation on the expanded Crout matrix in Table 13. Thus

$$x_{1.0} = x_1 - \qquad 5x_0 = x \ - \ 5$$

$$x_{2.0} = x_2 - \qquad 35x_0 = x^2 - 35$$
$$x_{3.0} = x_3 - \qquad 285x_0 = x^3 - 285$$
$$y_{0.0} = y \ - 4.83333x_0 = y - 4.83333$$

$$x_{2.01} = x_{2.0} - \quad 11x_{1.0} = x^2 - 11x + 20$$

$$x_{3.01} = x_{3.0} - \quad 107.4x_{1.0}$$
$$y_{0.01} = y_{0.0} - 1.11667x_{1.0}$$

$$x_{3.012} = x_{3.01} \ - 16.1875x_{2.01} = x^3 - 16.1875x^2 + 70.6625x - 71.75$$

$$y_{0.012} = y_{0.01} \ - \quad 0.005208x_{2.01}$$
$$y_{0.0123} = y_{0.012} + \quad 0.031595x_{3.012}.$$

Let us now write out some of the $y_{0 \cdot 01} \ldots$ in terms of lower forms:

$$y_{0 \cdot 0} = y - 4.8333$$
$$y_{0 \cdot 01} = (y - 4.83333) - 1.11667x_{1 \cdot 0} = y - 1.11667(x - 5) - 4.83333$$
$$= y - 1.11667x + 0.75000$$
$$y_{0 \cdot 012} = (y - 1.11667x + 0.75) - 0.00521x_{2 \cdot 01}$$
$$= (y - 1.11667x + 0.75) - 0.00521(x^2 - 11x + 20)$$
$$= y - 0.00521x^2 - 1.05938x + 0.64583$$
$$y_{0 \cdot 0123} = y_{0 \cdot 012} - 0.031595x_{3 \cdot 012}$$
$$= y_{0 \cdot 012} - 0.031595\{[(x^3 - 285) - 107.4(x - 5)] - 16.1875$$
$$(x^2 - 11x + 20)\}$$
$$= y_{0 \cdot 012} + 0.031595(x^3 - 16.1875x^2 + 70.6625x - 71.75).$$

If we now remark that $y_{0 \cdot 0} y_{0 \cdot 01} \ldots y_{0 \cdot 0123}$ are the residuals of the true y from the fitted polynomials, we see that the fitted polynomials themselves are

$$\begin{cases} y_0 = +4.83333 \\ y_1 = -0.75000 + 1.11667x \\ y_2 = -0.64583 + 1.05938x + 0.00521x^2 \\ y_3 = +1.62111 - 1.17320x + 0.51665x^2 - 0.031585x^3. \end{cases}$$

Note that $x_{1 \cdot 0}, x_{2 \cdot 01}, x_{3 \cdot 012}$ (boxed in the original set of formulae) are the orthogonal polynomials—without their normalization and with their highest power of x having a unit coefficient. The appropriate normalizing factor is found very simply, since it consists of the reciprocal of the square root of the corresponding principal diagonal term. Thus for

$$x_{1 \cdot 0} \quad \text{we need} \qquad\qquad = \frac{1}{\sqrt{60}}$$

$$x_{2 \cdot 01} \quad \text{we need} \quad \frac{1}{\sqrt{384}} = \frac{1}{8\sqrt{6}}$$

$$x_{3 \cdot 0123} \text{ we need } \frac{1}{\sqrt{1,872.9}} = \frac{80}{24\sqrt{20,810}}.$$

This is in complete agreement with the results of the determinantal orthogonal treatment. Thus we can, by using the parenthesized numbers in the regular Crout matrix, get the orthogonal polynomials and their normalization. We can also get the explicit fitted polynomial for any order via equations of this type, as was just demonstrated above. If our aim is merely to get these equations, however, we need not write out the orthogonal polynomials. We can treat the Crout matrix as the solution of the original powers-of-x problem by cutting off the matrix at the order of the equation desired and substituting in for the standard "back-solution," thereby generating the coefficients of the fitted polynomial directly.   For example, if we want the parabolic equation we merely consider the matrix to be:

$$
\begin{array}{cccc}
6 & (5) & (35) & (4.83333) \\
  & 60 & (11) & (1.11667) \\
  &   & 384 & (0.00521) \\
(0.64582) & (1.05936) & (0.00521) &
\end{array}
$$

The 0.00521 is already there, the $1.05936 = 1.11667 - 11(0.00521)$ and $0.64582 = 4.83333 - 35(0.00521) - 5(1.05936)$. This is easily done without recopying the matrix—merely by ignoring the other numbers.

The quadratic *orthogonal polynomial* may be obtained in the same fashion by bordering the matrix by zeros on the right (in place of the y column), except that we place *one* in the extreme bottom position.   Thus $x_{2.01}$ is given by

$$
\begin{array}{cccc}
6 & (5) & (35) & 0 \\
  & 60 & (11) & 0 \\
  &   & 384 & 1 \\
20 & -11 & 1 & \text{or} \quad (x^2 - 11x + 20)
\end{array}
$$

and the normalization is supplied by $\dfrac{1}{\sqrt{384}} = \dfrac{1}{8\sqrt{6}}$.

To construct the table of $p_n(x_i)$, we compute the polynomials and evaluate them at the x_i, probably by synthetic division.

The actual efficient computational form would seem to be as given in Table 15—or some simple variant of it which may suit the particular computer's fancy.   The first part of the table is the original matrix, with the computation falling below it.   The numbers in the four corners, cut off by dotted lines from the rest of the matrix, are the ones that have been computed at the end of the linear fit.   We look at the residual sum of squares (2.01667) and decide whether this is small enough (close enough fit) for our purpose.   If we decide to go on to fit a parabola, the next row and column of figures are added.   In the solid box (lower left) are the coefficients of the fitted polynomials, and a similar box could be added below it for the orthogonal polynomials if they were desired explicitly.

For a new set of y data on the same x's, we can replace the right-hand column of the original matrix and repeat those calculations that are affected—i.e., less than half the calculations need to be done over for any subsequent set.   This requires the recomputation of $\sum y^2$, $\sum y$, $\sum xy$, ..., $\sum x^m y$ (where m is the highest polynomial that we shall want to fit), as well as the repetition of the pertinent numbers in the Crout matrix.

TABLE 15

6	30	210	1,710	29
	210	1,710	14,994	212
		14,994	136,950	1,754
			1,281,930	15,434
				217

6	(5)	(35)	(285)	(4.83333)
30	60	(11)	(107.4)	(1.11667)
210	660	384	(16.1875)	(0.00521)
1,710	6,444	6,216	1,872.9	(−0.031595)
29	67	2	−59.175	

				SSR after the removal of a		SS removed
−0.75000	1.11667			76.83333	mean	140.16667
−0.64582	1.05936	0.00521		2.01667	line	74.81667
1.62117	−1.17325	0.51666	−0.031595	2.00625	parabola	0.01042
				0.13662	cubic	1.86963

The photometric problem

Returning to the problem of calcium in the presence of lanthanum, we find that Heidel and Fassel took their data at eight points which are almost logarithmically distributed. Lacking any internal evidence justifying a transformation, we chose to use the original units, and this section shows how we obtained the orthogonal polynomials used in Table 7.

In order to reduce the size of the numbers as much as possible, we shifted the x values until their mean value was zero by subtracting 0.650. Since a preliminary translation or change of scale can easily be allowed for at the end, and since the linear orthogonal polynomial is $x_i - x.$, this change will simplify our arithmetic. We have only to remember that the fitted functions, if needed explicitly (they usually are not!), will have to be written by replacing x with $x' - 0.650$ to return to the original x' variable.

Our matrix of the powers of x is

8	0	5.045	5.85796875
0	5.045	5.85796875	12.232582815
5.045	5.85796875	12.232582815	21.52292255859325
5.85796875	12.232582815	21.52292255859325	40.2678592900390625

from which we get

8	(0)	(0.630625)	(0.73224609375)
0	5.045	(1.161143459)	(2.424694314)
5.045	5.85796875	2.249137590	(1.611709979)
5.85796875	12.232582815	3.624957499	0.4757304287

where the terms are found exactly as were those of the previous illustration. With a desk calculator no figures need be written down other than those shown here. We now find the coefficients of the orthogonal polynomials by mentally retaining the figures in parentheses and appending a column of *zeros* and a *one* to their right. Thus, for the cubic orthogonal polynomial we envision:

	(0)	(0.630625)	(0.73224609375)	0
		(1.161143459)	(2.424694314)	0
			(1.1611709979)	0
0.2841385117	−0.5532678141	−1.1611709979	1	

where each figure on the bottom line is obtained by multiplying those to the right of it by the parenthesized figures above, adding them together, and subtracting from zero. Thus

$$0 - 1(2.424694314) - (-1.611709939)(1.161143459) = -0.5532678141$$

and

$$0 - (1)(1.611709979) = -1.611709979$$

gives this coefficient trivially. The bottom line is interpreted as

$$p_3(x_i) = N_j(x^3 - 1.611709979x^2 - 0.5532678141x + 0.2841385117).$$

The normalization $N.$ is the appropriate diagonal term to the $-\frac{1}{2}$ power,

$$N_3 = (2.249137590)^{-\frac{1}{2}} = 0.666794474.$$

The orthogonal polynomial coefficients, with their normalizations in parentheses, may be compactly written immediately below the previous matrix.

1	(0.3535533906)			
0	1	(0.445214617)		
−0.630625	−1.161143459	1	(0.66679474)	
+0.2841385117	−0.5532678141	−1.611709979	1	(1.449838430)

The values presented in Table 7 and repeated in Table 16 are found by evaluating each of these orthogonal polynomials by synthetic division at each of the x values and multiplying by the normalizing factor. This

TABLE 16

x'	x	p_1	p_2	p_3
0.025	−0.625	−0.27825914	+0.32387185	−0.35344732
0.050	−0.600	−0.26712877	+0.28409517	−0.26113967
0.125	−0.525	−0.23373767	+0.16976608	−0.02077122
0.250	−0.400	−0.17808585	−0.00411252	+0.26614980
0.375	−0.275	−0.12243402	−0.15715382	+0.42567940
0.625	−0.025	−0.01113037	−0.40072442	+0.43052555
1.250	+0.600	·+0.26712877	−0.64499768	−0.59738819
2.500	+1.850	+0.82364704	+0.42925534	+0.11039164
5.200	0	0	0	0

procedure gives polynomials normalized to *one*. Since there is no possibility of gaining the advantages of nice integer values by doing otherwise, we save ourselves the worries of applying the normalizing factor at some later point in the computations.

If explicit *polynomial* expressions for these fitted curves are necessary, it is not clear that the computation of the p_j effects any saving of labor, but usually these are not really the end product which is desired. Usually we want an equation that may be evaluated at a particular x, and the table of p_j allows this *more* easily than does the form

$$y_m = a_0 + a_1 x + ... + a_m x^m \qquad (5)$$

as long as we are interested only in the points x_i. For other points, the corresponding p_j can be computed directly from their polynomial expressions, but this labor is admittedly a little greater than substituting directly in equation (5). The balance to be struck here is the frequency with which this interpolative use of the polynomial is required versus the frequency with which the other uses will suffice.

More orthogonal fitting—equally spaced

We now return to the phthalic anhydride example of Chapter 6. The questions raised there, but still unexplored in most details, concerned the form of a common calibration curve for the analysis of phthalic anhydride in the presence of four similar organic acids. We wondered whether separate curves were perhaps justified but postponed these questions until the efficient mechanism for fitting such curves was available.

If we fit separate means and linear and quadratic terms to the individual and total columns of Table 10 (Chapter 6), we obtain the coefficients and sums of squares set forth in Table 17. The check marks indicate totals

TABLE 17

Acid	Mean	Sums of Squares			Regression Coefficients		
		Linear	Quadratic	Other	Mean	Linear	Quadratic
Succinic	259.2	608.4	743.143	1,805.257	7.2	−7.8	−7.286
Adipic	1,411.2	2,560.0	257.143	2,163.657	−16.8	−16.0	4.286
Sebacic	1,548.8	6,553.6	370.286	1,623.314	−17.6	−25.6	5.143
Itaconic	720.0	1,000.0	2,113.143	1,222.857	−12.0	−10.0	−12.286
Total	3,939.2	10,722.0	3,483.715	6,815.085			
All acids	1,920.8	8,820.9	360.071	40.229	−39.2	−59.4	−10.143
Additional	2,018.4 √	1,901.1	+3,123.644	+6,774.856	=11,799.6 √		

that were obtained by other calculations in the last chapter. If we were so optimistic as to fit cubic terms, the Other column of Table 17 would break into the pieces shown in Table 18, and we obtain the cubic regression coefficients of column C.

TABLE 18

Acid	Cubic	Quartic	C
Succinic	1,795.6	9.657	−13.4
Adipic	250.0	1,913.657	− 5.0
Sebacic	672.4	950.914	+ 8.2
Itaconic	1,210.0	12.857	+11.0
Total	3,928.0	2,887.085	
All acids	1.6	38.629	+ 0.8
Additional	3,926.4	2,848.456	

Tables 17 and 18 give a complete breakdown of the Sums of Squares into individual degrees of freedom. Such detail is useful for discovering physical mechanisms, but it is undesirable as a summary of our results. We therefore abstract the data already present in the bottom of these tables for a more conventional anova, Table 19.

What mean square yardstick shall we use to separate the statistical fluctuations from real physical systematic symptoms? The duplicate suggestion of 110 has been rejected as probably unsound, and the Interaction estimate of 983 is (hopefully) too large. In this example we have concluded that 983 is not too large, but the argument is a proof-by-denial (a favorite with mathematicians, inquisitors, and missionaries). If 110 were used, almost every factor in these tables would be significant—and the resultant calibrations that we would be forced to accept would be complex beyond the bounds of physical intuition. Since we believe in some order in our chemical universe, we reject the variance estimate as too small. The same argument succeeds in rejecting a mean square of about 400; the critical terms admitted to the realm of respectability are still not sufficiently homogeneous to satisfy our aesthetics. Note that succinic acid reserves almost all its polynomial behavior for the Cubic term, whereas adipic prefers the Mean, Linear, and Quartic. Sebacic needs only the Mean and the Linear (but *they* really explain a lot of the variability), whereas itaconic ignores all but Quadratic and Cubic.

Only when we finally take our critical value as 800 or more does a semblance of order appear—and this the dull order we obtained when the Row by Column Interaction term was interpreted as the realistic measure of day-to-day variability. So we seem to be stuck with it, squirm how we will. This is not statistics, but it *is* the only type of analysis these data can support. Further experiments are desirable, but until then we must live with the present treatment.

TABLE 19

		SS	DF	MS
Common	Mean	1,920.8	1	1,920.8
	Slope	8,820.9	1	8,820.9
	Quadratic	360.1	1	360.1
	Cubic	1.6	1	1.6
	Quartic	38.6	1	38.6
Separate	Means	2,018.4	3	672.8
	Slopes	1,901.1	3	633.7
	Quadratics	3,123.6	3	1,041.2
	Cubics	3,926.4	3	1,308.8
	Quartics	2,848.5	3	949.5
Total		24,960.0	20	

CHAPTER 8

The Use of Transformations

Although most of the data in this book exhibit a straight line or two when plotted for inspection, the reader should not infer that the numbers necessarily enjoyed such a property when they were first recorded. However much the analyst may wish that Nature's mold be linear, the simple truth is often found in curves. To gain the advantages given by lines, we may change either variable, or both—if we choose—and it is with the philosophy of such transformations that we here concern ourselves.

If only one variate bears a distribution, if only y is subject to random errors, for instance, then we may play with the other variate with considerable abandon—and this freedom often suffices to straighten out the graph. The statistical tests, comparisons, confidence limits, etc., may be applied to the transformed data, and the results thus obtained may, if desired, be transformed back to the original curvilinear scale. Since only y contains our statistical variation and since it is unchanged, effects of the transformation neither need be sought for nor guarded against.

For what purpose then, we may ask, would anyone bother to transform the y variate if he has all this freedom with x with which to play? The answer must lie concealed in the subtler structure of the data rather than in the gross presence of a line. For instance, the y variate may be transformed *to stabilize the variability*. Most of the line-fitting procedures assume that the errors in the y data are normally distributed, with the means of those distributions located along a line and *with the variances of the distributions being everywhere the same*. If we know our data become more variable as y grows larger, for instance, we will be tempted to use a logarithmic or a square-root scale for y to make the variability more nearly uniform. This stabilizing the variance is probably the most frequent reason for transforming the dependent variate.

Another standard assumption underlying most statistical superstructures is that of normality. Occasionally the experimenter knows enough about the distribution of his errors to assert not only that they are not normal, but that they have a long tail on the right that looks more or less like this (and he draws a sketch like Figure 46). Again if *log y* were used instead of *y*, the statistician would be happier because then the picture would look a great deal more like a normal distribution. So transformations of the dependent variable may occasionally restore normality to a previously lopsided distribution—an improvement which greatly increases everyone's peace of mind. Unfortunately experimenters do not usually have enough experience with their data to invoke such transformations, and it is safe to say that the data from one particular experiment almost never contains sufficient evidence to warrant such a transformation without *a priori* experience. Thus the *introduction of normality* is a valid but infrequent reason for transforming dependent variates.

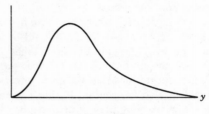

Figure 46

Finally we come to the subtlest and perhaps most important use of transformations: the *introduction of additivity into the model*. In the more complicated experiments where the analysis of variance is most important, we assumed that the several independent variables each contributed their part to the final measured quantity and that these parts were *added*. Thus if

$$y_{ij} = \mu + \xi_i + \eta_j + \epsilon_{ij} \tag{1}$$

then the variable *y* might be equal to an effect, ξ_i, ascribable to the day on which the measurements were taken and to another, η_j, attributable to the man who took them, as well as to random fluctuations, ϵ_{ij}, which are independent of both these variables, and also to a constant part, μ, which may be the quantity of principal interest (and may itself be a linear function of the independent non-statistical variate *x*). If such an additive model as (1) holds for *y*, it clearly is not true for log *y* or $\sqrt{y}$. By the same token, the experimenter may have good theoretical reason to expect additivity in a scale different from that on which the data were recorded. In such circumstances, a transformation is clearly needed and should unhesitatingly be made.

These three reasons for transforming the dependent variate have no obvious mathematical compulsion to be compatible; a transformation to introduce additivity might well throw out normality and mess up the constancy of variance beyond all recognition.   If, indeed, the choice should arise, then of course it must be made.   But usually the pleasant cloak of obscurity hides knowledge of all but one property from us—and so we cheerfully transform to vouchsafe unto ourselves this one desirable property while carefully refraining from other considerations about which query is futile.   Indeed, we can do naught else.

But there is a brighter side to this picture.   The gods who favor statisticians have frequently ordained that the world be well behaved and so we often find that a transformation to obtain one of these *desiderata* in fact achieves them all (well, *almost* achieves them!).   That the universe be statistically well ordered is perhaps just compensation for the existence of errors and variability in the first place.   It may seem strange that a statistician must ask for an act of faith when he links together the properties of additivity, normality, and homoscedasticity, and asserts that to achieve one is frequently (even usually) to approach all—but proof is lacking and only observation and experience may be quoted.   Plausibility arguments have been advanced, but they are rather unconvincing and hedged with restrictive assumptions.   For the present, at least, we must assume with Pippa that "All's right with the world."

Binomial data: Their curse and cure

Occasionally linear data arise from a binomial population rather than from a normal one.   An hypothetical example might be the fraction defective of some product as some independent variable x is gradually changed. Perhaps the decision about the defectiveness arose through the application of a go-nogo gage, or perhaps by a qualitative judgment of an inspector. If the gage was used, probably there is also a measurable variate, y, which might have a normal distribution—but the cost of measuring it denies it to us.   Economy forces a binomial model on us.   If the judgment is qualitative, of course we have only the binomial, and we must therefore live with it.

If we are examining the number of defectives in lots of size n, and if n is large enough, it is well known that

$$\frac{y - np}{\sqrt{np(1 - p)}},$$

where p is the (unknown) fraction defective,
is approximately normally distributed.   The only trouble is that n has to be about thirty before the approximation to normality becomes good

enough for anybody with a conscience, and it is not really very good for setting confidence limits even then.   And who ever had samples that big anyway?   Maybe biologists, but engineers usually do not.   So instead of trying to use this fact directly in fitting a line, it is often more convenient to transform y so that it is approximately normal, and then act as if it were completely orthodox.

The binomial distribution is unpleasant because the variance of the measured variate, y, is equal to $np(1 - p)$ and hence is a function of its expected value, np, as well as the sample size, n.   If we are trying to fit a line which essentially shows p as a function of some independent variable x, then as p changes so does the variance of the observed variate, y.

Several transformations have been proposed to stabilize the variance of binomial data, but they all stem from

$$Z_1 = \arcsin \sqrt{y/n} = \sin^{-1} (\text{fraction defective})^{1/2}.$$

A slightly more efficient angular transformation is

$$Z_2 = \arcsin \sqrt{(y + \tfrac{3}{8})/(n + \tfrac{3}{4})},$$

which was proposed by Anscombe [1], and a still more efficient transformation, proposed by Tukey [34], is

$$Z_3 = \arcsin \sqrt{y/(n + 1)} + \arcsin \sqrt{(y + 1)/(n + 1)}.$$

All three of these transformations are designed to stabilize the variance of the transformed variate—Z_1 and Z_2 tending to be normal with variance $1/(4n + 2)$, and Z_3 having a variance near $1/(n + \tfrac{1}{2})$.   The means are, of course, also different—but irrelevant to our discussion.   The variance of Z_3 is within 6 per cent of $(n + \tfrac{1}{2})^{-1}$ for almost all p and n where np is greater than *one*.

An alternative procedure for fitting a straight line to binomial data is to use the original scale but to weight these data in inverse proportion to their apparent variances.   The struggles of weighted arithmetic scarcely seem justified, however, especially if we believe that to stabilize the variance may also tend to introduce the other well-regulated behaviors we covet.   Accordingly, your author is somewhat less than enthusiastic for fitting in the untransformed scale.   We fit a line to several sets of data to bring out the pertinent information about the parameters of the line which may be enjoyed in common by these sets.   To combine them in the binomial scale is difficult; to fit in a normal one is easy.

We hasten to remark that in the setting of confidence limits for several sets of binomial data transformation to a normal scale may be avoided by methods of Freeman and Tukey [15], but these methods do not seem useful for line fitting.

Poisson data

If our data are from a Poisson distribution, we have the same problem of non-uniform variance as occurs with the binomial. Poisson data arise if we are plotting radiation counts for a fixed time interval, or numbers of telephone calls, or bacterial colonies—indeed, almost any *number* of random events occurring in a prescribed time or space. The variance of a Poisson variate, y, is identically equal to its mean, m, so that as the mean increases, so does the variate. Again several transformations have been proposed to stabilize this variance, the basic one being

$$\sqrt{y},$$

which was improved by Anscombe [1] to

$$\sqrt{y + \tfrac{3}{8}},$$

and a somewhat better one by Tukey [34]

$$\sqrt{y} + \sqrt{y + 1}.$$

This last transformation has a variance equal to *one* (plus or minus 6 per cent) for an expected value of y greater than one, and the two earlier transformations stabilize to a variance of approximately 0.25.

Logarithmic data

Although no clear rule may be safely offered for the taking of logarithms to reduce data to manageable configurations, nevertheless, this transformation is probably the commonest of them all. Almost all data that arise from growth phenomena where the change in a datum is apt to be proportional to its size and hence the errors are similarly afflicted are improved by transforming to their logarithms. Data that are *counts* of populations, vital statistics, census data, and the like are almost always improved by taking logs—be they bacteria or merely people. The late Charles Winsor frequently prescribed the taking of logs of all naturally occurring counts (plus *one*, to handle that embarrassing quantity *zero*) before analyzing them—no matter what the source. The number of times the prescription will harm the patient are few compared with the cures.

Engineering and physical-science applications of this transformation are less frequent, but still plentiful. Perhaps it is too easy to suggest that whenever an engineer feels impelled to plot his data on log paper, he ought to consider analyzing it in the same scale—but the truth lies somewhere near this suggestion, and we hereby propose it. An overdose of this medicine is not apt to kill the patient. The rather considerable palaver about log-normal distributions may be ignored since it merely refers to data whose logarithms are normally distributed. So transform away!

CHAPTER 9

The Rejection of Unwanted Data

The reader might suppose that this chapter should come much earlier in the book—that anyone analyzing data ought to learn how to get rid of the useless stuff right away so as to save his strength for the more valuable nuggets. But the plain truth is that physical scientists and engineers need not be encouraged to ignore an obstinate outlying datum—rather they need to be held in check. Most data that get to a statistician for analysis have already suffered from a more drastic screening than they would ever receive at his hands, and any words that he would write must plead primarily for less drastic measures. When a point bobs out of line, it is all too easy to decide that "The voltage was unsteady during the first part of this run" or that "Those chemicals weren't as pure as I should have had them," or "My hand wasn't very steady when I made that last adjustment." Self-criticism is vital to experimental success, and we are not suggesting that some statistical panacea is at hand either to mechanize or to sanctify what is an essentially subjective operation. We merely point out the dangers of *a posteriori* rejection of data on physical arguments—buttressed as they are by the prime scientific drive for simplicity and a well-ordering of results.

When we are faced with a set of data, together with a theory about how they should behave, we often find one or two stragglers who have wandered off from the rest. They lie farther from the line, they are separated from the others by a suspicious gap—they just "don't look right." If we have physical explanations for the anomalous behavior, the explanations should probably govern the eventual disposition of these data. This course is fraught with the dangers decried above, but until more adequate statistical techniques are known, we have little choice.

Whatever our method of throwing the rascals out, it ultimately rests on an assumption that the rascals belong to a family different from the rest of the data. This difference may be one of mean value—the rascals are merely trying to be somewhere else and have been rather successful. Or the family difference may be in the variability—here a wild fellow from the

224

wild family will be noticed and perhaps rejected, whereas one of his accidentally conforming brethren will remain undetected. Perhaps the family differences are more complicated—normal versus rectangular distributions, for example—but we have trouble enough providing theories for the simpler hypotheses.

To construct a rejection scheme we rely on a guilt-by-lack-of-association principle (perhaps we should call it lack of conformity). We estimate the dispersion of the principal underlying population and then test the suspected datum for abnormal deviations. (Statisticians tend to be more tolerant than physical scientists, who in turn are more lenient than politicians.) Either the test can be a squared deviation versus an estimated variance, or it can be a rangized version in which a gap is compared with the sample range. In either test we must guard against the obvious fact that only extremes will be tested, and to reject them too easily may cost us heavily by leading to that false sense of security conferred by stable data. The casual levels of confidence we have been using for other problems (5 per cent, 10 per cent) are usually far too lenient for a rejection scheme, which probably should operate from 0.1 per cent to 1 per cent.

Samples from a normal population

The obvious statistic to test a straggler, if there is only one to be tested and if we believe all the rest form a normal population, is

$$\frac{x_n - x.}{s} = R_n$$

where x_n is the suspected non-conformist,

$\quad$ $x.$ is the mean of all the *other* observations,

$\quad$ s $\;$ is the estimate of the population standard deviation based on the *other* observations.

Others may prefer to base the mean and standard deviation estimate on *all* the data, rather than to exclude the point in question—but these refinements are of no analytical consequence, since both these statistics are simple monotone functions of each other and a test for one will automatically yield a test for the other. Grubbs [16] has tabled still another statistic

$$\frac{S_n^2}{S^2} = \frac{\sum\limits_{}^{n-1} (x_i - \bar{x}_n)^2}{\sum\limits_{}^{n} (x_i - \bar{x})^2} = \left[1 + \frac{(n-1)}{n(n-2)} R_n^2\right]^{-1}$$

where the numerator excludes the suspect (x_n) both from the summation and from the mean, $\bar{x}_n$. The second equality shows the relation to our statistic. A brief table of the percentage points of R_n is included in Appendix Table 17.

As with all classical statistics, doubts inevitably arise about the normal assumption, and advocates of quick-and-not-too-dirty statistics have offered rangized tests. Dixon [12] has tabled percentage points for several statistics, the simplest of which is

$$r_{10} = \frac{x_n - x_{n-1}}{x_n - x_1},$$

in which the gap between the subject and his nearest neighbor is compared with the entire sample range. Critical values are available in Table 16 of the Appendix. This test seems to be almost indistinguishable from Grubbs' for samples up to 25 and is considerably simpler to use.

Both versions of this straggler test lead to another nasty suspicion—perhaps *more than one* datum is from a foreign population. Perhaps two at the top are strangers, or two at the top and one at the bottom—and so on. Perhaps the range used for comparison ought not to include the data being tested. Once this train of thought is started, it becomes difficult to stop. Dixon [12] has given critical values for several of these statistics. Grubbs [16] has tabled only the tests for the single extreme and the test for the *two* largest (or smallest).

These tests all presuppose that the main population variance must be estimated from the sample containing the outlier, that no independent estimate is available. If, however, an independent estimate is at hand, the multiple-comparison techniques of Tukey [34] et al. are at our disposal. Such a situation occurs if we have several samples and are testing whether one of the sample *means* is an outlier (the sample variance can be estimated from the *within* sample variability). With these larger configurations of data, the problem of testing and rejecting discrepant data becomes somewhat simpler to understand and less susceptible to dangerous wishful thinking.

Samples from a line

When we wish to test a point that seems too far off a line, we try to reduce the problem to one already solved by removing the line and looking at the residuals. Most of our line-fitting models have assumed that these deviations are normal, that they all come from populations with zero mean and a common unknown variance, σ^2. So all we ought to do is question the obstinate one about his right to belong to this homogeneous group of residuals.

The only trouble with this theory is the fitted line. The deviations from the (unknown) true line may very well be normal with zero mean and a common variance, but unfortunately the line we removed is necessarily imperfect—and contributes to all the residuals.   That the residuals from a particular fitted line are *dependent* is obvious, but whether this dependence seriously warps the rejection probability levels of the normal tests is not entirely clear.   Intuitively, I think not, but I cannot prove it and so my intuition may merely represent wishful thinking.

The first example in Chapter 2, the calcium oxide analyses, originally showed one datum different from those given in this book.   The original data, together with their residuals from the fitted least-squares line, are given in Table 1.   A glance at the residuals suggests that the datum for

TABLE 1

x	y	$y - y_f$
4.0	3.7	-0.05
8.0	7.8	0.07
12.5	12.1	-0.11
16.0	15.6	-0.09
20.0	19.8	0.13
25.0	24.5	-0.14
31.0	31.1	0.49
36.0	35.5	-0.08
40.0	39.4	-0.16
40.0	39.5	-0.06
232.5	229.0	0.00

31 ml. CaO is from a different population than the others.   Accordingly, we are tempted to omit it from the analysis.   To check on our intuition, however, we applied the outlier tests, both of which are now illustrated.

The classical statistic gives

$$\frac{y_n - y.}{s} = \frac{0.490 - (-0.054)}{0.119} = 4.57,$$

which is significant at the 2 per cent level.   (We used the mean and standard deviation of the residuals from the line fitted to the ten points here.   Perhaps we should use the deviation, mean, and s from fitting a new line to the nine points, but that statistic is clearly very close to the present one—and, in fact, gives 4.33 instead of 4.57.)

The rangized version is

$$\frac{r_n - r_{n-1}}{r_n - r_1} = \frac{0.49 - (0.13)}{(0.49) - (-0.16)} = 0.554.$$

This value is significant at about the 1 per cent level.

Finally, in the interests of expositional aesthetics, a new datum was inserted in Chapter 2 (to avoid that missing-tooth look) by consulting a random number table for a new residual. The variance of the population from which the random choice was made was chosen to be approximately 0.01, the estimated size of the variance of the other nine residuals.

CHAPTER 10

Cumulative Data: The Fading Line

Some data fit lines naturally, but others have lines thrust upon them. From the first chapter it has been our plea and thesis that a realistic model is worth more than all the blindly applied least-squares technique in the world. In this chapter we examine a common type of engineering data in which a line seems to lurk but has misled more often than helped. We cannot hope to cover all the misuses of linear models, but we hope that the present example from a cumulative data experiment will suffice to illuminate the dangers.

An abrasion test

Common practice in abrasion or wear tests decrees that the substance under test be abraded for several successive periods and that the weight (or thickness) be recorded at the end of each period. The quantity of interest is the rate of wear, a quantity that can easily be conceived as the slope of the line summarizing *weight* versus *number of abrasions*. More conventionally, the total loss of weight is plotted against the number of abrasions, and a line is fitted that has a mild moral obligation to go through the origin. There is nothing wrong with this method of collecting data, but—at the same time—we may be tempted to pour these data uncritically into the standard line-fitting formulae without considering what answer we want.

An unsatisfactory example

In a rubber abrasion test J. M. Brust collected the first two columns of numbers of Table 1, being the total loss in weight (milligrams) versus the total number of revolutions of the abrading machine.

Our first reaction is to conclude that the average rate of wear is probably 266/10 or 26.6 mg. per 1,000 revolutions—and indeed this should be our last reaction as well, unless further data turn up to lend credence to some more complicated model. Some readers doubtless will feel that we are

TABLE 1

1,000 rpm	Lost	Residual
0	0	0.0
1	36	9.4
2	66	12.8
3	94	14.2
4	111	4.6
5	133	0.0
6	161	1.4
7	190	3.8
8	214	1.2
9	240	0.6
10	266	0.0

ignoring a line here—a line through the origin whose slope demands fitting by the formula $\sum xy/\sum x^2$, but another group will point out that the *differences* of the successive weights each estimate the slope and hence we should average *them*. This second approach leads directly to our arithmetic but leaves a faintly uncomfortable feeling because the successive differences may contain weighing errors and hence are not independent.

Such statistical quandaries can be resolved only by carefully returning to the mathematical model of the physical behavior we expect. Why should the weight loss vary? Clearly weighing errors could occur. Perhaps the abrading machine was not operating uniformly. And perhaps the rubber sample was not uniform. Ideally each datum should give new and independent insight into the abrasion resistance of the rubber. Unfortunately, each total weight depends not only on the amount removed since the last weighing but also on all the previous history of the test. Thus a simple model might be

$$w_i = \mu_i + \epsilon_i = \mu_{i-1} - \xi_i + \epsilon_i,$$

where μ_{i-1} is the true weight lost up to the previous weighing,

     ξ_i is the true weight removed since the previous weighing,

     ϵ_i is the weighing error.

(Repeated weighings would add a *j* subscript to w_i and ϵ_i but would otherwise leave the model unchanged.) It is clear that an isolated soft spot in our specimen would produce a high value for μ_i which would then intrude itself upon all subsequent weighings unless fortuitously canceled by a subsequent hard region. Thus local effects do not appear *once* in these data; they appear, unhappily, forever after. The conventional straight-line fitting, as pointed out by J. Mandell [24], would weight these effects out of all proportion to their significance. Since the last datum contains all the previous effects, a slope fitted by it alone is adequate. Of course, if known discontinuities in the line occur, the uncontaminated differences (i.e., those not adjacent to the discontinuities) may be averaged for the slope estimate.

Weighing errors can be reduced by repeated weighings, and since they pose no interesting questions of data treatment, we shall not discuss them further. If we suspect the uniformity of the abrading machine operation, we could possibly arrange the simultaneous abrasion of a known uniform standard sample jointly with the test specimen. We would then have a third column of data, and the slope of interest would be taken from a plot of y versus this third variable.

Finally, suppose the test specimen is not uniform. Perhaps the concept of rate of wear is no longer useful because of a large variability, or perhaps a systematic change in the resistance leads to a smooth curve with changing slope. We must then ask what it is we wish to estimate—and why. Perhaps we should ignore these data entirely. (In the words of W. C. Randalls, "What isn't worth doing at all isn't worth doing well!")

If we decide that weighing errors are not serious and that the departures from linearity are due to unsystematic variation in the abraded material, then we will probably remove the simple line fitted between the origin and the last point to look at the residuals. In our example we get the third column of Table 1. These particular residuals do not look random, and it is not clear whether the rate-of-wear concept can be justified for any except gross uses. Without further information the cause of these probably systematic deviations cannot be found.

With repeated weighings to give an estimate of the smallest category of experimental variability, it should be possible to examine the residuals from the fitted line to determine whether they are due solely to weighing inaccuracies or to more material causes. If they appear to be systematically curved, a parabolic term could be extracted and tested for its likelihood of random occurrence. In fact, once the line has faded out of the picture any of the classical analysis of variance techniques are at our disposal and should present no problems. The difficult questions are still those of physical interpretation.

References

1. Anscombe, F. J., "The Transformation of Poisson, Binomial, and Negative-Binomial Data," *Biometrika*, **35** (1948), 246–254.
2. Askovitz, S. I., "A Short-Cut Graphic Method for Fitting the Best Straight Line to a Series of Points According to the Criterion of Least Squares," *JASA*, **52** (1957), 13–17.
3. Bartlett, M. S., "Properties of Sufficiency and Statistical Tests," *Proc. Roy. Soc. (London)*, **A160** (1937), 268–282.
4. Berkson, J., "Are There Two Regressions?", *JASA*, **45** (1950), 164–180.
5. Box, G. E. P., "Non-normality and Test on Variances," *Biometrika*, **40** (1953), 318–335.
6. Brown, G. W. and A. M. Mood, "On Median Tests for Linear Hypotheses," *Proceedings of the Second Berkeley Symposium on Mathematical Statistics and Probability*, University of California Press, Berkeley, 1950, 154–166.
7. Brownlee, K. A., *Industrial Experimentation*, Chemical Publishing Co., Brooklyn, 1947.
8. Cochran, W. G., "The Distribution of the Largest of a Set of Estimated Variances as a Function of their Total," *Ann. Eugenics*, **11** (1941), 45–52.
9. Cohen, A. C., Jr., "Estimating the Mean and Variance of Normal Populations from Singly Truncated and Doubly Truncated Samples," *Ann. Math. Stat.*, **21** (1950), 557–569.
10. Daniels, H. E., "A Distribution-Free Test for Regression Parameters," *Ann. Math. Stat.*, **25** (1954), 499–513.
11. David, F. N., *Tables of the Ordinates and Probability Integral of the Distribution of the Correlation Coefficient in Small Samples*, Cambridge University Press, Cambridge, England, 1938. Also in *Biometrika Tables for Statisticians*, Vol. 1, Tables 13–15.
12. Dixon, W. J., "Ratios Involving Extreme Values," *Ann. Math. Stat.*, **22** (1951), 68–78.
13. Eisenhart, C., *see* Swed, F. S.
14. Fisher, R. A. and F. Yates, *Statistical Tables for Biological Agricultural and Medical Research*, Oliver & Boyd, London, 1943, Table XXIII, Orthogonal Polynomials.
15. Freeman, M. F. and J. W. Tukey, "Transformations Related to the Angular and Square-Root," *Ann. Math. Stat.*, **21** (1950), 607–611.
16. Grubbs, F. E., "Sample Criteria for Testing Outlying Observations," *Ann. Math. Stat.*, **21** (1950), 27–58.
17. ——— and C. L. Weaver, "Best Unbiased Estimate of Population Standard Deviation Based on Group Ranges," *JASA*, **42** (1947), 224–241.

18. Hald, A., *Statistical Tables and Formulas*, John Wiley & Sons, New York, 1952.
19. Hartley, H. O., "Maximum F-Ratio as a Short Cut Test for Heterogeneity of Variance," *Biometrika*, **37** (1950), 308–312.
20. Holt, S. B., "The Genetics of Dermal Ridges," *Ann. Eugenics*, **17** (1952), 140–161.
21. Ladaski, M. and M. Szwarc, "Studies of the Variations in Bond Dissociation Energies of Aromatic Compounds," *Proc. Roy. Soc. (London)*, **A219** (1953), 341–352.
22. Link, R. F., *see* Tukey, J. W.
23. Lord, E., "The Use of Range in the Analysis of Variance," *Biometrika*, **34** (1947), 41–67.
24. Mandell, J., "Fitting a Straight Line to Certain Types of Cumulative Data," *JASA*, **52** (1957), 552–566.
25. Mann, H. B., and D. R. Whitney, "On a Test of Whether One of Two Random Variables is Stochastically Larger than the Other," *Ann. Math. Stat.*, **18** (1947), 50–60.
26. Milne, W E., *Numerical Calculus*, Princeton University Press, Princeton, N.J., 1949.
27. Nair, K. R. and M. P. Shrivastava, "On a Simple Method of Curve Fitting," *Sankhya*, **6** (1942–1943), 121–132.
28. Noether, G. E., "Use of the Range Instead of the Standard Deviation," *JASA*, **50** (1955), 1040–1055.
29. Snedecor, G., *Statistical Methods*, Iowa State College Press, Ames, Iowa, 1956.
30. Stone, H. and Eichelberger, "Titration of Dissolved Oxygen Using Acid-Chromous Reagent," *Anal. Chem.*, **23** (1951), 868–871.
31. Swed, F. S. and C. Eisenhart, "Tables for Testing Randomness of Grouping in a Sequence of Alternatives," *Ann. Math. Stat.*, **14** (1943), 66–87.
32. Trinder, P., "Titrimetric Determination of Sodium in Biological Fluids," *Analyst*, **78** (1953), 180–183.
33. Tukey, J. W., "Components in Regression," *Biometrics*, **7** (1951), 33–69.
34. ———, *Notes on Quick and Denormalized Methods of Analyzing Data.* Dittoed handout, 1950. Contains tables by R. F. Link, D. L. Wallace, et al.
35. ———, "Standard Methods of Analyzing Data," *Proceedings of the 1949 Computation Seminar*, IBM, New York, 1951.
36. Wald, A., "The Fitting of Straight Lines if Both Variables are Subject to Error," *Ann. Math. Stat.*, **11** (1940), 284–300.
37. ——— and J. Wolfowitz, "Tolerance Limits for a Normal Distribution," *Ann. Math. Stat.*, **17** (1946), 208–215.
38. Wallace, D. L., *see* Tukey, J. W.
39. Walsh, J. E., "On the Range-Midrange Test and Some Tests with Bounded Significance Levels," *Ann. Math. Stat.*, **20** (1949), 257–267.
40. Wilcoxon, F., *Some Rapid Approximate Statistical Procedures*, Insecticide and Fungicide Section, Stamford Research Laboratories, American Cyanamide Co.
41. Wilks, S. S., "Statistical Prediction with Special Reference to the Problem of Tolerance Limits, *Ann. Math. Stat.*, **13** (1942), 400–409.
42. Yates, F., *see* Fisher, R. A.

Additional Bibliography

The following articles, although not cited specifically in this book, discuss topics within its scope. Occasional comments have been added which may serve to guide the reader who is searching for further material.

Allen, R. G. D., "The Assumptions of Linear Regression," *Economica*, **6** N.S. (1939), 191–204.

The author points out the need for knowing two out of the three quantities λ_u, λ_v, r_{uv}—and suggests r and one of the λ's as preferable to the two λ's, in view of the limits on r that might otherwise be violated. Also suggested is r and the *ratio* of the λ's. He defines

$$\lambda_u = \frac{\sigma_u}{\sigma_x} \quad \text{and} \quad \lambda_v = \frac{\sigma_v}{\sigma_y}$$

to be *intensities* of the deviations of x and y, where

$$\begin{cases} x = \xi \text{ (true value)} + u \text{ (deviation)} \\ y = \eta \qquad\qquad\quad + v \end{cases}$$

He discusses the effect of several specific cases:

1. $\lambda_u = 0$ (x known without error).
2. $r_{uv} = 0$ (no correlations between the errors).
3. $r_{uv} = \pm 1$ (perfect correlations between the errors).
4. $\dfrac{r_{uv}\sigma_u\sigma_v}{\sigma_u - \sigma_v{}^2} = \dfrac{\sigma_{xy}\sigma_x\sigma_y}{\sigma_x{}^2 - \sigma_y{}^2}$ [error ellipse major axis coincides with (x, y) ellipse major axis].

These points are treated simply and competently with geometrical arguments.

Anscombe, F., "Sampling Theory of the Negative Binomial and Logarithmic Series Distribution," *Biometrika*, **37** (1950), 358–382.

A comprehensive review of the art.

Bartlett, M. S., "The Use of Transformations," *Biometrics*, **3** (1947), 39–52.

One of the better expository papers on this subject. He discusses:

1. Square root—if data are Poisson.
2. Logarithmic.
3. Inverse sine—for binomial data.
4. Others.

Bartlett, M. S., "The fitting of straight lines if both variables are subject to error," *Biometrics*, **5** (1948), 207–212.

Bross, I., "Fiducial Intervals for Variance Components," *Biometrics*, **6** (1950), 136–144.
Bross's suggestions have since been modified by Tukey, but this is the basic article on this subject.

Dixon, W. J. and F. J. Massey, Jr., *Introduction to Statistical Analysis*, McGraw-Hill, New York, 1951.

Dixon W. J. and A. M. Mood, "The Statistical Sign Test," *JASA*, **41** (1946), 557–566.
The definitive exposition of the sign test, with derivations and approximate tables of significance levels.

Durbin J. and G. S. Watson, "Testing for Serial Correlation in Least Squares Regression I," *Biometrika*, **37** (1950), 409–428.

Ehrenberg, A. S. C., "The Unbiased Estimation of Heterogeneous Error Variances," *Biometrika*, **37** (1950), 347–357.

Ferris, C. D., F. E. Grubb, and C. L. Weaver, "Operating Characteristics for the Common Statistical Test of Significance," *Ann. Math. Stat.*, **17** (1946), 178–197.
An important paper whose title is self-explanatory. Curves are given for

$$\chi^2 \quad \text{testing} \quad \sigma_1 = \sigma \quad \text{against} \quad \sigma_1 > \sigma$$
$$\chi^2 \quad \text{testing} \quad \sigma_1 = \sigma \quad \text{against} \quad \sigma_1 < \sigma$$
$$F_{n_1 n_2} \quad \text{testing} \quad \sigma_1 = \sigma \quad \text{against} \quad \sigma_1 > \sigma_2$$
$$\text{normal} \quad \text{testing} \quad \mu = a \quad \text{against} \quad \mu \neq a$$
$$t \quad \text{testing} \quad \mu = a \quad \text{against} \quad \mu \neq a$$

Haldane, J. B. S., "The Fitting of Binomial Distributions," *Ann. Eugenics*, **11** (1941), 179–187.
Maximum-likelihood fit is shown. Fisher also shows it to be better than fitting by moments. This paper is good for methodology.

Hartley, H. O., "The Estimation of Non-linear Parameters by 'Internal Least Squares'," *Biometrika*, **35** (1948), 32–45.
An important paper which suggests fitting the *linear* second-order *difference* equation which corresponds to the linear second-order differential equation which generates the *non-linear law* we want fitted to data. (The justification is that the physical laws are usually linear, and hence *they* should be fitted.) The techniques for exponential and other curves are illustrated, using cumulative sums of variables.

Housner, G. W. and J. F. Brennan, "The Estimation of Linear Trends," *Ann. Math. Stat.*, **19** (1948), 380–388.
An important paper—the bivariate error problem fitted without estimates of the error variances.

Hsu, C. T., "On Samples from a Normal Bivariate Population," *Ann. Math. Stat.*, **11** (1940), 410–426.

Jessop, W. N., "A Critical Review of Work Relating to One-Line Representations of the Relationship between Two Variables," U.S. Steel Co. Ltd. Statistical Section, Research and Development Department, *Stat. Sect. R.*001.1950, 18 pages typewritten.
A good review of the distinction between regression lines in a bivariate population and estimation of a functional relation between two variables. It includes references to Wald, Berkson, Lindley, Roos, Pearson, Bartlett, and others. He distinguishes Berkson's cases and emphasizes the presence or lack of consistency of various estimates.
No attempt is made to complicate the models.

Jows, H., "Linear Regression Functions with Neglected Variables," *JASA*, **41** (1946), 356–369.

Kendall, M. G., "Regression, Structure, and Functional Relationship, Part I," *Biometrika*, **38** (1951), 11–25.

A comprehensive discussion of the history of regression, from the strictly bivariate problems through to the functional-dependence-with-error type.   His interest is that of the mathematician, and he shows what situations may be treated (exactly) with what assumptions.   He tends to regret the unfortunate cases where these assumptions are not satisfied, without suggesting any real faith in approximate solutions.

He refers regularly to Lindley and to Kendall, and intends to write Part II on stochastic regression problems.

One important regression problem he brings up—both variates in error and a functional (linear) relation between the true variables: (*a*) estimation of the true relation $y = f(x)$, and (*b*) estimation of the predictor for the true y from the observed (erroneous) $x', y = f(x')$.   Typically he worries about the nuisance that if f in the first estimation is linear, the f in the second cannot be unless everything is normal.

Kummel, C. H., "Reduction of Observation Equations Which Contain More Than One Observed Quantity," *Analyst*, **6** (1879), 97–105.

A widely quoted but seldom read article which points out the need for estimates of precision of the measurements when fitting with both variates in error.

Lindley, D. V., "Regression Lines and Linear Functional Relationships," *Supp. J. Royal Stat. Soc.*, **9** (1947).

Moore, G. H. and W. A. Wallis, "Time Series Significance Tests Based on Signs of Differences," *JASA*, **38** (1943), 153–164.

Mosteller, F., "A *k*-Sample Slippage Test for an Extreme Population," *Ann. Math. Stat.*, **19** (1948), 58–65.

Tables are given for testing which of k samples is from the extreme population—all populations being of the same form.   The tables actually are the probabilities of getting one of k samples of size n, each having r or more observations larger than those of the other $k - 1$ samples.

Derivations are given and a discussion of the power.   The case of two samples ($k = 2$) is interesting, as the tables give the probabilities that r values of one will exceed the largest of the other (a trivial order statistic of the Wilksian school, but it shows the basis for all these tests).

Mosteller, F. and J. W. Tukey, "The Uses and Usefulness of Binomial Probability Paper," *JASA*, **44** (1949), 174–212.

A long article giving a quite thorough introduction to binomial probability paper, including many cases which at first sight seem unrelated, i.e., F tests, etc.

This paper will repay study.   Because the emphasis is on procedure, its weakness lies in the lack of explanation of *why* something is done at some crucial points.

Murphy, R. B., "Non-parametric Tolerance Limits," *Ann. Math. Stat.*, **19** (1948), 581–589.

Graphs are given for Wilk tolerance limits on populations with continuous c.d.f. $-a = 0.90, 0.95, 0.99$.

Examples are given for one- and two-variate problems.

Samples from m to 500 items in size are covered, where m is the number of items dropped from the extremes to set the limits.

Nair, K. R., "Table of Confidence Interval for the Median in Samples from Any Continuous Population," *Sankhya*, **4** (1940), 551–558.

The table is essentially a 0.95 and 0.99 extract from the cumulative binomial distribution, like that of Dixon and Mood in the sign test, but with four figure probabilities given as well.

Works of Thompson and Savur are discussed.

Nair, K. R., "Median Tests by Randomization," *Sankhya*, **4** (1940), 543–550.

Nair discusses Fisher's method of analyzing two samples by randomization—i.e., a test in which the probabilities are calculated for all possible samples which could be observed from the data at hand, should there be no difference between these samples, and then seeing what was obtained.

Nair, K. R. and K. S. Banerjee, "A Note on Fitting Straight Lines If Both Variables Are Subject to Errors," *Sankhya*, **6** (1942–1943), 331.

Points out that Nair and Shrivastava method works here too—and that Wald's is a generalization of it.

Olmstead, P. S. and J. W. Tukey, "A Corner Test for Association," *Ann. Math. Stat.*, **18** (1947), 495–513.

See also Dixon, W. J. and F. J. Massey.

The initial reference to this non-parametric test for association (essentially a nonparametric 2 × 2 table).

Pearson, K., "On Lines And Planes of Closest Fit to Systems of Points in Space," *Phil. Mag.* (6), **2** (1901), 559–572.

Pearson gives the major axis of the correlation ellipses as the line of best fit for both variates in error (where both variates are plotted in units of their standard deviations). He assumes standard deviations and correlations between all variables to be known—in *n* dimensions.

He thinks in terms of one *n* variate population, not as a series of *n* variate populations strung out along an $n - 1$ plane or along a one-dimensional line.

Roos, C. F., "A General Variant Criterion of Fit for Lines and Planes: When All Variates Are Subject to Error," *Metron*, **13** (1937).

Satterthwaite, F. E., "Synthesis of Variance," *Psychometrika*, **6** (1941), 309–316.

A study of the distribution of a linear combination of χ^2 variates—giving the approximation commonly used for the effective number of degrees of freedom.

Sukhatme, P. V., "On Fisher and Behren's Test of Significance for the Difference in Means of Two Normal Samples," *Sankhya*, **4** (1938), 39–48.

A discussion of the Fisher-Behren's test, giving 5 per cent points of *d* in terms of n, n', θ:

$$d = \frac{\bar{x}' - \bar{x}}{\sqrt{s^2 + s'^2}} = t' \cos \theta - t \sin \theta$$

$$\tan \theta = s/s'$$

$$\left. \begin{array}{l} n_1 = 6, 8, 12, 24, \infty \\ n_2 = 6, 8, 12, 24, \infty \\ \theta = 0°(15°)\,90° \end{array} \right\} \quad \text{four significant figures.}$$

Swaroop, S., *Tables of the Exact Values of Probabilities for Testing the Significance of Differences between Properties Based on Pairs of Small Samples.*

Tables to be applied to the 2 × 2 where one set of marginal totals are equal: i.e., with two samples of equal size, *n*, one treatment caused a score of m_1/n, the other sample experiment m_2/n. Probability of random occurrence of $m_1 m_2$ is given for $n = 5, 10,$

15, 20, 30, 50 in Table A—as well as cumulative tables (B) for the same n, i.e., occurrence of m_1 *or more extreme* values keeping marginal totals.   Table B is asserted to be that which χ^2 on the 2×2 approaches for large samples.

$$\text{Table A} = \frac{(n!)^2(m_1 + m_2)!(2n - m_1 - m_2)!}{(2n)!m_1!m_2!(n - m_1)!(n - m_2)!}$$

Thompson, C. M. and M. Merrington, "Tables for Testing the Homogeneity of a Set of Estimated Variances," *Biometrika*, **33** (1946), 296–304.   (Tables reprinted in E. S. Pearson and H. O. Hartley, *Biometrika Tables for Statisticians*, Vol. 1.)

A very complete article giving 1 per cent and 5 per cent tables with instructions for their use (which is simple if approximate results are desired—complicated if exact tests are needed).

The test is Bartlett's, modified.   The statistic is

$$M = N \ln \left\{ \frac{\sum\limits_i N_i s_i^2}{N} \right\} - \sum (\nu_i \ln s_i^2)$$

$$N = \sum \nu_i;$$

ν_i are the number of degrees of freedom in s_i^2.

Wald, A., "A Note on the Analysis of Variance with Unequal Class Frequencies," *Ann. Math. Stat.*, **11** (1940), 96–100.

Limits, exact, for the ratio $\dfrac{\sigma'^2}{\sigma^2} = \lambda^2$ are given, but they demand solution of a complicated algebraic equation.   Limits on the exact limits are then given which seem simple to compute.

$\lambda_1^2{}'$ and $\lambda_1^2{}''$ enclose the lower confidence limit, λ_1^2

where $\lambda_1^2{}' = \dfrac{1}{m'} \left(\dfrac{F_m{}'}{F_2} - 1 \right)$,

$\qquad \lambda_1^2{}'' = \dfrac{1}{m''} \left(\dfrac{F_m{}''}{F_2} - 1 \right)$.

$\lambda_2^2{}'$ and $\lambda_2^2{}''$ enclose the upper confidence limit, λ_2^2

where $\lambda_2^2{}' = \dfrac{1}{m'} \left(\dfrac{F_m{}'}{F_1} - 1 \right)$,

$\qquad \lambda_2^2{}'' = \dfrac{1}{m''} \left(\dfrac{F_m{}''}{F_1} - 1 \right)$,

$\left. \begin{matrix} m' \text{ is the smallest} \\ m'' \text{ is the largest} \end{matrix} \right\}$ of the m_1, the class frequencies,

and $F_m{}^* = \dfrac{m(N - p) \sum\limits_{j=1}^{p} (x._j - x..)^2}{(p - 1) \sum\limits_i \sum\limits_j (x_{ij} - x._j)^2}$

Walsh, J. E., "Applications of Some Significance Tests for the Median Which are Valid under Very General Conditions," *JASA*, **44** (1949), 342–355.

This paper gives a variety of tests useful to find confidence limits for the population median at various levels near the conventional ones.

Tests with bounded significance levels are included as a special group.

Walsh, J. E., "Some Significance Tests for the Median Which are Valid under Very General Conditions," *Ann. Math. Stat.*, **20** (1949), 64–81.

Essentially the same tests as in the *JASA* paper by the same author—but with a lengthier discussion of the mathematical derivation. Not as interesting to the applied man as the other paper.

Walsh, J. E., "Some Significance Tests Based on Order Statistics," *Ann. Math. Stat.*, **17** (1946), 44–52.

A collection designed primarily to test a single new statistic against an expression of the type

$$a_m \sum_1^m y_i - b_m y_{(u)}$$

where a_m, b_m are specified functions of m (the number in the sample against which tested) and $y_{(u)}$ is the u largest of y_i. This is generalized to allow x to be a *sum of r new* sample values, and the y_i can each be a sum of s *past* sample values plus another sum of *relatively weighted* past sample values (but *not* order statistics). These tests are less useful than the ones given in the other papers by the same author.

Wilcoxon, F., "Probability Tables for Individual Comparisons by Ranking Methods," *Biometrics*, **3** (1947), 119–122.

The author derives his ranking test, referring to Mann and Whitney's tables. He gives brief tables for n 5(1)20 $P = 0.01$

0.02

0.05

which seem to be based on a normal approximation—and are rounded off to the nearest (conservative?) integer so that the probability is *not* exactly the level indicated. The true probability is not given.

Wilcoxon, F., "Individual Comparisons by Ranking Methods," *Biometrics Bull.*, **1** (1945), 80–83.

A brief account of a test for equality of two samples by sums of rank order, giving a small table of critical values. Also the same data for a paired comparison test (similar technique). The first test was later treated more fully by Mann and Whitney.

Appendix

TABLE 1
Critical Values of t *

DF	\multicolumn{5}{c}{Two-Sided Risk}
	10%	5%	2.5%	1%	0.5%
1	6.31	12.7	25.5	63.7	127
2	2.92	4.30	6.21	9.92	14.1
3	2.35	3.18	4.18	5.84	7.45
4	2.13	2.78	3.50	4.60	5.60
5	2.01	2.57	3.16	4.03	4.77
6	1.94	2.45	2.97	3.71	4.32
7	1.89	2.36	2.84	3.50	4.03
8	1.86	2.31	2.75	3.36	3.83
9	1.83	2.26	2.69	3.25	3.69
10	1.81	2.23	2.63	3.17	3.58
11	1.80	2.20	2.59	3.11	3.50
12	1.78	2.18	2.56	3.05	3.43
13	1.77	2.16	2.53	3.01	3.37
14	1.76	2.14	2.51	2.98	3.33
15	1.75	2.13	2.49	2.95	3.29
16	1.75	2.12	2.47	2.92	3.25
17	1.74	2.11	2.46	2.90	3.22
18	1.73	2.10	2.45	2.88	3.20
19	1.73	2.09	2.43	2.86	3.17
20	1.72	2.09	2.42	2.85	3.15
21	1.72	2.08	2.41	2.83	3.14
22	1.72	2.07	2.41	2.82	3.12
23	1.71	2.07	2.40	2.81	3.10
24	1.71	2.06	2.39	2.80	3.09
25	1.71	2.06	2.38	2.79	3.08
26	1.71	2.06	2.38	2.78	3.07
27	1.70	2.05	2.37	2.77	3.06
28	1.70	2.05	2.37	2.76	3.05
29	1.70	2.05	2.36	2.76	3.04
30	1.70	2.04	2.36	2.75	3.03
40	1.68	2.02	2.33	2.70	2.97
60	1.67	2.00	2.30	2.66	2.91
120	1.66	1.98	2.27	2.62	2.86
∞	1.64	1.96	2.24	2.58	2.81
	5%	2·5%	1.25%	0·5%	0·25%
	\multicolumn{5}{c}{One-Sided Risk}

* By permission from *Introduction to Statistical Analysis*, by W. J. Dixon and F. J. Massey. Copyright, 1951. McGraw-Hill Book Company, Inc.

TABLE 2

Critical Values of χ^2*

DF	Percentiles									
	0.5	1	2.5	5	10	90	95	97.5	99	99.5
1	0.000039	0.00016	0.00098	0.0039	0.0158	2.71	3.84	5.02	6.63	7.88
2	0.0100	0.0201	0.0506	0.1026	0.2107	4.61	5.99	7.38	9.21	10.60
3	0.0717	0.115	0.216	0.352	0.584	6.25	7.81	9.35	11.34	12.84
4	0.207	0.297	0.484	0.711	1.064	7.78	9.49	11.14	13.28	14.86
5	0.412	0.554	0.831	1.15	1.61	9.24	11.07	12.83	15.09	16.75
6	0.676	0.872	1.24	1.64	2.20	10.64	12.59	14.45	16.81	18.55
7	0.989	1.24	1.69	2.17	2.83	12.02	14.07	16.01	18.48	20.28
8	1.34	1.65	2.18	2.73	3.49	13.36	15.51	17.53	20.09	21.96
9	1.73	2.09	2.70	3.33	4.17	14.68	16.92	19.02	21.67	23.59
10	2.16	2.56	3.25	3.94	4.87	15.99	18.31	20.48	23.21	25.19
11	2.60	3.05	3.82	4.57	5.58	17.28	19.68	21.92	24.73	26.76
12	3.07	3.57	4.40	5.23	6.30	18.55	21.03	23.34	26.22	28.30
13	3.57	4.11	5.01	5.89	7.04	19.81	22.36	24.74	27.69	29.82
14	4.07	4.66	5.63	6.57	7.79	21.06	23.68	26.12	29.14	31.32
15	4.60	5.23	6.26	7.26	8.55	22.31	25.00	27.49	30.58	32.80
16	5.14	5.81	6.91	7.96	9.31	23.54	26.30	28.85	32.00	34.27
18	6.26	7.01	8.23	9.39	10.86	25.99	28.87	31.53	34.81	37.16
20	7.43	8.26	9.59	10.85	12.44	28.41	31.41	34.17	37.57	40.00
24	9.89	10.86	12.40	13.85	15.66	33.20	36.42	39.36	42.98	45.56
30	13.79	14.95	16.79	18.49	20.60	40.26	43.77	46.98	50.89	53.67
40	20.71	22.16	24.43	26.51	29.05	51.81	55.76	59.34	63.69	66.77
60	35.53	37.48	40.48	43.19	46.46	74.40	79.08	83.30	88.38	91.95
120	83.85	86.92	91.58	95.70	100.62	140.23	146.57	152.21	158.95	163.64

For large values of degrees of freedom the approximate formula

$$\chi_\alpha^2 = \tfrac{1}{2}(z_\alpha + \sqrt{2n-1})^2,$$

where z_α is the normal deviate and n is the number of degrees of freedom, may be used. For example $\chi_{0.99}^2 = \tfrac{1}{2}(2.326 + 10.909)^2 = 87.6$ for the 99th percentile for 60 degrees of freedom.

* By permission from *Introduction to Statistical Analysis*, by W. J. Dixon and F. J. Massey. Copyright, 1951. McGraw-Hill Book Company, Inc.

Critical Values of the χ^2/DF Distribution *

DF	Percentiles									
	0.5	1	2.5	5	10	90	95	97.5	99	99.5
1	0.000039	0.00016	0.00098	0.0039	0.0158	2.71	3.84	5.02	6.63	7.88
2	0.00501	0.0101	0.0253	0.0513	0.1054	2.30	3.00	3.69	4.61	5.30
3	0.0239	0.0383	0.0719	0.117	0.195	2.08	2.60	3.12	3.78	4.28
4	0.0517	0.0743	0.121	0.178	0.266	1.94	2.37	2.79	3.32	3.72
5	0.0823	0.111	0.166	0.229	0.322	1.85	2.21	2.57	3.02	3.35
6	0.113	0.145	0.206	0.273	0.367	1.77	2.10	2.41	2.80	3.09
7	0.141	0.177	0.241	0.310	0.405	1.72	2.01	2.29	2.64	2.90
8	0.168	0.206	0.272	0.342	0.436	1.67	1.94	2.19	2.51	2.74
9	0.193	0.232	0.300	0.369	0.463	1.63	1.88	2.11	2.41	2.62
10	0.216	0.256	0.325	0.394	0.487	1.60	1.83	2.05	2.32	2.52
11	0.237	0.278	0.347	0.416	0.507	1.57	1.79	1.99	2.25	2.43
12	0.256	0.298	0 367	0.435	0.525	1.55	1.75	1.94	2.18	2.36
13	0.274	0.316	0.385	0.453	0.542	1.52	1.72	1.90	2.13	2.29
14	0.291	0.333	0.402	0.469	0.556	1.50	1.69	1.87	2.08	2.24
15	0.307	0.349	0.417	0.484	0.570	1.49	1.67	1.83	2.04	2.19
16	0.321	0.363	0.432	0.498	0.582	1.47	1.64	1.80	2.00	2.14
18	0.348	0.390	0.457	0.522	0.604	1.44	1.60	1.75	1.93	2.06
20	0.372	0.413	0.480	0.543	0.622	1.42	1.57	1.71	1.88	2.00
24	0.412	0.452	0.517	0.577	0.652	1.38	1.52	1.64	1.79	1.90
30	0.460	0.498	0.560	0.616	0.687	1.34	1.46	1.57	1.70	1.79
40	0.518	0.554	0.611	0.663	0.726	1.30	1.39	1.48	1.59	1.67
60	0.592	0.625	0.675	0.720	0.774	1.24	1.32	1.39	1.47	1.53
120	0.699	0.724	0.763	0.798	0.839	1.17	1.22	1.27	1.32	1.36
∞	1.00	1.00	1.00	1.00	1.000	1.00	1.00	1.00	1.00	1.00

The values in the above tables were computed from percentiles of the F distribution. Interpolation should be performed using reciprocals of the degrees of freedom.

* By permission from *Introduction to Statistical Analysis*, by W. J. Dixon and F. J. Massey. Copyright, 1951.   McGraw-Hill Book Company, Inc.

Critical Values of the F Distribution *
F Distribution, Upper 5 Per Cent Points ($F_{0.95}$)

Degrees of freedom for numerator

Degrees of freedom for denominator	1	2	3	4	5	6	7	8	9	10	12	15	20	24	30	40	60	120	∞
1	161.4	199.5	215.7	224.6	230.2	234.0	236.8	238.9	240.5	241.9	243.9	245.9	248.0	249.1	250.1	251.1	252.2	253.3	254.3
2	18.5	19.0	19.2	19.3	19.3	19.3	19.4	19.4	19.4	19.4	19.4	19.4	19.4	19.5	19.5	19.5	19.5	19.5	19.5
3	10.1	9.55	9.28	9.12	9.01	8.94	8.89	8.85	8.81	8.79	8.74	8.70	8.66	8.64	8.62	8.59	8.57	8.55	8.53
4	7.71	6.94	6.59	6.39	6.26	6.16	6.09	6.04	6.00	5.96	5.91	5.86	5.80	5.77	5.75	5.72	5.69	5.66	5.63
5	6.61	5.79	5.41	5.19	5.05	4.95	4.88	4.82	4.77	4.74	4.68	4.62	4.56	4.53	4.50	4.46	4.43	4.40	4.36
6	5.99	5.14	4.76	4.53	4.39	4.28	4.21	4.15	4.10	4.06	4.00	3.94	3.87	3.84	3.81	3.77	3.74	3.70	3.67
7	5.59	4.74	4.35	4.12	3.97	3.87	3.79	3.73	3.68	3.64	3.57	3.51	3.44	3.41	3.38	3.34	3.30	3.27	3.23
8	5.32	4.46	4.07	3.84	3.69	3.58	3.50	3.44	3.39	3.35	3.28	3.22	3.15	3.12	3.08	3.04	3.01	2.97	2.93
9	5.12	4.26	3.86	3.63	3.48	3.37	3.29	3.23	3.18	3.14	3.07	3.01	2.94	2.90	2.86	2.83	2.79	2.75	2.71
10	4.96	4.10	3.71	3.48	3.33	3.22	3.14	3.07	3.02	2.98	2.91	2.85	2.77	2.74	2.70	2.66	2.62	2.58	2.54
11	4.84	3.98	3.59	3.36	3.20	3.09	3.01	2.95	2.90	2.85	2.79	2.72	2.65	2.61	2.57	2.53	2.49	2.45	2.40
12	4.75	3.89	3.49	3.26	3.11	3.00	2.91	2.85	2.80	2.75	2.69	2.62	2.54	2.51	2.47	2.43	2.38	2.34	2.30
13	4.67	3.81	3.41	3.18	3.03	2.92	2.83	2.77	2.71	2.67	2.60	2.53	2.46	2.42	2.38	2.34	2.30	2.25	2.21
14	4.60	3.74	3.34	3.11	2.96	2.85	2.76	2.70	2.65	2.60	2.53	2.46	2.39	2.35	2.31	2.27	2.22	2.18	2.13
15	4.54	3.68	3.29	3.06	2.90	2.79	2.71	2.64	2.59	2.54	2.48	2.40	2.33	2.29	2.25	2.20	2.16	2.11	2.07
16	4.49	3.63	3.24	3.01	2.85	2.74	2.66	2.59	2.54	2.49	2.42	2.35	2.28	2.24	2.19	2.15	2.11	2.06	2.01
17	4.45	3.59	3.20	2.96	2.81	2.70	2.61	2.55	2.49	2.45	2.38	2.31	2.23	2.19	2.15	2.10	2.06	2.01	1.96
18	4.41	3.55	3.16	2.93	2.77	2.66	2.58	2.51	2.46	2.41	2.34	2.27	2.19	2.15	2.11	2.06	2.02	1.97	1.92
19	4.38	3.52	3.13	2.90	2.74	2.63	2.54	2.48	2.42	2.38	2.31	2.23	2.16	2.11	2.07	2.03	1.98	1.93	1.88
20	4.35	3.49	3.10	2.87	2.71	2.60	2.51	2.45	2.39	2.35	2.28	2.20	2.12	2.08	2.04	1.99	1.95	1.90	1.84
21	4.32	3.47	3.07	2.84	2.68	2.57	2.49	2.42	2.37	2.32	2.25	2.18	2.10	2.05	2.01	1.96	1.92	1.87	1.81
22	4.30	3.44	3.05	2.82	2.66	2.55	2.46	2.40	2.34	2.30	2.23	2.15	2.07	2.03	1.98	1.94	1.89	1.84	1.78
23	4.28	3.42	3.03	2.80	2.64	2.53	2.44	2.37	2.32	2.27	2.20	2.13	2.05	2.01	1.96	1.91	1.86	1.81	1.76
24	4.26	3.40	3.01	2.78	2.62	2.51	2.42	2.36	2.30	2.25	2.18	2.11	2.03	1.98	1.94	1.89	1.84	1.79	1.73
25	4.24	3.39	2.99	2.76	2.60	2.49	2.40	2.34	2.28	2.24	2.16	2.09	2.01	1.96	1.92	1.87	1.82	1.77	1.71
30	4.17	3.32	2.92	2.69	2.53	2.42	2.33	2.27	2.21	2.16	2.09	2.01	1.93	1.89	1.84	1.79	1.74	1.68	1.62
40	4.08	3.23	2.84	2.61	2.45	2.34	2.25	2.18	2.12	2.08	2.00	1.92	1.84	1.79	1.74	1.69	1.64	1.58	1.51
60	4.00	3.15	2.76	2.53	2.37	2.25	2.17	2.10	2.04	1.99	1.92	1.84	1.75	1.70	1.65	1.59	1.53	1.47	1.39
120	3.92	3.07	2.68	2.45	2.29	2.17	2.09	2.02	1.96	1.91	1.83	1.75	1.66	1.61	1.55	1.50	1.43	1.35	1.25
∞	3.84	3.00	2.60	2.37	2.21	2.10	2.01	1.94	1.88	1.83	1.75	1.67	1.57	1.52	1.46	1.39	1.32	1.22	1.00

Interpolation should be performed using reciprocals of the degrees of freedom.

* This table is abridged with permission of Professor E. S. Pearson from E. S. Pearson and H. O. Hartley, *Biometrika Tables for Statisticians*, Vol. 1. The original computations appear in C. M. Thompson and M. Merrington, "Tables of the Percentage Points of the Inverted Beta (*F*) Distribution," *Biometrika*, 33 (1943), 73.

F Distribution, Upper 2.5 Per Cent Points ($F_{0.975}$)

	Degrees of freedom for numerator																		
Degrees of freedom for denominator	1	2	3	4	5	6	7	8	9	10	12	15	20	24	30	40	60	120	∞
1	647.8	799.5	864.2	899.6	922	937	948	957	963	969	977	985	993	997	1,001	1,006	1,010	1,014	1,018
2	38.5	39.0	39.2	39.2	39.3	39.3	39.4	39.4	39.4	39.4	39.4	39.4	39.4	39.5	39.5	39.5	39.5	39.5	39.5
3	17.4	16.0	15.4	15.1	14.9	14.7	14.6	14.5	14.5	14.4	14.3	14.3	14.2	14.1	14.1	14.0	14.0	13.9	13.9
4	12.2	10.7	9.98	9.60	9.36	9.20	9.07	8.98	8.90	8.84	8.75	8.66	8.56	8.51	8.46	8.41	8.36	8.31	8.26
5	10.0	8.43	7.76	7.39	7.15	6.98	6.85	6.76	6.68	6.62	6.52	6.43	6.33	6.28	6.23	6.18	6.12	6.07	6.02
6	8.81	7.26	6.60	6.23	5.99	5.82	5.70	5.60	5.52	5.46	5.37	5.27	5.17	5.12	5.07	5.01	4.96	4.90	4.85
7	8.07	6.54	5.89	5.52	5.29	5.12	4.99	4.90	4.82	4.76	4.67	4.57	4.47	4.42	4.36	4.31	4.25	4.20	4.14
8	7.57	6.06	5.42	5.05	4.82	4.65	4.53	4.43	4.36	4.30	4.20	4.10	4.00	3.95	3.89	3.84	3.78	3.73	3.67
9	7.21	5.71	5.08	4.72	4.48	4.32	4.20	4.10	4.03	3.96	3.87	3.77	3.67	3.61	3.56	3.51	3.45	3.39	3.33
10	6.94	5.46	4.83	4.47	4.24	4.07	3.95	3.85	3.78	3.72	3.62	3.52	3.42	3.37	3.31	3.26	3.20	3.14	3.08
11	6.72	5.26	4.63	4.28	4.04	3.88	3.76	3.66	3.59	3.53	3.43	3.33	3.23	3.17	3.12	3.06	3.00	2.94	2.88
12	6.55	5.10	4.47	4.12	3.89	3.73	3.61	3.51	3.44	3.37	3.28	3.18	3.07	3.02	2.96	2.91	2.85	2.79	2.72
13	6.41	4.97	4.35	4.00	3.77	3.60	3.48	3.39	3.31	3.25	3.15	3.05	2.95	2.89	2.84	2.78	2.72	2.66	2.60
14	6.30	4.86	4.24	3.89	3.66	3.50	3.38	3.29	3.21	3.15	3.05	2.95	2.84	2.79	2.73	2.67	2.61	2.55	2.49
15	6.20	4.77	4.15	3.80	3.58	3.41	3.29	3.20	3.12	3.06	2.96	2.86	2.76	2.70	2.64	2.59	2.52	2.46	2.40
16	6.12	4.69	4.08	3.73	3.50	3.34	3.22	3.12	3.05	2.99	2.89	2.79	2.68	2.63	2.57	2.51	2.45	2.38	2.32
17	6.04	4.62	4.01	3.66	3.44	3.28	3.16	3.06	2.98	2.92	2.82	2.72	2.62	2.56	2.50	2.44	2.38	2.32	2.25
18	5.98	4.56	3.95	3.61	3.38	3.22	3.10	3.01	2.93	2.87	2.77	2.67	2.56	2.50	2.44	2.38	2.32	2.26	2.19
19	5.92	4.51	3.90	3.56	3.33	3.17	3.05	2.96	2.88	2.82	2.72	2.62	2.51	2.45	2.39	2.33	2.27	2.20	2.13
20	5.87	4.46	3.86	3.51	3.29	3.13	3.01	2.91	2.84	2.77	2.68	2.57	2.46	2.41	2.35	2.29	2.22	2.16	2.09
21	5.83	4.42	3.82	3.48	3.25	3.09	2.97	2.87	2.80	2.73	2.64	2.53	2.42	2.37	2.31	2.25	2.18	2.11	2.04
22	5.79	4.38	3.78	3.44	3.22	3.05	2.93	2.84	2.76	2.70	2.60	2.50	2.39	2.33	2.27	2.21	2.14	2.08	2.00
23	5.75	4.35	3.75	3.41	3.18	3.02	2.90	2.81	2.73	2.67	2.57	2.47	2.36	2.30	2.24	2.18	2.11	2.04	1.97
24	5.72	4.32	3.72	3.38	3.15	2.99	2.87	2.78	2.70	2.64	2.54	2.44	2.33	2.27	2.21	2.15	2.08	2.01	1.94
25	5.69	4.29	3.69	3.35	3.13	2.97	2.85	2.75	2.68	2.61	2.51	2.41	2.30	2.24	2.18	2.12	2.05	1.98	1.91
30	5.57	4.18	3.59	3.25	3.03	2.87	2.75	2.65	2.57	2.51	2.41	2.31	2.20	2.14	2.07	2.01	1.94	1.87	1.79
40	5.42	4.05	3.46	3.13	2.90	2.74	2.62	2.53	2.45	2.39	2.29	2.18	2.07	2.01	1.94	1.88	1.80	1.72	1.64
60	5.29	3.93	3.34	3.01	2.79	2.63	2.51	2.41	2.33	2.27	2.17	2.06	1.94	1.88	1.82	1.74	1.67	1.58	1.48
120	5.15	3.80	3.23	2.89	2.67	2.52	2.39	2.30	2.22	2.16	2.05	1.94	1.82	1.76	1.69	1.61	1.53	1.43	1.31
∞	5.02	3.69	3.12	2.79	2.57	2.41	2.29	2.19	2.11	2.05	1.94	1.83	1.71	1.64	1.57	1.48	1.39	1.27	1.00

Interpolation should be performed using reciprocals of the degrees of freedom.

F Distribution, Upper 1 Per Cent Points ($F_{0.99}$)

Degrees of freedom for denominator	Degrees of freedom for numerator																		
	1	2	3	4	5	6	7	8	9	10	12	15	20	24	30	40	60	120	∞
1	4,052	5,000	5,403	5,625	5,764	5,859	5,928	5,982	6,027	6,056	6,106	6,157	6,209	6,235	6,261	6,287	6,313	6,339	6,366
2	98.5	99.0	99.2	99.2	99.3	99.3	99.4	99.4	99.4	99.4	99.4	99.4	99.4	99.5	99.5	99.5	99.5	99.5	99.5
3	34.1	30.8	29.5	28.7	28.2	27.9	27.7	27.5	27.3	27.2	27.1	26.9	26.7	26.6	26.5	26.4	26.3	26.2	26.1
4	21.2	18.0	16.7	16.0	15.5	15.2	15.0	14.8	14.7	14.5	14.4	14.2	14.0	13.9	13.8	13.7	13.7	13.6	13.5
5	16.3	13.3	12.1	11.4	11.0	10.7	10.5	10.3	10.2	10.1	9.89	9.72	9.55	9.47	9.38	9.29	9.20	9.11	9.02
6	13.7	10.9	9.78	9.15	8.75	8.47	8.26	8.10	7.98	7.87	7.72	7.56	7.40	7.31	7.23	7.14	7.06	6.97	6.88
7	12.2	9.55	8.45	7.85	7.46	7.19	6.99	6.84	6.72	6.62	6.47	6.31	6.16	6.07	5.99	5.91	5.82	5.74	5.65
8	11.3	8.65	7.59	7.01	6.63	6.37	6.18	6.03	5.91	5.81	5.67	5.52	5.36	5.28	5.20	5.12	5.03	4.95	4.86
9	10.6	8.02	6.99	6.42	6.06	5.80	5.61	5.47	5.35	5.26	5.11	4.96	4.81	4.73	4.65	4.57	4.48	4.40	4.31
10	10.0	7.56	6.55	5.99	5.64	5.39	5.20	5.06	4.94	4.85	4.71	4.56	4.41	4.33	4.25	4.17	4.08	4.00	3.91
11	9.65	7.21	6.22	5.67	5.32	5.07	4.89	4.74	4.63	4.54	4.40	4.25	4.10	4.02	3.94	3.86	3.78	3.69	3.60
12	9.33	6.93	5.95	5.41	5.06	4.82	4.64	4.50	4.39	4.30	4.16	4.01	3.86	3.78	3.70	3.62	3.54	3.45	3.36
13	9.07	6.70	5.74	5.21	4.86	4.62	4.44	4.30	4.19	4.10	3.96	3.82	3.66	3.59	3.51	3.43	3.34	3.25	3.17
14	8.86	6.51	5.56	5.04	4.69	4.46	4.28	4.14	4.03	3.94	3.80	3.66	3.51	3.43	3.35	3.27	3.18	3.09	3.00
15	8.68	6.36	5.42	4.89	4.56	4.32	4.14	4.00	3.89	3.80	3.67	3.52	3.37	3.29	3.21	3.13	3.05	2.96	2.87
16	8.53	6.23	5.29	4.77	4.44	4.20	4.03	3.89	3.78	3.69	3.55	3.41	3.26	3.18	3.10	3.02	2.93	2.84	2.75
17	8.40	6.11	5.18	4.67	4.34	4.10	3.93	3.79	3.68	3.59	3.46	3.31	3.16	3.08	3.00	2.92	2.83	2.75	2.65
18	8.29	6.01	5.09	4.58	4.25	4.01	3.84	3.71	3.60	3.51	3.37	3.23	3.08	3.00	2.92	2.84	2.75	2.66	2.57
19	8.18	5.93	5.01	4.50	4.17	3.94	3.77	3.63	3.52	3.43	3.30	3.15	3.00	2.92	2.84	2.76	2.67	2.58	2.49
20	8.10	5.85	4.94	4.43	4.10	3.87	3.70	3.56	3.46	3.37	3.23	3.09	2.94	2.86	2.78	2.69	2.61	2.52	2.42
21	8.02	5.78	4.87	4.37	4.04	3.81	3.64	3.51	3.40	3.31	3.17	3.03	2.88	2.80	2.72	2.64	2.55	2.46	2.36
22	7.95	5.72	4.82	4.31	3.99	3.76	3.59	3.45	3.35	3.26	3.12	2.98	2.83	2.75	2.67	2.58	2.50	2.40	2.31
23	7.88	5.66	4.76	4.26	3.94	3.71	3.54	3.41	3.30	3.21	3.07	2.93	2.78	2.70	2.62	2.54	2.45	2.35	2.26
24	7.82	5.61	4.72	4.22	3.90	3.67	3.50	3.36	3.26	3.17	3.03	2.89	2.74	2.66	2.58	2.49	2.40	2.31	2.21
25	7.77	5.57	4.68	4.18	3.85	3.63	3.46	3.32	3.22	3.13	2.99	2.85	2.70	2.62	2.54	2.45	2.36	2.27	2.17
30	7.56	5.39	4.51	4.02	3.70	3.47	3.30	3.17	3.07	2.98	2.84	2.70	2.55	2.47	2.39	2.30	2.21	2.11	2.01
40	7.31	5.18	4.31	3.83	3.51	3.29	3.12	2.99	2.89	2.80	2.66	2.52	2.37	2.29	2.20	2.11	2.02	1.92	1.80
60	7.08	4.98	4.13	3.65	3.34	3.12	2.95	2.82	2.72	2.63	2.50	2.35	2.20	2.12	2.03	1.94	1.84	1.73	1.60
120	6.85	4.79	3.95	3.48	3.17	2.96	2.79	2.66	2.56	2.47	2.34	2.19	2.03	1.95	1.86	1.76	1.66	1.53	1.38
∞	6.63	4.61	3.78	3.32	3.02	2.80	2.64	2.51	2.41	2.32	2.18	2.04	1.88	1.79	1.70	1.59	1.47	1.32	1.00

Interpolation should be performed using reciprocals of the degrees of freedom.

Critical Values of the F Distribution, Upper 0.5 Per Cent Points ($F_{0.995}$)

						Degrees of freedom for numerator												
	1	2	3	4	5	6	7	8	9	10	12	15	20	24	30	40	60	∞
1	16,211	20,000	21,615	22,500	23,056	23,437	23,715	23,925	24,091	24,224	24,426	24,630	24,836	24,940	25,044	25,148	25,253	25,465
2	198	199	199	199	199	199	199	199	199	199	199	199	199	199	199	199	199	200
3	55.6	49.8	47.5	46.2	45.4	44.8	44.4	44.1	43.9	43.7	43.4	43.1	42.8	42.6	42.5	42.3	42.1	41.8
4	31.3	26.3	24.3	23.2	22.5	22.0	21.6	21.4	21.1	21.0	20.7	20.4	20.2	20.0	19.9	19.8	19.6	19.3
5	22.8	18.3	16.5	15.6	14.9	14.5	14.2	14.0	13.8	13.6	13.4	13.1	12.9	12.8	12.7	12.5	12.4	12.1
6	18.6	14.5	12.9	12.0	11.5	11.1	10.8	10.6	10.4	10.3	10.0	9.81	9.59	9.47	9.36	9.24	9.12	8.88
7	16.2	12.4	10.9	10.1	9.52	9.16	8.89	8.68	8.51	8.38	8.18	7.97	7.75	7.65	7.53	7.42	7.31	7.08
8	14.7	11.0	9.60	8.81	8.30	7.95	7.69	7.50	7.34	7.21	7.01	6.81	6.61	6.50	6.40	6.29	6.18	5.95
9	13.6	10.1	8.72	7.96	7.47	7.13	6.88	6.69	6.54	6.42	6.23	6.03	5.83	5.73	5.62	5.52	5.41	5.19
10	12.8	9.43	8.08	7.34	6.87	6.54	6.30	6.12	5.97	5.85	5.66	5.47	5.27	5.17	5.07	4.97	4.86	4.64
11	12.2	8.91	7.60	6.88	6.42	6.10	5.86	5.68	5.54	5.42	5.24	5.05	4.86	4.76	4.65	4.55	4.44	4.23
12	11.8	8.51	7.23	6.52	6.07	5.76	5.52	5.35	5.20	5.09	4.91	4.72	4.53	4.43	4.33	4.23	4.12	3.90
13	11.4	8.19	6.93	6.23	5.79	5.48	5.25	5.08	4.94	4.82	4.64	4.46	4.27	4.17	4.07	3.97	3.87	3.65
14	11.1	7.92	6.68	6.00	5.56	5.26	5.03	4.86	4.72	4.60	4.43	4.25	4.06	3.96	3.86	3.76	3.66	3.44
15	10.8	7.70	6.48	5.80	5.37	5.07	4.85	4.67	4.54	4.42	4.25	4.07	3.88	3.79	3.69	3.58	3.48	3.26
16	10.6	7.51	6.30	5.64	5.21	4.91	4.69	4.52	4.38	4.27	4.10	3.92	3.73	3.64	3.54	3.44	3.33	3.11
17	10.4	7.35	6.16	5.50	5.07	4.78	4.56	4.39	4.25	4.14	3.97	3.79	3.61	3.51	3.41	3.31	3.21	2.98
18	10.2	7.21	6.03	5.37	4.96	4.66	4.44	4.28	4.14	4.03	3.86	3.68	3.50	3.40	3.30	3.20	3.10	2.87
19	10.1	7.09	5.92	5.27	4.85	4.56	4.34	4.18	4.04	3.93	3.76	3.59	3.40	3.31	3.21	3.11	3.00	2.78
20	9.94	6.99	5.82	5.17	4.76	4.47	4.26	4.09	3.96	3.85	3.68	3.50	3.32	3.22	3.12	3.02	2.92	2.69
21	9.83	6.89	5.73	5.09	4.68	4.39	4.18	4.01	3.88	3.77	3.60	3.43	3.24	3.15	3.05	2.95	2.84	2.61
22	9.73	6.81	5.65	5.02	4.61	4.32	4.11	3.94	3.81	3.70	3.54	3.36	3.18	3.08	2.98	2.88	2.77	2.55
23	9.63	6.73	5.58	4.95	4.54	4.26	4.05	3.88	3.75	3.64	3.47	3.30	3.12	3.02	2.92	2.82	2.71	2.48
24	9.55	6.66	5.52	4.89	4.49	4.20	3.99	3.83	3.69	3.59	3.42	3.25	3.06	2.97	2.87	2.77	2.66	2.43
25	9.48	6.60	5.46	4.84	4.43	4.15	3.94	3.78	3.64	3.54	3.37	3.20	3.01	2.92	2.82	2.72	2.61	2.38
30	9.18	6.35	5.24	4.62	4.23	3.95	3.74	3.58	3.45	3.34	3.18	3.01	2.82	2.73	2.63	2.52	2.42	2.18
40	8.83	6.07	4.98	4.37	3.99	3.71	3.51	3.35	3.22	3.12	2.95	2.78	2.60	2.50	2.40	2.30	2.18	1.93
60	8.49	5.79	4.73	4.14	3.76	3.49	3.29	3.13	3.01	2.90	2.74	2.57	2.39	2.29	2.19	2.08	1.96	1.69
120	8.18	5.54	4.50	3.92	3.55	3.28	3.09	2.93	2.81	2.71	2.54	2.37	2.19	2.09	1.98	1.87	1.75	1.43
∞	7.88	5.30	4.28	3.72	3.35	3.09	2.90	2.74	2.62	2.52	2.36	2.19	2.00	1.90	1.79	1.67	1.53	1.00

Degrees of freedom for denominator

Interpolation should be performed using reciprocals of the degrees of freedom.

TABLE 4

Critical Values of τ_ϵ for Testing the Deviations of the Means of Small Samples *

$$\tau_\epsilon = \frac{u_\epsilon(1, n)}{d_n\sqrt{n}} \leqslant \frac{|x. - M|}{W(1, n)}$$

Number in the Sample n	Two-Sided Risk			
	10%	5%	2%	1%
2	3.196	6.353	15.910	31.828
3	0.885⁻	1.304	2.111	3.008
4	0.529	0.717	1.023	1.316
5	0.388	0.507	0.685⁺	0.843
6	0.312	0.399	0.523	0.628
7	0.263	0.333	0.429	0.507
8	0.230	0.288	0.366	0.429
9	0.205⁻	0.255⁺	0.322	0.374
10	0.186	0.230	0.288	0.333
11	0.170	0.210	0.262	0.302
12	0.158	0.194	0.241	0.277
13	0.147	0.181	0.224	0.256
14	0.138	0.170	0.209	0.239
15	0.131	0.160	0.197	0.224
	5%	2.5%	1%	0.5%
		One-Sided Risk		

For samples of size greater than about 12 the range $W(1, n)$ becomes inefficient and it is advisable to estimate dispersion by the sum of the ranges of m subsamples, using Table 5 to find the factor for confidence limits.

* This test is discussed in Chapter 2, page 60. The table is reproduced by permission of Professor E. S. Pearson from E. Lord, "Range in Place of the Standard Deviation in the *t*-Test," *Biometrika*, **34** (1947), 41–67, from which it was abridged.

TABLE 5

Critical Values of $T_\epsilon(N)$ for Testing the Deviations of Means of Larger Samples *

$$T_\epsilon(N) = \frac{u_\epsilon(m, n)}{md_n\sqrt{mn}} \leqslant \frac{|x. - M|}{W(m, n)}$$

N	m	n	10%	5%	2%	1%
				Two-Sided Risk		
12–13	2	6	0.101	0.125	0.155	0.178
14–15	2	7	0.087	0.106	0.131	0.150
16–17	2	8	0.076	0.094	0.115	0.130
18–19	2	9	0.0685	0.0835	0.102	0.116
20	2	10	0.0624	0.0760	0.0926	0.105
21–23	3	7	0.0462	0.0562	0.0683	0.0772
24–26	3	8	0.0409	0.0495	0.0600	0.0677
27	3	9	0.0367	0.0444	0.0537	0.0604
28–29	4	7	0.0297	0.0358	0.0433	0.0487
30–31	3	10	0.0336	0.0405	0.0488	0.0549
32–34	4	8	0.0262	0.0317	0.0381	0.0428
35	5	7	0.0211	0.0253	0.0306	0.0343
36–39	4	9	0.0237	0.0284	0.0343	0.0384
40–41	5	8	0.0187	0.0224	0.0272	0.0302
42–44	6	7	0.0160	0.0192	0.0231	0.0259
45–47	5	9	0.0169	0.0203	0.0243	0.0272
48	6	8	0.0142	0.0170	0.0205	0.0228
49	7	7	0.0126	0.0152	0.0183	0.0203
50–53	5	10	0.0154	0.0184	0.0221	0.0247

$|x. - M| \geqslant W(m, n) \cdot T_\epsilon(N)$

Split the sample randomly into m subsamples, each of size n. $W(m, n)$ is the sum of the ranges of each subsample.

$$\left[T_\epsilon(N) = \frac{u(m, n)}{m\sqrt{m}\sqrt{n}d_n} \right]$$

$$= \frac{u(m, n)}{md_n\sqrt{N}}$$

m	$m\sqrt{m}$
2	2.828
3	5.196
4	8.000
5	11.18

m, n	$\sqrt{n}d_n$	$m\sqrt{m}$
6	6.21	14.70
7	7.155	18.5
8	8.05	22.7
9	8.91	27.0
10	9.73	31.6

* Discussion of this test is found in Chapter 2, page 61.

TABLE 6

Critical Values of the Factor for Testing the Significant Difference between the Means of Two Small Samples of Equal Size p*

$$r_{\epsilon}(p) = \frac{u_{\epsilon}(2, p)}{d_p \sqrt{2p}} \leqslant \frac{|x_1. - x_2.|}{(w_1 + w_2)}$$

Number in the Sample p	Two-Sided Risk			
	10%	5%	2%	1%
2	1.161	1.715	2.776	3.958
3	0.487	0.636	0.858	1.047
4	0.322	0.407	0.523	0.618
5	0.246	0.306	0.386	0.448
6	0.203	0.249	0.311	0.357
7	0.174	0.213	0.263	0.300
8	0.153	0.187	0.229	0.261
9	0.137	0.167	0.205	0.232
10	0.125	0.152	0.186	0.209
12	0.107	0.130	0.157	0.178
14	0.094	0.114	0.138	0.155
16	0.085	0.102	0.124	0.139
	5%	2.5%	1%	0.5%
			One-Sided Risk	

* This test is discussed in Chapter 2, page 62.

APPENDIX

TABLE 7

Critical Values of $R_\epsilon(p)$ for Testing the Significant Difference between the Means of Two Larger Samples of Equal Size p*

$$R_\epsilon(p) = \frac{u(2m, n)}{md_n\sqrt{2mn}} \leqslant \frac{|x_1. - x_2.|}{W(2m, n)}$$

Size of Each Sample			Two-Sided Risk			
p	m	n	10%	5%	2%	1%
12–13	2	6	0.0688	0.0823	0.1010	0.1139
14–15	2	7	0.0593	0.0716	0.0866	0.0974
16–17	2	8	0.0525	0.0633	0.0763	0.0857
18–19	2	9	0.0474	0.0570	0.0688	0.0769
20	2	10	0.0432	0.0518	0.0627	0.0699
21–23	3	7	0.0319	0.0384	0.0462	0.0518
24–26	3	8	0.0284	0.0340	0.0408	0.0457
27	3	9	0.0255	0.0307	0.0368	0.0408
28–29	4	7	0.0206	0.0248	0.0297	0.0331
30–31	3	10	0.0233	0.0280	0.0336	0.0373
32–34	4	8	0.0183	0.0219	0.0262	0.0293
35	5	7	0.0148	0.0177	0.0211	0.0235
36–39	4	9	0.0166	0.0198	0.0237	0.0264
40–41	5	8	0.0130	0.0156	0.0187	0.0208
42–44	6	7	0.0112	0.0134	0.0160	0.0178
45–47	5	9	0.0118	0.0141	0.0168	0.0187
48	6	8	0.0099	0.0119	0.0142	0.0158
49	7	7	0.0089	0.0106	0.0127	0.0140
50–53	5	10	0.0108	0.0129	0.0154	0.0171
			5%	2.5%	1%	0.5%
				One-Sided Risk		

* Discussion of this test is found in Chapter 2, page 62.

TABLE 8

Factor from the Range to the Adjustment for Extreme Values *

Number in the Sample		Two-Sided Risk			
		10%	5%	2%	1%
2		2.66	5.85	15.41	31.33
3		0.40	0.80	1.61	2.52
4	Outside	0.06	0.24	0.54	0.87
5	Inside	0.08	0.02	0.21	0.35
6		0.15	0.07	0.06	0.16
7		0.20	0.12	0.02	0.05
8		0.24	0.17	0.08	0.02
9		0.26	0.20	0.12	0.07
10		0.28	0.22	0.15	0.11
		5%	2.5%	1%	0.5%
			One-Sided Risk		

The adjusted extreme value limits are for a typical value.

* See Chapter 2, page 63. This table was distributed by J. W. Tukey in a dittoed paper, *Notes on Quick and Denormalized Methods of Analyzing Data*, and is reprinted here with his permission.

TABLE 9

Ratio of the Separation of the Crossovermost Values to the Sum of Ranges *

$$k_\epsilon(p) = \frac{y_{21} - y_{1p}}{w_1 + w_2}$$

Number per Group, p	Two-Sided Risk, ϵ			
	10%	5%	2%	1%
2	0.66	1.21	2.28	3.46
3	0.00	0.16	0.39	0.58
4	−0.17	−0.08	0.05	0.16
5	−0.26	−0.19	−0.10	−0.03

Negative signs indicate that the samples overlap, thereby creating a negative separation. Table by R. F. Link.

* This statistic is discussed on page 65 of Chapter 2. The table was distributed by J. W. Tukey in a dittoed paper, *Notes on Quick and Denormalized Methods of Analyzing Data*, and is reprinted here with his permission.

TABLE 10

Critical Tallies for the Sign Test *

Number of Cases	Two-Sided Risk			
	10%	5%	2%	1%
5	0.3			
6	0.6	0.2		
7	0.9	0.5	0.1	
8	1.2	0.8	0.4	0.1
9	1.6	1.2	0.7	0.4
10	1.9	1.5	1.0	0.6
11	2.3	1.8	1.3	0.9
12	2.7	2.2	1.6	1.2
13	3.1	2.5	1.9	1.6
14	3.5	2.9	2.3	1.9
15	3.8	3.2	2.6	2.2
16	4.2	3.6	3.0	2.5
17	4.6	3.9	3.3	2.9
18	5.0	4.3	3.7	3.2
19	5.4	4.7	4.0	3.6
20	5.8	5.1	4.4	3.9
21	6.3	5.5	4.8	4.3
22	6.7	5.8	5.1	4.6
23	7.1	6.4	5.5	5.0
24	7.5	6.7	5.9	5.4
25	7.9	7.1	6.3	5.7
26	8.3	7.5	6.7	6.0
27	8.7	7.9	7.0	6.3
28	9.1	8.3	7.4	6.7
29	9.6	8.7	7.8	7.1
30	10.0	9.2	8.2	7.5
31	10.4	9.6	8.6	7.9
32	10.8	10.0	9.0	8.3
33	11.3	10.4	9.4	8.7
34	11.7	10.8	9.8	9.1
35	12.1	11.2	10.2	9.5
36	12.6	11.6	10.6	9.9
37	13.0	12.1	11.0	10.3
38	13.4	12.5	11.4	10.7
39	13.8	12.9	11.8	11.1
40	14.3	13.4	12.2	11.5
41	14.7	13.8	12.6	11.9
42	15.1	14.2	13.0	12.3
43	15.6	14.7	13.4	12.7
44	16.0	15.1	13.8	13.1
45	16.5	15.5	14.2	13.5
46	16.9	15.9	14.6	13.9
47	17.3	16.4	15.0	14.3
48	17.8	16.8	15.4	14.7
49	18.2	17.2	15.8	15.1
50	18.7	17.6	16.3	15.5

Extreme values tally "zero," next to extreme "one," and so on.

* This statistic is discussed in Chapter 2, page 67. The table was distributed by J. W. Tukey in a dittoed paper, *Notes on Quick and Denormalized Methods of Analyzing Data*, and is reprinted here with his permission.

TABLE 11

Critical Tallies for Wilcoxon's Method for Setting Confidence Limits on the Mean of a Sample *

Number of Values	Two-Sided Percentages			
	10%	5%	2%	1%
5	0.6	—	—	—
6	2.1	0.6	—	—
7	3.7	2.1	0.3	—
8	5.8	3.7	1.6	0.3
9	8.1	5.7	3.1	1.6
10	10.8	8.1	5.1	3.1
11	13.9	10.8	7.3	5.1
12	17.5	13.8	9.8	7.2
13	21.4	17.2	12.7	9.8
14	25.7	21.1	15.9	12.7
15	30.4	25.3	19.6	15.9
16	35.6	29.9	23.6	19.5
17	41.2	34.9	28.0	23.4
18	47.2	40.3	32.7	27.7
19	53.6	46.1	37.8	32.4
20	60.4	52.3	43.4	37.5
21	67.5	58.9	49.3	42.9
22	75.3	66.0	55.6	48.7
23	83.9	73.4	62.3	54.9
24	91.9	81.3	69.4	61.5
25	100.9	89.5	76.9	68.5
	5%	2.5%	1%	0.5%
		One-Sided Percentages		

Means of each pair of observations formed graphically. Extreme means tally "zero," next to extreme means tally "one," and so on.

* This test is discussed in Chapter 2, page 69. The table was distributed by J. W. Tukey in a dittoed paper, *Notes on Quick and Denormalized Methods of Analyzing Data*, and is reprinted here with his permission.

TABLE 12

Critical Tallies for the Kendall-Slope Count for Setting Confidence Limits
on the Slope of a Fitted Line *

Number of Cases	Two-Sided Risk			
	10%	5%	2%	1%
4	0.1	–	–	–
5	1.1	0.5	0.1	–
6	2.6	1.9	1.1	0.5
7	4.5	3.5	2.5	1.9
8	6.8	5.6	4.3	3.5
9	9.6	8.2	6.6	5.6
10	12.8	11.1	9.3	8.1
11	16.4	14.5	12.4	11.0
12	20.5	18.3	15.9	14.2
13	25.0	22.5	19.8	18.0
14	30.0	27.2	24.1	22.1
15	35.3	32.3	28.8	26.6
16	41.2	37.8	34.0	31.5
17	47.5	43.8	39.6	36.9
18	54.2	50.2	45.7	42.6
19	61.5	57.1	52.1	48.8
20	69.1	64.4	59.1	55.5
	5%	2.5%	1%	0.5%
	One-Sided Risk			

Every segment joining two points is laid off to the right of a common origin by a tracing-through technique. Those of extreme slope are tallied "zero," those of next-to-extreme slope are tallied "one," and so on.

* This test is discussed in Chapter 2, page 70. The table was distributed by J. W. Tukey in a dittoed paper, *Notes on Quick and Denormalized Methods of Analyzing Data*, and is reprinted here with his permission.

TABLE 13

Critical Tallies for the Kendall-*p* Count for Setting Confidence Limits on the Differences between Two Sample Means *

	Two-Sided $\frac{5\%}{1\%}$ Risk					
	Number in One Group					
Number in Other Group	3	4	5	6	7	8
4		0.8	1.6	2.4	3.3	4.1
		—	—	0.0	0.7	1.3
5	0.4	1.6	2.8	3.9	5.1	6.3
	—	—	0.3	1.2	2.0	2.8
6	1.0	2.4	3.9	5.4	6.9	8.5
	—	0.0	1.2	2.2	3.3	4.5
7	1.5	3.3	5.1	6.9	8.8	10.7
	—	0.7	2.0	3.3	4.8	6.2
8	2.0	4.1	6.3	8.5	10.7	13.0
	—	1.3	2.8	4.5	6.2	7.9
9	2.5	5.0	7.5	10.0	12.6	15.3
	0.1	1.8	3.6	5.6	7.6	9.7
10	3.0	5.8	8.7	11.6	14.6	17.6
	0.5	2.4	4.5	6.7	9.1	11.5
11	3.6	6.7	9.9	13.2	16.5	19.9
	0.8	2.9	5.3	7.9	10.6	13.3
12	4.1	7.5	11.1	14.8	18.5	22.3
	1.1	3.4	6.2	9.1	12.1	15.2
13	4.6	8.4	12.3	16.3	20.4	
	1.4	4.0	7.0	10.3	13.6	
14	5.4	9.2	13.5	17.9		
	1.7	4.6	7.9	11.4		
15	5.6	10.1	14.8			
	2.0	5.2	8.8			
16	6.2	11.0				
	2.3	5.7				
17	6.7					
	2.6					

Form all differences $A - B$ by tracing through. Tally extreme differences "zero," next-to-extreme "one," and so on.

* This test is discussed in Chapter 2, page 72. The table was distributed by J. W. Tukey in a dittoed paper, *Notes on Quick and Denormalized Methods of Analyzing Data*, and is reprinted here with his permission.

TABLE 14

Critical Values of $u(m, n)$ and d_n *

10 Per Cent Points of $u = u(m, n)$

n \ m	1	2	3	4	5	6	8	10	15	20	30	60
2	5.04	2.62	2.20	2.03	1.94	1.89	1.82	1.78	1.73	1.71	1.69	1.67(1)
3	2.59	2.02	1.88	1.81	1.77	1.75+	1.72	1.71	1.69	1.67	1.66	1.66(1)
4	2.18	1.88	1.79	1.75+	1.73	1.72	1.70	1.69	1.67	1.67	1.66	1.65+
5	2.02	1.81	1.75+	1.73	1.71	1.70	1.68	1.68	1.67	1.66	1.66	1.65
6	1.94	1.78	1.73	1.71	1.70	1.69	1.68	1.67	1.66	1.66	1.65+	1.65−
7	1.88	1.76	1.72	1.70	1 69	1.68	1.67	1.67	1.66	1.66	1.65+	1.65−
8	1.85	1.74	1.71	1.69	1.68	1.68	1.67	1.66	1.66	1.65+	1.65+	1.65−
9	1.82	1.73	1.70	1.69	1.68	1.67	1.67	1.66	1.66	1.65+	1.65	1.65−
10	1.81	1.72	1.70	1.68	1.68	1.67	1.66	1.66	1.65+	1.65+	1.65	1.65−
12	1.78	1.71	1.69	1.68	1.67	1.67	1.66	1.66	1.65+	1.65+	1.65−	1.65−
14	1.76	1.70	1.68	1.67	1.67	1.66	1.66	1.66	1.65+	1.65	1.65−	1.65−
16	1 75	1.70	1.68	1.67	1.67	1.66	1.66	1.65+	1.65+	1 65	1.65−	1.65−
18	1˙74	1.69	1.68	1.67	1.66	1.66	1.66	1.65+	1.65+	1.65−	1.65−	1.65−
20	1.73	1.69	1.67	1.67	1.66	1.66	1.66	1.65+	1.65	1.65−	1.65−	1.65−

5 Per Cent Points of $u = u(m, n)$

n \ m	1	2	3	4	5	6	8	10	15	20	30	60
2	10.14	3.87	2.98	2.66	2.49	2.38	2.26	2.20	2.11	2.07	2.03	2.00(2)
3	3.82	2.64	2.37	2.25	2.19	2.14	2.09	2.07	2.03	2.01	1.99	1.98(1)
4	2.95+	2.37	2.22	2.15−	2.11	2.08	2.05	2.03	2.01	2.00	1.98	1.97
5	2.63	2.25+	2.15−	2.10	2.07	2.05	2.03	2.01	2.00	1.99	1.98	1.97(1)
6	2.48	2.19	2.11	2.07	2.05−	2.03	2.01	2.00	1.99	1.98	1.97	1.97(1)
7	2.38	2.15+	2.09	2.05+	2.03	2.02	2.01	2.00	1.98	1.98	1.97	1.97(1)
8	2.32	2.13	2.07	2.04	2.02	2.01	2.00	1.99	1.98	1.98	1.97	1.97(1)
9	2.27	2.11	2.06	2.03	2.02	2.01	2.00	1.99	1.98	1.97	1.97	1.96
10	2.24	2.09	2.05−	2.02	2.01	2.00	1.99	1.98	1.98	1.97	1.97	1.96
12	2.19	2.07	2.03	2.01	2.00	2.00	1.99	1.98	1.97	1.97	1.97	1.96
14	2.16	2.06	2.02	2.01	2.00	1.99	1.98	1.98	1.97	1.97	1.97	1.96
16	2.14	2.05−	2.02	2.00	1.99	1.99	1.98	1.98	1.97	1.97	1.97	1.96
18	2.12	2.04	2.01	2.00	1.99	1.99	1.98	1.98	1.97	1.97	1.97	1.96
20	2.11	2.03	2.01	2.00	1.99	1.98	1.98	1.97	1.97	1.97	1.96	1.96

The numbers in brackets in the column headed $m = 60$ indicate the number of units that must be subtracted in the second decimal place to obtain the level for $m = 120$ and the same value of n. Where no figure is given $u(120, n) = u(60, n)$ to second decimal place accuracy. For example, for the 5 per cent level, $u(120,2) = 1.98$.

* This statistic is discussed in Chapter 2, page 60. The table is reproduced by permission of Professor E. S. Pearson from E. Lord, "Range in Place of the Standard Deviation in the t-Test," *Biometrika*, **34** (1947), 63–67.

2 Per Cent Points of $u = u(m, n)$

n \ m	1	2	3	4	5	6	8	10	15	20	30	60
2	25.39	6.27	4.27	3.60	3.27	3.08	2.86	2.73	2.59	2.52	2.45+	2.39(3)
3	6.19	3.56	3.05−	2.84	2.72	2.65−	2.56	2.51	2.45−	2.42	2.39	2.36(2)
4	4.21	3.05−	2.77	2.65−	2.58	2.53	2.48	2.45−	2.41	2.39	2.37	2.35−(1)
5	3.56	2.84	2.65−	2.56	2.51	2.48	2.44	2.42	2.39	2.37	2.36	2.34(1)
6	3.25−	2.73	2.58	2.51	2.47	2.45−	2.42	2.40	2.37	2.36	2.35+	2.34(1)
7	3.07	2.66	2.54	2.48	2.45+	2.43	2.40	2.39	2.37	2.36	2.35−	2.34(1)
8	2.95+	2.61	2.51	2.46	2.43	2.42	2.39	2.38	2.36	2.35+	2.34	2.34(1)
9	2.87	2.58	2.49	2.45−	2.42	2.41	2.39	2.37	2.36	2.35+	2.34	2.33
10	2.81	2.55+	2.47	2.44	2.41	2.40	2.38	2.37	2.35+	2.35−	2.34	2.33
12	2.72	2.51	2.45−	2.42	2.40	2.39	2.37	2.36	2.35+	2.34	2.34	2.33
14	2.67	2.49	2.43	2.41	2.39	2.38	2.37	2.36	2.35−	2.34	2.34	2.33
16	2.63	2.47	2.42	2.40	2.38	2.37	2.36	2.35+	2.35−	2.34	2.34	2.33
18	2.60	2.46	2.41	2.39	2.38	2.37	2.36	2.35+	2.34	2.34	2.33	2.33
20	2.58	2.45−	2.41	2.39	2.37	2.37	2.36	2.35−	2.34	2.34	2.33	2.33

1 Per Cent Points of $u = u(m, n)$

n \ m	1	2	3	4	5	6	8	10	15	20	30	60
2	50.79	8.93	5.49	4.43	3.93	3.64	3.32	3.14	2.93	2.84	2.75−	2.66(4)
3	8.82	4.34	3.60	3.30	3.14	3.03	2.91	2.84	2.75−	2.70	2.66	2.62(2)
4	5.42	3.60	3.20	3.02	2.92	2.86	2.79	2.74	2.68	2.66	2.63	2.60(1)
5	4.38	3.29	3.02	2.90	2.83	2.79	2.73	2.70	2.66	2.64	2.62	2.60(1)
6	3.90	3.13	2.93	2.83	2.78	2.74	2.70	2.67	2.64	2.62	2.61	2.59(1)
7	3.63	3.03	2.87	2.79	2.75−	2.72	2.68	2.66	2.63	2.62	2.60	2.59(1)
8	2.45+	2.97	2.83	2.76	2.72	2.70	2.67	2.65−	2.62	2.61	2.60	2.59(1)
9	3.33	2.92	2.80	2.74	2.71	2.68	2.66	2.64	2.62	2.61	2.60	2.59(1)
10	3.24	2.88	2.78	2.72	2.69	2.67	2.65−	2.63	2.61	2.60	2.59	2.59(1)
12	3.12	2.83	2.74	2.70	2.68	2.66	2.64	2.62	2.61	2.60	2.59	2.58
14	3.05−	2.80	2.72	2.69	2.66	2.65−	2.63	2.62	2.60	2.60	2.59	2.58
16	2.99	2.78	2.71	2.67	2.65+	2.64	2.62	2.61	2.60	2.60	2.59	2.58
18	2.95−	2.76	2.70	2.66	2.65−	2.63	2.62	2.61	2.60	2.59	2.59	2.58
20	2.92	2.74	2.69	2.66	2.64	2.63	2.62	2.61	2.60	2.59	2.59	2.58

The numbers in brackets in the column headed $m = 60$ indicate the number of units that must be subtracted in the second decimal place to obtain the level for $m = 120$ and the same value of n. Where no figure is given $u(120, n) = u(60, n)$ to second decimal place accuracy. For example, for the 2 per cent level $u(120, 5) = 2.33$.

Functions of the Expected Value of the Range in a Sample of Size n from a $N(0;1)$ Population

n	d_n	$1/d_n$	$\sqrt{n}$	$d_n\sqrt{n}$
2	1.1284	0.8862	1.4142	1.5958
3	1.6926	0.5908	1.7321	2.9316
4	2.0588	0.4857	2.0000	4.1175
5	2.3259	0.4299	2.2361	5.2009
6	2.5344	0.3946	2.4495	6.2080
7	2.7044	0.3698	2.6458	7.1551
8	2.8472	0.3512	2.8284	8.0531
9	2.9700	0.3367	3.0000	8.9101
10	3.0775	0.3249	3.1623	9.7319
11	3.1729	0.3152	3.3166	10.5232
12	3.2585	0.3069	3.4641	11.2876
13	3.3360	0.2998	3.6056	12.0281
14	3.4068	0.2935	3.7417	12.7469
15	3.4718	0.2880	3.8730	13.4463
16	3.5320	0.2831	4.0000	14.1279
17	3.5879	0.2787	4.1231	14.7932
18	3.6401	0.2747	4.2426	15.4435
19	3.6890	0.2711	4.3589	16.0798
20	3.7350	0.2677	4.4721	16.7032

TABLE 15

Percentage Points of the Ratio, $s^2_{max.}/s^2_{min.}$*

Upper 5 Per Cent Points

v \ k	2	3	4	5	6	7	8	9	10	11	12
2	39.0	87.5	142	202	266	333	403	475	550	626	704
3	15.4	27.8	39.2	50.7	62.0	72.9	83.5	93.9	104	114	124
4	9.60	15.5	20.6	25.2	29.5	33.6	37.5	41.1	44.6	48.0	51.4
5	7.15	10.8	13.7	16.3	18.7	20.8	22.9	24.7	26.5	28.2	29.9
6	5.82	8.38	10.4	12.1	13.7	15.0	16.3	17.5	18.6	19.7	20.7
7	4.99	6.94	8.44	9.70	10.8	11.8	12.7	13.5	14.3	15.1	15.8
8	4.43	6.00	7.18	8.12	9.03	9.78	10.5	11.1	11.7	12.2	12.7
9	4.03	5.34	6.31	7.11	7.80	8.41	8.95	9.45	9.91	10.3	10.7
10	3.72	4.85	5.67	6.34	6.92	7.42	7.87	8.28	8.66	9.01	9.34
12	3.28	4.16	4.79	5.30	5.72	6.09	6.42	6.72	7.00	7.25	7.48
15	2.86	3.54	4.01	4.37	4.68	4.95	5.19	5.40	5.59	5.77	5.93
20	2.46	2.95	3.29	3.54	3.76	3.94	4.10	4.24	4.37	4.49	4.59
30	2.07	2.40	2.61	2.78	2.91	3.02	3.12	3.21	3.29	3.36	3.39
60	1.67	1.85	1.96	2.04	2.11	2.17	2.22	2.26	2.30	2.33	2.36
∞	1.00	1.00	1.00	1.00	1.00	1.00	1.00	1.00	1.00	1.00	1.00

* This test is discussed in Chapter 3, page 89. The table is reproduced with the permission of Professor E. S. Pearson from E. S. Pearson and H. O. Hartley, *Biometrika Tables for Statisticians*, Vol. 1, Table 31.

TABLE 16

Critical Values of $r_{10}(n)$ for Testing the Extreme Datum from a Sample of n *

$$r_{10} = \frac{x_n - x_{n-1}}{x_n - x_1}$$

Size of the Sample n	One-Sided Risk			
	5%	2%	1%	0.5%
3	0.941	0.976	0.988	0.994
4	0.765	0.846	0.889	0.926
5	0.642	0.729	0.780	0.821
6	0.560	0.644	0.698	0.740
7	0.507	0.586	0.637	0.680
8	0.468	0.543	0.590	0.634
9	0.437	0.510	0.555	0.598
10	0.412	0.483	0.527	0.568
11	0.392	0.460	0.502	0.542
12	0.376	0.441	0.482	0.522
13	0.361	0.425	0.465	0.503
14	0.349	0.411	0.450	0.488
15	0.338	0.399	0.438	0.475
16	0.329	0.388	0.426	0.463
18	0.313	0.370	0.407	0.442
20	0.300	0.356	0.391	0.425
25	0.277	0.329	0.362	0.393
30	0.260	0.309	0.341	0.372

* A discussion of this test will be found in Chapter 9, page 226.   The table is abridged, with permission, from Table 1 of W. J. Dixon, "Ratios Involving Extreme Values," *Ann. Math. Stat.*, **22** (1951), 68–78.

TABLE 17

Critical Values of R_n for Determining Whether to Reject an Extreme
Observation from a Sample of n *

$$R_n = \frac{x_n - x.}{s}$$

where $x.$ is the mean of the *other* $n - 1$ observations
and s^2 is $\sum\limits^{n-1} (x_i - x.)^2/(n - 2)$.

| Sample Size | One-Sided Risk | | |
n	5%	2.5%	1%
3	123	–	31.4
4	7.17	–	16.27
5	5.08	–	9.00
6	4.34	–	6.85
7	3.98	–	5.88
8	3.77	–	5.33
9	3.63	–	4.98
10	3.54	–	4.75
11	3.48	–	4.58
12	3.42	–	4.45
14	3.36	–	4.28
16	3.32	–	4.17
18	3.30	–	4.08
20	3.28	–	4.02
25	3.26	–	3.94

* This test is discussed in Chapter 9, page 225.

Index

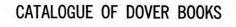

CATALOGUE OF DOVER BOOKS

BOOKS EXPLAINING SCIENCE AND MATHEMATICS

General

WHAT IS SCIENCE?, Norman Campbell. This excellent introduction explains scientific method, role of mathematics, types of scientific laws. Contents: 2 aspects of science, science & nature, laws of science, discovery of laws, explanation of laws, measurement & numerical laws, applications of science. 192pp. 5⅜ x 8. S43 Paperbound **$1.25**

THE COMMON SENSE OF THE EXACT SCIENCES, W. K. Clifford. Introduction by James Newman, edited by Karl Pearson. For 70 years this has been a guide to classical scientific and mathematical thought. Explains with unusual clarity basic concepts, such as extension of meaning of symbols, characteristics of surface boundaries, properties of plane figures, vectors, Cartesian method of determining position, etc. Long preface by Bertrand Russell. Bibliography of Clifford. Corrected, 130 diagrams redrawn. 249pp. 5⅜ x 8.
T61 Paperbound **$1.60**

SCIENCE THEORY AND MAN, Erwin Schrödinger. This is a complete and unabridged reissue of SCIENCE AND THE HUMAN TEMPERAMENT plus an additional essay: "What is an Elementary Particle?" Nobel laureate Schrödinger discusses such topics as nature of scientific method, the nature of science, chance and determinism, science and society, conceptual models for physical entities, elementary particles and wave mechanics. Presentation is popular and may be followed by most people with little or no scientific training. "Fine practical preparation for a time when laws of nature, human institutions . . . are undergoing a critical examination without parallel," Waldemar Kaempffert, N. Y. TIMES. 192pp. 5⅜ x 8.
T428 Paperbound **$1.35**

FADS AND FALLACIES IN THE NAME OF SCIENCE, Martin Gardner. Examines various cults, quack systems, frauds, delusions which at various times have masqueraded as science. Accounts of hollow-earth fanatics like Symmes; Velikovsky and wandering planets; Hoerbiger; Bellamy and the theory of multiple moons; Charles Fort; dowsing, pseudoscientific methods for finding water, ores, oil. Sections on naturopathy, iridiagnosis, zone therapy, food fads, etc. Analytical accounts of Wilhelm Reich and orgone sex energy; L. Ron Hubbard and Dianetics; A. Korzybski and General Semantics; many others. Brought up to date to include Bridey Murphy, others. Not just a collection of anecdotes, but a fair, reasoned appraisal of eccentric theory. Formerly titled IN THE NAME OF SCIENCE. Preface. Index. x + 384pp. 5⅜ x 8. T394 Paperbound **$1.50**

A DOVER SCIENCE SAMPLER, edited by George Barkin. 64-page book, sturdily bound, containing excerpts from over 20 Dover books, explaining science. Edwin Hubble, George Sarton, Ernst Mach, A. d'Abro, Galileo, Newton, others, discussing island universes, scientific truth, biological phenomena, stability in bridges, etc. Copies limited; no more than 1 to a customer,
FREE

POPULAR SCIENTIFIC LECTURES, Hermann von Helmholtz. Helmholtz was a superb expositor as well as a scientist of genius in many areas. The seven essays in this volume are models of clarity, and even today they rank among the best general descriptions of their subjects ever written. "The Physiological Causes of Harmony in Music" was the first significant physiological explanation of musical consonance and dissonance. Two essays, "On the Interaction of Natural Forces" and "On the Conservation of Force," were of great importance in the history of science, for they firmly established the principle of the conservation of energy. Other lectures include "On the Relation of Optics to Painting," "On Recent Progress in the Theory of Vision," "On Goethe's Scientific Researches," and "On the Origin and Significance of Geometrical Axioms." Selected and edited with an introduction by Professor Morris Kline. xii + 286pp. 5⅜ x 8½. T799 Paperbound **$1.45**

BOOKS EXPLAINING SCIENCE AND MATHEMATICS

Physics

CONCERNING THE NATURE OF THINGS, Sir William Bragg. Christmas lectures delivered at the Royal Society by Nobel laureate. Why a spinning ball travels in a curved track; how uranium is transmuted to lead, etc. Partial contents: atoms, gases, liquids, crystals, metals, etc. No scientific background needed; wonderful for intelligent child. 32pp. of photos, 57 figures. xii + 232pp. 5⅜ x 8. T31 Paperbound **$1.50**

THE RESTLESS UNIVERSE, Max Born. New enlarged version of this remarkably readable account by a Nobel laureate. Moving from sub-atomic particles to universe, the author explains in very simple terms the latest theories of wave mechanics. Partial contents: air and its relatives, electrons & ions, waves & particles, electronic structure of the atom, nuclear physics. Nearly 1000 illustrations, including 7 animated sequences. 325pp. 6 x 9.
T412 Paperbound **$2.00**

CATALOGUE OF DOVER BOOKS

FROM EUCLID TO EDDINGTON: A STUDY OF THE CONCEPTIONS OF THE EXTERNAL WORLD, Sir Edmund Whittaker. A foremost British scientist traces the development of theories of natural philosophy from the western rediscovery of Euclid to Eddington, Einstein, Dirac, etc. The inadequacy of classical physics is contrasted with present day attempts to understand the physical world through relativity, non-Euclidean geometry, space curvature, wave mechanics, etc. 5 major divisions of examination: Space; Time and Movement; the Concepts of Classical Physics; the Concepts of Quantum Mechanics; the Eddington Universe. 212pp. 5⅜ x 8.
T491 Paperbound **$1.35**

PHYSICS, THE PIONEER SCIENCE, L. W. Taylor. First thorough text to place all important physical phenomena in cultural-historical framework; remains best work of its kind. Exposition of physical laws, theories· developed chronologically, with great historical, illustrative experiments diagrammed, described, worked out mathematically. Excellent physics text for self-study as well as class work. Vol. 1: Heat, Sound: motion, acceleration, gravitation, conservation of energy, heat engines, rotation, heat, mechanical energy, etc. 211 illus. 407pp. 5⅜ x 8. Vol. 2: Light, Electricity: images, lenses, prisms, magnetism, Ohm's law, dynamos, telegraph, quantum theory, decline of mechanical view of nature, etc. Bibliography. 13 table appendix. Index. 551 illus. 2 color plates. 508pp. 5⅜ x 8.
Vol. 1 S565 Paperbound **$2.00**
Vol. 2 S566 Paperbound **$2.00**
The set **$4.00**

A SURVEY OF PHYSICAL THEORY, Max Planck. One of the greatest scientists of all time, creator of the quantum revolution in physics, writes in non-technical terms of his own discoveries and those of other outstanding creators of modern physics. Planck wrote this book when science had just crossed the threshold of the new physics, and he communicates the excitement felt then as he discusses electromagnetic theories, statistical methods, evolution of the concept of light, a step-by-step description of how he developed his own momentous theory, and many more of the basic ideas behind modern physics. Formerly "A Survey of Physics." Bibliography. Index. 128pp. 5⅜ x 8.
S650 Paperbound **$1.15**

THE ATOMIC NUCLEUS, M. Korsunsky. The only non-technical comprehensive account of the atomic nucleus in English. For college physics students, etc. Chapters cover: Radioactivity, the Nuclear Model of the Atom, the Mass of Atomic Nuclei, the Disintegration of Atomic Nuclei, the Discovery of the Positron, the Artificial Transformation of Atomic Nuclei, Artificial Radioactivity, Mesons, the Neutrino, the Structure of Atomic Nuclei and Forces Acting Between Nuclear Particles, Nuclear Fission, Chain Reaction, Peaceful Uses, Thermoculear Reactions. Slightly abridged edition. Translated by G. Yankovsky. 65 figures. Appendix includes 45 photographic illustrations. 413 pp. 5⅜ x 8.
S1052 Paperbound **$2.00**

PRINCIPLES OF MECHANICS SIMPLY EXPLAINED, Morton Mott-Smith. Excellent, highly readable introduction to the theories and discoveries of classical physics. Ideal for the layman who desires a foundation which will enable him to understand and appreciate contemporary developments in the physical sciences. Discusses: Density, The Law of Gravitation, Mass and Weight, Action and Reaction, Kinetic and Potential Energy, The Law of Inertia, Effects of Acceleration, The Independence of Motions, Galileo and the New Science of Dynamics, Newton and the New Cosmos, The Conservation of Momentum, and other topics. Revised edition of "This Mechanical World." Illustrated by E. Kosa, Jr. Bibliography and Chronology. Index. xiv + 171pp. 5⅜ x 8½.
T1067 Paperbound **$1.00**

THE CONCEPT OF ENERGY SIMPLY EXPLAINED, Morton Mott-Smith. Elementary, non-technical exposition which traces the story of man's conquest of energy, with particular emphasis on the developments during the nineteenth century and the first three decades of our own century. Discusses man's earlier efforts to harness energy, more recent experiments and discoveries relating to the steam engine, the engine indicator, the motive power of heat, the principle of excluded perpetual motion, the bases of the conservation of energy, the concept of entropy, the internal combustion engine, mechanical refrigeration, and many other related topics. Also much biographical material. Index. Bibliography. 33 illustrations. ix + 215pp. 5⅜ x 8½.
T1071 Paperbound **$1.25**

HEAT AND ITS WORKINGS, Morton Mott-Smith. One of the best elementary introductions to the theory and attributes of heat, covering such matters as the laws governing the effect of heat on solids, liquids and gases, the methods by which heat is measured, the conversion of a substance from one form to another through heating and cooling, evaporation, the effects of pressure on boiling and freezing points, and the three ways in which heat is transmitted (conduction, convection, radiation). Also brief notes on major experiments and discoveries. Concise, but complete, it presents all the essential facts about the subject in readable style. Will give the layman and beginning student a first-rate background in this major topic in physics. Index. Bibliography. 50 illustrations. x + 165pp. 5⅜ x 8½. T978 Paperbound **$1.15**

THE STORY OF ATOMIC THEORY AND ATOMIC ENERGY, J. G. Feinberg. Wider range of facts on physical theory, cultural implications, than any other similar source. Completely non-technical. Begins with first atomic theory, 600 B.C., goes through A-bomb, developments to 1959. Avogadro, Rutherford, Bohr, Einstein, radioactive decay, binding energy, radiation danger, future benefits of nuclear power, dozens of other topics, told in lively, related, informal manner. Particular stress on European atomic research. "Deserves special mention . . . authoritative," Saturday Review. Formerly "The Atom Story." New chapter to 1959. Index. 34 illustrations. 251pp. 5⅜ x 8.
T625 Paperbound **$1.60**

THE STRANGE STORY OF THE QUANTUM, AN ACCOUNT FOR THE GENERAL READER OF THE GROWTH OF IDEAS UNDERLYING OUR PRESENT ATOMIC KNOWLEDGE, B. Hoffmann. Presents lucidly and expertly, with barest amount of mathematics, the problems and theories which led to modern quantum physics. Dr. Hoffmann begins with the closing years of the 19th century, when certain trifling discrepancies were noticed, and with illuminating analogies and examples takes you through the brilliant concepts of Planck, Einstein, Pauli, de Broglie, Bohr, Schroedinger, Heisenberg, Dirac, Sommerfeld, Feynman, etc. This edition includes a new, long postscript carrying the story through 1958. "Of the books attempting an account of the history and contents of our modern atomic physics which have come to my attention, this is the best," H. Margenau, Yale University, in "American Journal of Physics." 32 tables and line illustrations. Index. 275pp. 5⅜ x 8. T518 Paperbound $1.50

THE EVOLUTION OF SCIENTIFIC THOUGHT FROM NEWTON TO EINSTEIN, A. d'Abro. Einstein's special and general theories of relativity, with their historical implications, are analyzed in non-technical terms. Excellent accounts of the contributions of Newton, Riemann, Weyl, Planck, Eddington, Maxwell, Lorentz and others are treated in terms of space and time, equations of electromagnetics, finiteness of the universe, methodology of science. 21 diagrams. 482pp. 5⅜ x 8. T2 Paperound $2.25

THE RISE OF THE NEW PHYSICS, A. d'Abro. A half-million word exposition, formerly titled THE DECLINE OF MECHANISM, for readers not versed in higher mathematics. The only thorough explanation, in everyday language, of the central core of modern mathematical physical theory, treating both classical and modern theoretical physics, and presenting in terms almost anyone can understand the equivalent of 5 years of study of mathematical physics. Scientifically impeccable coverage of mathematical-physical thought from the Newtonian system up through the electronic theories of Dirac and Heisenberg and Fermi's statistics. Combines both history and exposition; provides a broad yet unified and detailed view, with constant comparison of classical and modern views on phenomena and theories. "A must for anyone doing serious study in the physical sciences," JOURNAL OF THE FRANKLIN INSTITUTE. "Extraordinary faculty . . . to explain ideas and theories of theoretical physics in the language of daily life," ISIS. First part of set covers philosophy of science, drawing upon the practice of Newton, Maxwell, Poincaré, Einstein, others, discussing modes of thought, experiment, interpretations of causality, etc. In the second part, 100 pages explain grammar and vocabulary of mathematics, with discussions of functions, groups, series, Fourier series, etc. The remainder is devoted to concrete, detailed coverage of both classical and quantum physics, explaining such topics as analytic mechanics, Hamilton's principle, wave theory of light, electromagnetic waves, groups of transformations, thermodynamics, phase rule, Brownian movement, kinetics, special relativity, Planck's original quantum theory, Bohr's atom, Zeeman effect, Broglie's wave mechanics, Heisenberg's uncertainty, Eigen-values, matrices, scores of other important topics. Discoveries and theories are covered for such men as Alembert, Born, Cantor, Debye, Euler, Foucault, Galois, Gauss, Hadamard, Kelvin, Kepler, Laplace, Maxwell, Pauli, Rayleigh, Volterra, Weyl, Young, more than 180 others. Indexed. 97 illustrations. ix + 982pp. 5⅜ x 8. T3 Volume 1, Paperbound $2.25 / T4 Volume 2, Paperbound $2.25

SPINNING TOPS AND GYROSCOPIC MOTION, John Perry. Well-known classic of science still unsurpassed for lucid, accurate, delightful exposition. How quasi-rigidity is induced in flexible and fluid bodies by rapid motions; why gyrostat falls, top rises; nature and effect on climatic conditions of earth's precessional movement; effect of internal fluidity on rotating bodies, etc. Appendixes describe practical uses to which gyroscopes have been put in ships, compasses, monorail transportation. 62 figures. 128pp. 5⅜ x 8. T416 Paperbound $1.00

THE UNIVERSE OF LIGHT, Sir William Bragg. No scientific training needed to read Nobel Prize winner's expansion of his Royal Institute Christmas Lectures. Insight into nature of light, methods and philosophy of science. Explains lenses, reflection, color, resonance, polarization, x-rays, the spectrum, Newton's work with prisms, Huygens' with polarization, Crookes' with cathode ray, etc. Leads into clear statement of 2 major historical theories of light, corpuscle and wave. Dozens of experiments you can do. 199 illus., including 2 full-page color plates. 293pp. 5⅜ x 8. S538 Paperbound $1.85

THE STORY OF X-RAYS FROM RÖNTGEN TO ISOTOPES, A. R. Bleich. Non-technical history of x-rays, their scientific explanation, their applications in medicine, industry, research, and art, and their effect on the individual and his descendants. Includes amusing early reactions to Röntgen's discovery, cancer therapy, detections of art and stamp forgeries, potential risks to patient and operator, etc. Illustrations show x-rays of flower structure, the gall bladder, gears with hidden defects, etc. Original Dover publication. Glossary. Bibliography. Index. 55 photos and figures. xiv + 186pp. 5⅜ x 8. T662 Paperbound $1.35

ELECTRONS, ATOMS, METALS AND ALLOYS, Wm. Hume-Rothery. An introductory-level explanation of the application of the electronic theory to the structure and properties of metals and alloys, taking into account the new theoretical work done by mathematical physicists. Material presented in dialogue-form between an "Old Metallurgist" and a "Young Scientist." Their discussion falls into 4 main parts: the nature of an atom, the nature of a metal, the nature of an alloy, and the structure of the nucleus. They cover such topics as the hydrogen atom, electron waves, wave mechanics, Brillouin zones, co-valent bonds, radioactivity and natural disintegration, fundamental particles, structure and fission of the nucleus,etc. Revised, enlarged edition. 177 illustrations. Subject and name indexes. 407pp. 5⅜ x 8½. S1046 Paperbound $2.25

OUT OF THE SKY, H. H. Nininger. A non-technical but comprehensive introduction to "meteoritics", the young science concerned with all aspects of the arrival of matter from outer space. Written by one of the world's experts on meteorites, this work shows how, despite difficulties of observation and sparseness of data, a considerable body of knowledge has arisen. It defines meteors and meteorites; studies fireball clusters and processions, meteorite composition, size, distribution, showers, explosions, origins, craters, and much more. A true connecting link between astronomy and geology. More than 175 photos, 22 other illustrations. References. Bibliography of author's publications on meteorites. Index. viii + 336pp. 5⅜ x 8.
T519 Paperbound **$1.85**

SATELLITES AND SCIENTIFIC RESEARCH, D. King-Hele. Non-technical account of the manmade satellites and the discoveries they have yielded up to the autumn of 1961. Brings together information hitherto published only in hard-to-get scientific journals. Includes the life history of a typical satellite, methods of tracking, new information on the shape of the earth, zones of radiation, etc. Over 60 diagrams and 6 photographs. Mathematical appendix. Bibliography of over 100 items. Index. xii + 180pp. 5⅜ x 8½.
T703 Paperbound **$2.00**

BOOKS EXPLAINING SCIENCE AND MATHEMATICS

Mathematics

CHANCE, LUCK AND STATISTICS: THE SCIENCE OF CHANCE, Horace C. Levinson. Theory of probability and science of statistics in simple, non-technical language. Part I deals with theory of probability, covering odd superstitions in regard to "luck," the meaning of betting odds, the law of mathematical expectation, gambling, and applications in poker, roulette, lotteries, dice, bridge, and other games of chance. Part II discusses the misuse of statistics, the concept of statistical probabilities, normal and skew frequency distributions, and statistics applied to various fields—birth rates, stock speculation, insurance rates, advertising, etc. "Presented in an easy humorous style which I consider the best kind of expository writing," Prof. A. C. Cohen, Industry Quality Control. Enlarged revised edition. Formerly titled "The Science of Chance." Preface and two new appendices by the author. Index. xiv + 365pp. 5⅜ x 8.
T1007 Paperbound **$1.85**

PROBABILITIES AND LIFE, Emile Borel. Translated by M. Baudin. Non-technical, highly readable introduction to the results of probability as applied to everyday situations. Partial contents: Fallacies About Probabilities Concerning Life After Death; Negligible Probabilities and the Probabilities of Everyday Life; Events of Small Probability; Application of Probabilities to Certain Problems of Heredity; Probabilities of Deaths, Diseases, and Accidents; On Poisson's Formula. Index. 3 Appendices of statistical studies and tables. vi + 87pp. 5⅜ x 8½.
T121 Paperbound **$1.00**

GREAT IDEAS OF MODERN MATHEMATICS: THEIR NATURE AND USE, Jagjit Singh. Reader with only high school math will understand main mathematical ideas of modern physics, astronomy, genetics, psychology, evolution, etc., better than many who use them as tools, but comprehend little of their basic structure. Author uses his wide knowledge of non-mathematical fields in brilliant exposition of differential equations, matrices, group theory, logic, statistics, problems of mathematical foundations, imaginary numbers, vectors, etc. Original publication. 2 appendices. 2 indexes. 65 illustr. 322pp. 5⅜ x 8.
S587 Paperbound **$1.75**

MATHEMATICS IN ACTION, O. G. Sutton. Everyone with a command of high school algebra will find this book one of the finest possible introductions to the application of mathematics to physical theory. Ballistics, numerical analysis, waves and wavelike phenomena, Fourier series, group concepts, fluid flow and aerodynamics, statistical measures, and meteorology are discussed with unusual clarity. Some calculus and differential equations theory is developed by the author for the reader's help in the more difficult sections. 88 figures. Index. viii + 236pp. 5⅜ x 8.
T440 Clothbound **$3.50**

THE FOURTH DIMENSION SIMPLY EXPLAINED, edited by H. P. Manning. 22 essays, originally Scientific American contest entries, that use a minimum of mathematics to explain aspects of 4-dimensional geometry: analogues to 3-dimensional space, 4-dimensional absurdities and curiosities (such as removing the contents of an egg without puncturing its shell), possible measurements and forms, etc. Introduction by the editor. Only book of its sort on a truly elementary level, excellent introduction to advanced works. 82 figures. 251pp. 5⅜ x 8.
T711 Paperbound **$1.35**

MATHEMATICS—INTERMEDIATE TO ADVANCED

General

INTRODUCTION TO APPLIED MATHEMATICS, Francis D. Murnaghan. A practical and thoroughly sound introduction to a number of advanced branches of higher mathematics. Among the selected topics covered in detail are: vector and matrix analysis, partial and differential equations, integral equations, calculus of variations, Laplace transform theory, the vector triple product, linear vector functions, quadratic and bilinear forms, Fourier series, spherical harmonics, Bessel functions, the Heaviside expansion formula, and many others. Extremely useful book for graduate students in physics, engineering, chemistry, and mathematics. Index. 111 study exercises with answers. 41 illustrations. ix + 389pp. 5⅜ x 8½.
S1042 Paperbound **$2.00**

OPERATIONAL METHODS IN APPLIED MATHEMATICS, H. S. Carslaw and J. C. Jaeger. Explanation of the application of the Laplace Transformation to differential equations, a simple and effective substitute for more difficult and obscure operational methods. Of great practical value to engineers and to all workers in applied mathematics. Chapters on: Ordinary Linear Differential Equations with Constant Coefficients;; Electric Circuit Theory; Dynamical Applications; The Inversion Theorem for the Laplace Transformation; Conduction of Heat; Vibrations of Continuous Mechanical Systems; Hydrodynamics; Impulsive Functions; Chains of Differential Equations; and other related matters. 3 appendices. 153 problems, many with answers. 22 figures. xvi + 359pp. 5⅜ x 8½.
S1011 Paperbound **$2.25**

APPLIED MATHEMATICS FOR RADIO AND COMMUNICATIONS ENGINEERS, C. E. Smith. No extraneous material here!—only the theories, equations, and operations essential and immediately useful for radio work. Can be used as refresher, as handbook of applications and tables, or as full home-study course. Ranges from simplest arithmetic through calculus, series, and wave forms, hyperbolic trigonometry, simultaneous equations in mesh circuits, etc. Supplies applications right along with each math topic discussed. 22 useful tables of functions, formulas, logs, etc. Index. 166 exercises, 140 examples, all with answers. 95 diagrams. Bibliography. x + 336pp. 5⅜ x 8.
S141 Paperbound **$1.75**

Algebra, group theory, determinants, sets, matrix theory

ALGEBRAS AND THEIR ARITHMETICS, L. E. Dickson. Provides the foundation and background necessary to any advanced undergraduate or graduate student studying abstract algebra. Begins with elementary introduction to linear transformations, matrices, field of complex numbers; proceeds to order, basal units, modulus, quaternions, etc.; develops calculus of linears sets, describes various examples of algebras including invariant, difference, nilpotent, semi-simple. "Makes the reader marvel at his genius for clear and profound analysis," Amer. Mathematical Monthly. Index. xii + 241pp. 5⅜ x 8.
S616 Paperbound **$1.50**

THE THEORY OF EQUATIONS WITH AN INTRODUCTION TO THE THEORY OF BINARY ALGEBRAIC FORMS, W. S. Burnside and A. W. Panton. Extremely thorough and concrete discussion of the theory of equations, with extensive detailed treatment of many topics curtailed in later texts. Covers theory of algebraic equations, properties of polynomials, symmetric functions, derived functions, Horner's process, complex numbers and the complex variable, determinants and methods of elimination, invariant theory (nearly 100 pages), transformations, introduction to Galois theory, Abelian equations, and much more. Invaluable supplementary work for modern students and teachers. 759 examples and exercises. Index in each volume. Two volume set. Total of xxiv + 604pp. 5⅜ x 8.
S714 Vol I Paperbound **$1.85**
S715 Vol II Paperbound **$1.85**
The set **$3.70**

COMPUTATIONAL METHODS OF LINEAR ALGEBRA, V. N. Faddeeva, translated by **C. D. Benster.** First English translation of a unique and valuable work, the only work in English presenting a systematic exposition of the most important methods of linear algebra—classical and contemporary. Shows in detail how to derive numerical solutions of problems in mathematical physics which are frequently connected with those of linear algebra. Theory as well as individual practice. Part I surveys the mathematical background that is indispensable to what follows. Parts II and III, the conclusion, set forth the most important methods of solution, for both exact and iterative groups. One of the most outstanding and valuable features of this work is the 23 tables, double and triple checked for accuracy. These tables will not be found elsewhere. Author's preface. Translator's note. New bibliography and index. x + 252pp. 5⅜ x 8.
S424 Paperbound **$1.95**

ALGEBRAIC EQUATIONS, E. Dehn. Careful and complete presentation of Galois' theory of algebraic equations; theories of Lagrange and Galois developed in logical rather than historical form, with a more thorough exposition than in most modern books. Many concrete applications and fully-worked-out examples. Discusses basic theory (very clear exposition of the symmetric group); isomorphic, transitive, and Abelian groups; applications of Lagrange's and Galois' theories; and much more. Newly revised by the author. Index. List of Theorems. xi + 208pp. 5⅜ x 8.
S697 Paperbound **$1.45**

CATALOGUE OF DOVER BOOKS

Differential equations, ordinary and partial; integral equations

INTRODUCTION TO THE DIFFERENTIAL EQUATIONS OF PHYSICS, L. Hopf. Especially valuable to the engineer with no math beyond elementary calculus. Emphasizing intuitive rather than formal aspects of concepts, the author covers an extensive territory. Partial contents: Law of causality, energy theorem, damped oscillations, coupling by friction, cylindrical and spherical coordinates, heat source, etc. Index. 48 figures. 160pp. 5⅜ x 8.
S120 Paperbound **$1.25**

INTRODUCTION TO THE THEORY OF LINEAR DIFFERENTIAL EQUATIONS, E. G. Poole. Authoritative discussions of important topics, with methods of solution more detailed than usual, for students with background of elementary course in differential equations. Studies existence theorems, linearly independent solutions; equations with constant coefficients; with uniform analytic coefficients; regular singularities; the hypergeometric equation; conformal representation; etc. Exercises. Index. 210pp. 5⅜ x 8.
S629 Paperbound **$1.65**

DIFFERENTIAL EQUATIONS FOR ENGINEERS, P. Franklin. Outgrowth of a course given 10 years at M. I. T. Makes most useful branch of pure math accessible for practical work. Theoretical basis of D.E.'s; solution of ordinary D.E.'s and partial derivatives arising from heat flow, steady-state temperature of a plate, wave equations; analytic functions; convergence of Fourier Series. 400 problems on electricity, vibratory systems, other topics. Formerly "Differential Equations for Electrical Engineers." Index 41 illus. 307pp. 5⅜ x 8.
S601 Paperbound **$1.65**

DIFFERENTIAL EQUATIONS, F. R. Moulton. A detailed, rigorous exposition of all the non-elementary processes of solving ordinary differential equations. Several chapters devoted to the treatment of practical problems, especially those of a physical nature, which are far more advanced than problems usually given as illustrations. Includes analytic differential equations; variations of a parameter; integrals of differential equations; analytic implicit functions; problems of elliptic motion; sine-amplitude functions; deviation of formal bodies; Cauchy-Lipschitz process; linear differential equations with periodic coefficients; differential equations in infinitely many variations; much more. Historical notes. 10 figures. 222 problems. Index. xv + 395pp. 5⅜ x 8.
S451 Paperbound **$2.00**

DIFFERENTIAL AND INTEGRAL EQUATIONS OF MECHANICS AND PHYSICS (DIE DIFFERENTIAL-UND INTEGRALGLEICHUNGEN DER MECHANIK UND PHYSIK), edited by P. Frank and R. von Mises. Most comprehensive and authoritative work on the mathematics of mathematical physics available today in the United States: the standard, definitive reference for teachers, physicists, engineers, and mathematicians—now published (in the original German) at a relatively inexpensive price for the first time! Every chapter in this 2,000-page set is by an expert in his field: Carathéodory, Courant, Frank, Mises, and a dozen others. Vol I, on mathematics, gives concise but complete coverages of advanced calculus, differential equations, integral equations, and potential, and partial differential equations. Index. xxiii + 916pp. Vol. II (physics): classical mechanics, optics, continuous mechanics, heat conduction and diffusion, the stationary and quasi-stationary electromagnetic field, electromagnetic oscillations, and wave mechanics. Index. xxiv + 1106pp. Two volume set. Each volume available separately. 5⅝ x 8⅜.
S787 Vol I Clothbound **$7.50**
S788 Vol II Clothbound **$7.50**
The set **$15.00**

LECTURES ON CAUCHY'S PROBLEM, J. Hadamard. Based on lectures given at Columbia, Rome, this discusses work of Riemann, Kirchhoff, Volterra, and the author's own research on the hyperbolic case in linear partial differential equations. It extends spherical and cylindrical waves to apply to all (normal) hyperbolic equations. Partial contents: Cauchy's problem, fundamental formula, equations with odd number, with even number of independent variables; method of descent. 32 figures. Index. iii + 316pp. 5⅜ x 8.
S105 Paperbound **$1.75**

THEORY OF DIFFERENTIAL EQUATIONS, A. R. Forsyth. Out of print for over a decade, the complete 6 volumes (now bound as 3) of this monumental work represent the most comprehensive treatment of differential equations ever written. Historical presentation includes in 2500 pages every substantial development. Vol. 1, 2: EXACT EQUATIONS, PFAFF'S PROBLEM; ORDINARY EQUATIONS, NOT LINEAR: methods of Grassmann, Clebsch, Lie, Darboux; Cauchy's theorem; branch points; etc. Vol. 3, 4: ORDINARY EQUATIONS, NOT LINEAR; ORDINARY LINEAR EQUATIONS: Zeta Fuchsian functions, general theorems on algebraic integrals, Brun's theorem, equations with uniform periodic coffiecients, etc. Vol. 4, 5: PARTIAL DIFFERENTIAL EQUATIONS: 2 existence-theorems, equations of theoretical dynamics, Laplace transformations, general transformation of equations of the 2nd order, much more. Indexes. Total of 2766pp. 5⅜ x 8.
S576-7-8 Clothbound: the set **$15.00**

PARTIAL DIFFERENTIAL EQUATIONS OF MATHEMATICAL PHYSICS, A. G. Webster. A keystone work in the library of every mature physicist, engineer, researcher. Valuable sections on elasticity, compression theory, potential theory, theory of sound, heat conduction, wave propagation, vibration theory. Contents include: deduction of differential equations, vibrations, normal functions, Fourier's series, Cauchy's method, boundary problems, method of Riemann-Volterra. Spherical, cylindrical, ellipsoidal harmonics, applications, etc. 97 figures. vii + 440pp. 5⅜ x 8.
S263 Paperbound **$2.00**

ELEMENTARY CONCEPTS OF TOPOLOGY, P. Alexandroff. First English translation of the famous brief introduction to topology for the beginner or for the mathematician not undertaking extensive study. This unusually useful intuitive approach deals primarily with the concepts of complex, cycle, and homology, and is wholly consistent with current investigations. Ranges from basic concepts of set-theoretic topology to the concept of Betti groups. "Glowing example of harmony between intuition and thought," David Hilbert. Translated by A. E. Farley. Introduction by D. Hilbert. Index. 25 figures. 73pp. 5⅜ x 8.   S747 Paperbound **$1.00**

Number theory

INTRODUCTION TO THE THEORY OF NUMBERS, L. E. Dickson. Thorough, comprehensive approach with adequate coverage of classical literature, an introductory volume beginners can follow. Chapters on divisibility, congruences, quadratic residues & reciprocity, Diophantine equations, etc. Full treatment of binary quadratic forms without usual restriction to integral coefficients. Covers infinitude of primes, least residues, Fermat's theorem, Euler's phi function, Legendre's symbol, Gauss's lemma, automorphs, reduced forms, recent theorems of Thue & Siegel, many more. Much material not readily available elsewhere. 239 problems. Index. I figure. viii + 183pp. 5⅜ x 8.   S342 Paperbound **$1.65**

ELEMENTS OF NUMBER THEORY, I. M. Vinogradov. Detailed 1st course for persons without advanced mathematics; 95% of this book can be understood by readers who have gone no farther than high school algebra. Partial contents: divisibility theory, important number theoretical functions, congruences, primitive roots and indices, etc. Solutions to both problems and exercises. Tables of primes, indices, etc. Covers almost every essential formula in elementary number theory! Translated from Russian. 233 problems, 104 exercises. viii + 227pp. 5⅜ x 8.   S259 Paperbound **$1.60**

THEORY OF NUMBERS and DIOPHANTINE ANALYSIS, R. D. Carmichael. These two complete works in one volume form one of the most lucid introductions to number theory, requiring only a firm foundation in high school mathematics. "Theory of Numbers," partial contents: Eratosthenes' sieve, Euclid's fundamental theorem, G.C.F. and L.C.M. of two or more integers, linear congruences, etc "Diophantine Analysis": rational triangles, Pythagorean triangles, equations of third, fourth, higher degrees, method of functional equations, much more. "Theory of Numbers": 76 problems. Index. 94pp. "Diophantine Analysis": 222 problems. Index. 118pp. 5⅜ x 8.   S529 Paperbound **$1.35**

Numerical analysis, tables

MATHEMATICAL TABLES AND FORMULAS, Compiled by Robert D. Carmichael and Edwin R. Smith. Valuable collection for students, etc. Contains all tables necessary in college algebra and trigonometry, such as five-place common logarithms, logarithmic sines and tangents of small angles, logarithmic trigonometric functions, natural trigonometric functions, four-place antilogarithms, tables for changing from sexagesimal to circular and from circular to sexagesimal measure of angles, etc. Also many tables and formulas not ordinarily accessible, including powers, roots, and reciprocals, exponential and hyperbolic functions, ten-place logarithms of prime numbers, and formulas and theorems from analytical and elementary geometry and from calculus. Explanatory introduction. viii + 269pp. 5⅜ x 8½.   S111 Paperbound **$1.00**

MATHEMATICAL TABLES, H. B. Dwight. Unique for its coverage in one volume of almost every function of importance in applied mathematics, engineering, and the physical sciences. Three extremely fine tables of the three trig functions and their inverse functions to thousandths of radians; natural and common logarithms; squares, cubes; hyperbolic functions and the inverse hyperbolic functions; $(a^2 + b^2)$ exp. ½a; complete elliptic integrals of the 1st and 2nd kind; sine and cosine integrals; exponential integrals Ei(x) and Ei(— x); binomial coefficients; factorials to 250; surface zonal harmonics and first derivatives; Bernoulli and Euler numbers and their logs to base of 10; Gamma function; normal probability integral; over 60 pages of Bessel functions; the Riemann Zeta function. Each table with formulae generally used, sources of more extensive tables, interpolation data, etc. Over half have columns of differences, to facilitate interpolation. Introduction. Index. viii + 231pp. 5⅜ x 8.   S445 Paperbound **$2.00**

TABLES OF FUNCTIONS WITH FORMULAE AND CURVES, E. Jahnke & F. Emde. The world's most comprehensive 1-volume English-text collection of tables, formulae, curves of transcendent functions. 4th corrected edition, new 76-page section giving tables, formulae for elementary functions—not in other English editions. Partial contents: sine, cosine, logarithmic integral; factorial function; error integral; theta functions; elliptic integrals, functions; Legendre, Bessel, Riemann, Mathieu, hypergeometric functions, etc. Supplementary books. Bibliography. Indexed. "Out of the way functions for which we know no other source," SCIENTIFIC COMPUTING SERVICE, Ltd. 212 figures. 400pp. 5⅜ x 8.   S133 Paperbound **$2.00**

CHEMISTRY AND PHYSICAL CHEMISTRY

ORGANIC CHEMISTRY, F. C. Whitmore. The entire subject of organic chemistry for the practicing chemist and the advanced student. Storehouse of facts, theories, processes found elsewhere only in specialized journals. Covers aliphatic compounds (500 pages on the properties and synthetic preparation of hydrocarbons, halides, proteins, ketones, etc.), alicyclic compounds, aromatic compounds, heterocyclic compounds, organophosphorus and organometallic compounds. Methods of synthetic preparation analyzed critically throughout. Includes much of biochemical interest. "The scope of this volume is astonishing," INDUSTRIAL AND ENGINEERING CHEMISTRY. 12,000-reference index. 2387-item bibliography. Total of x + 1005pp. 5⅜ x 8. Two volume set.
S700 Vol I Paperbound **$2.25**
S701 Vol II Paperbound **$2.25**
The set **$4.50**

THE MODERN THEORY OF MOLECULAR STRUCTURE, Bernard Pullman. A reasonably popular account of recent developments in atomic and molecular theory. Contents: The Wave Function and Wave Equations (history and bases of present theories of molecular structure); The Electronic Structure of Atoms (Description and classification of atomic wave functions, etc.); Diatomic Molecules; Non-Conjugated Polyatomic Molecules; Conjugated Polyatomic Molecules; The Structure of Complexes. Minimum of mathematical background needed. New translation by David Antin of "La Structure Moléculaire." Index. Bibliography. vii + 87pp. 5⅜ x 8½.
S987 Paperbound **$1.00**

CATALYSIS AND CATALYSTS, Marcel Prettre, Director, Research Institute on Catalysis. This brief book, translated into English for the first time, is the finest summary of the principal modern concepts, methods, and results of catalysis. Ideal introduction for beginning chemistry and physics students. Chapters: Basic Definitions of Catalysis (true catalysis and generalization of the concept of catalysis); The Scientific Bases of Catalysis (Catalysis and chemical thermodynamics, catalysis and chemical kinetics); Homogeneous Catalysis (acid-base catalysis, etc.); Chain Reactions; Contact Masses; Heterogeneous Catalysis (Mechanisms of contact catalyses, etc.); and Industrial Applications (acids and fertilizers, petroleum and petroleum chemistry, rubber, plastics, synthetic resins, and fibers). Translated by David Antin. Index. vi + 88pp. 5⅜ x 8½.
S998 Paperbound **$1.00**

POLAR MOLECULES, Pieter Debye. This work by Nobel laureate Debye offers a complete guide to fundamental electrostatic field relations, polarizability, molecular structure. Partial contents: electric intensity, displacement and force, polarization by orientation, molar polarization and molar refraction, halogen-hydrides, polar liquids, ionic saturation, dielectric constant, etc. Special chapter considers quantum theory. Indexed. 172pp. 5⅜ x 8.
S64 Paperbound **$1.65**

THE ELECTRONIC THEORY OF ACIDS AND BASES, W. F. Luder and Saverio Zuffanti. The first full systematic presentation of the electronic theory of acids and bases—treating the theory and its ramifications in an uncomplicated manner. Chapters: Historical Background; Atomic Orbitals and Valence; The Electronic Theory of Acids and Bases; Electrophilic and Electrodotic Reagents; Acidic and Basic Radicals; Neutralization; Titrations with Indicators; Displacement; Catalysis; Acid Catalysis; Base Catalysis; Alkoxides and Catalysts; Conclusion. Required reading for all chemists. Second revised (1961) eidtion, with additional examples and references. 3 figures. 9 tables. Index. Bibliography xii + 165pp. 5⅜ x 8.
S201 Paperbound **$1.50**

KINETIC THEORY OF LIQUIDS, J. Frenkel. Regarding the kinetic theory of liquids as a generalization and extension of the theory of solid bodies, this volume covers all types of arrangements of solids, thermal displacements of atoms, interstitial atoms and ions, orientational and rotational motion of molecules, and transition between states of matter. Mathematical theory is developed close to the physical subject matter. 216 bibliographical footnotes. 55 figures. xi + 485pp. 5⅜ x 8.
S95 Paperbound **$2.55**

THE PRINCIPLES OF ELECTROCHEMISTRY, D. A. MacInnes. Basic equations for almost every subfield of electrochemistry from first principles, referring at all times to the soundest and most recent theories and results; unusually useful as text or as reference. Covers coulometers and Faraday's Law, electrolytic conductance, the Debye-Hueckel method for the theoretical calculation of activity coefficients, concentration cells, standard electrode potentials, thermodynamic ionization constants, pH, potentiometric titrations, irreversible phenomena, Planck's equation, and much more. "Excellent treatise," AMERICAN CHEMICAL SOCIETY JOURNAL. "Highly recommended," CHEMICAL AND METALLURGICAL ENGINEERING. 2 Indices. Appendix. 585-item bibliography. 137 figures. 94 tables. ii + 478pp. 5⅜ x 8⅜.
S52 Paperbound **$2.45**

THE PHASE RULE AND ITS APPLICATION, Alexander Findlay. Covering chemical phenomena of 1, 2, 3, 4, and multiple component systems, this "standard work on the subject" (NATURE, London), has been completely revised and brought up to date by A. N. Campbell and N. O. Smith. Brand new material has been added on such matters as binary, tertiary liquid equilibria, solid solutions in ternary systems, quinary systems of salts and water. Completely revised to triangular coordinates in ternary systems, clarified graphic representation, solid models, etc. 9th revised edition. Author, subject indexes. 236 figures. 505 footnotes, mostly bibliographic. xii + 494pp. 5⅜ x 8.
S91 Paperbound **$2.50**

PHYSICS

General physics

FOUNDATIONS OF PHYSICS, R. B. Lindsay & H. Margenau. Excellent bridge between semi-popular works & technical treatises. A discussion of methods of physical description, construction of theory; valuable for physicist with elementary calculus who is interested in ideas that give meaning to data, tools of modern physics. Contents include symbolism, mathematical equations; space & time foundations of mechanics; probability; physics & continua; electron theory; special & general relativity; quantum mechanics; causality. "Thorough and yet not overdetailed. Unreservedly recommended," NATURE (London). Unabridged, corrected edition. List of recommended readings. 35 illustrations. xi + 537pp. 5⅜ x 8.
S377 Paperbound **$2.75**

FUNDAMENTAL FORMULAS OF PHYSICS, ed. by D. H. Menzel. Highly useful, fully descriptive reference and study text, ranging from simple to highly sophisticated operations. Mathematics integrated into text—each chapter stands as short textbook of field represented. Vol. 1: Statistics, Physical Constants, Special Theory of Relativity, Hydrodynamics, Aerodynamics, Boundary Value Problems in Math. Physics; Viscosity, Electromagnetic Theory, etc. Vol. 2: Sound, Acoustics, Geometrical Optics, Electron Optics, High-Energy Phenomena, Magnetism, Biophysics, much more. Index. Total of 800pp. 5⅜ x 8.
Vol. 1 S595 Paperbound **$2.00**
Vol. 2 S596 Paperbound **$2.00**

MATHEMATICAL PHYSICS, D. H. Menzel. Thorough one-volume treatment of the mathematical techniques vital for classic mechanics, electromagnetic theory, quantum theory, and relativity. Written by the Harvard Professor of Astrophysics for junior, senior, and graduate courses, it gives clear explanations of all those aspects of function theory, vectors, matrices, dyadics, tensors, partial differential equations, etc., necessary for the understanding of the various physical theories. Electron theory, relativity, and other topics seldom presented appear here in considerable detail. Scores of definitions, conversion factors, dimensional constants, etc. "More detailed than normal for an advanced text . . . excellent set of sections on Dyadics, Matrices, and Tensors," JOURNAL OF THE FRANKLIN INSTITUTE. Index. 193 problems, with answers. x + 412pp. 5⅜ x 8.
S56 Paperbound **$2.00**

THE SCIENTIFIC PAPERS OF J. WILLARD GIBBS. All the published papers of America's outstanding theoretical scientist (except for "Statistical Mechanics" and "Vector Analysis"). Vol I (thermodynamics) contains one of the most brilliant of all 19th-century scientific papers—the 300-page "On the Equilibrium of Heterogeneous Substances," which founded the science of physical chemistry, and clearly stated a number of highly important natural laws for the first time; 8 other papers complete the first volume. Vol II includes 2 papers on dynamics, 8 on vector analysis and multiple algebra, 5 on the electromagnetic theory of light, and 6 miscellaneous papers. Biographical sketch by H. A. Bumstead. Total of xxxvi + 718pp. 5⅝ x 8⅜.
S721 Vol I Paperbound **$2.50**
S722 Vol II Paperbound **$2.00**
The set **$4.50**

BASIC THEORIES OF PHYSICS, Peter Gabriel Bergmann. Two-volume set which presents a critical examination of important topics in the major subdivisions of classical and modern physics. The first volume is concerned with classical mechanics and electrodynamics: mechanics of mass points, analytical mechanics, matter in bulk, electrostatics and magnetostatics, electromagnetic interaction, the field waves, special relativity, and waves. The second volume (Heat and Quanta) contains discussions of the kinetic hypothesis, physics and statistics, stationary ensembles, laws of thermodynamics, early quantum theories, atomic spectra, probability waves, quantization in wave mechanics, approximation methods, and abstract quantum theory. A valuable supplement to any thorough course or text.
Heat and Quanta: Index. 8 figures. x + 300pp. 5⅜ x 8½.
S968 Paperbound **$2.00**
Mechanics and Electrodynamics: Index. 14 figures. vii + 280pp. 5⅜ x 8½.
S969 Paperbound **$1.75**

THEORETICAL PHYSICS, A. S. Kompaneyets. One of the very few thorough studies of the subject in this price range. Provides advanced students with a comprehensive theoretical background. Especially strong on recent experimentation and developments in quantum theory. Contents: Mechanics (Generalized Coordinates, Lagrange's Equation, Collision of Particles, etc.), Electrodynamics (Vector Analysis, Maxwell's equations, Transmission of Signals, Theory of Relativity, etc.), Quantum Mechanics (the Inadequacy of Classical Mechanics, the Wave Equation, Motion in a Central Field, Quantum Theory of Radiation, Quantum Theories of Dispersion and Scattering, etc.), and Statistical Physics (Equilibrium Distribution of Molecules in an Ideal Gas, Boltzmann statistics, Bose and Fermi Distribution, Thermodynamic Quantities, etc.). Revised to 1961. Translated by George Yankovsky, authorized by Kompaneyets. 137 exercises. 56 figures. 529pp. 5⅜ x 8½. S972 Paperbound **$2.50**

ANALYTICAL AND CANONICAL FORMALISM IN PHYSICS, André Mercier. A survey, in one volume, of the variational principles (the key principles—in mathematical form—from which the basic laws of any one branch of physics can be derived) of the several branches of physical theory, together with an examination of the relationships among them. Contents: the Lagrangian Formalism, Lagrangian Densities, Canonical Formalism, Canonical Form of Electrodynamics, Hamiltonian Densities, Transformations, and Canonical Form with Vanishing Jacobian Determinant. Numerous examples and exercises. For advanced students, teachers, etc. 6 figures. Index. viii + 222pp. 5⅜ x 8½.
S1077 Paperbound **$1.75**

MATHEMATICAL PUZZLES AND RECREATIONS

AMUSEMENTS IN MATHEMATICS, Henry Ernest Dudeney. The foremost British originator of mathematical puzzles is always intriguing, witty, and paradoxical in this classic, one of the largest collections of mathematical amusements. More than 430 puzzles, problems, and paradoxes. Mazes and games, problems on number manipulation, unicursal and other route problems, puzzles on measuring, weighing, packing, age, kinship, chessboards, joining, crossing river, plane figure dissection, and many others. Solutions. More than 450 illustrations. vii + 258pp. 5⅜ x 8. T473 Paperbound **$1.25**

SYMBOLIC LOGIC and THE GAME OF LOGIC, Lewis Carroll. "Symbolic Logic" is not concerned with modern symbolic logic, but is instead a collection of over 380 problems posed with charm and imagination, using the syllogism, and a fascinating diagrammatic method of drawing conclusions. In "The Game of Logic," Carroll's whimsical imagination devises a logical game played with 2 diagrams and counters (included) to manipulate hundreds of tricky syllogisms. The final section, "Hit or Miss" is a lagniappe of 101 additional puzzles in the delightful Carroll manner. Until this reprint edition, both of these books were rarities costing up to $15 each. Symbolic Logic: Index, xxxi + 199pp. The Game of Logic: 96pp. Two vols. bound as one. 5⅜ x 8. T492 Paperbound **$1.50**

MAZES AND LABYRINTHS: A BOOK OF PUZZLES, W. Shepherd. Mazes, formerly associated with mystery and ritual, are still among the most intriguing of intellectual puzzles. This is a novel and different collection of 50 amusements that embody the principle of the maze: mazes in the classical tradition; 3-dimensional, ribbon, and Möbius-strip mazes; hidden messages; spatial arrangements; etc.—almost all built on amusing story situations. 84 illustrations. Essay on maze psychology. Solutions. xv + 122pp. 5⅜ x 8. T731 Paperbound **$1.00**

MATHEMATICAL RECREATIONS, M. Kraitchik. Some 250 puzzles, problems, demonstrations of recreational mathematics for beginners & advanced mathematicians. Unusual historical problems from Greek, Medieval, Arabic, Hindu sources: modern problems based on "mathematics without numbers," geometry, topology, arithmetic, etc. Pastimes derived from figurative numbers, Mersenne numbers, Fermat numbers; fairy chess, latruncles, reversi, many topics. Full solutions. Excellent for insights into special fields of math. 181 illustrations. 330pp. 5⅜ x 8. T163 Paperbound **$1.75**

MATHEMATICAL PUZZLES OF SAM LOYD, Vol. I, selected and edited by M. Gardner. Puzzles by the greatest puzzle creator and innovator. Selected from his famous "Cyclopedia of Puzzles," they retain the unique style and historical flavor of the originals. There are posers based on arithmetic, algebra, probability, game theory, route tracing, topology, counter, sliding block, operations research, geometrical dissection. Includes his famous "14-15" puzzle which was a national craze, and his "Horse of a Different Color" which sold millions of copies. 117 of his most ingenious puzzles in all, 120 line drawings and diagrams. Solutions. Selected references. xx + 167pp. 5⅜ x 8. T498 Paperbound **$1.00**

MY BEST PUZZLES IN MATHEMATICS, Hubert Phillips ("Caliban"). Caliban is generally considered the best of the modern problemists. Here are 100 of his best and wittiest puzzles, selected by the author himself from such publications as the London Daily Telegraph, and each puzzle is guaranteed to put even the sharpest puzzle detective through his paces. Perfect for the development of clear thinking and a logical mind. Complete solutions are provided for every puzzle. x + 107pp. 5⅜ x 8½. T91 Paperbound **$1.00**

MY BEST PUZZLES IN LOGIC AND REASONING, H. Phillips ("Caliban"). 100 choice, hitherto unavailable puzzles by England's best-known problemist. No special knowledge needed to solve these logical or inferential problems, just an unclouded mind, nerves of steel, and fast reflexes. Data presented are both necessary and just sufficient to allow one unambiguous answer. More than 30 different types of puzzles, all ingenious and varied, many one of a kind, that will challenge the expert, please the beginner. Original publication. 100 puzzles, full solutions. x + 107pp. 5⅜ x 8½. T119 Paperbound **$1.00**

MATHEMATICAL PUZZLES FOR BEGINNERS AND ENTHUSIASTS, G. Mott-Smith. 188 mathematical puzzles to test mental agility. Inference, interpretation, algebra, dissection of plane figures, geometry, properties of numbers, decimation, permutations, probability, all enter these delightful problems. Puzzles like the Odic Force, How to Draw an Ellipse, Spider's Cousin, more than 180 others. Detailed solutions. Appendix with square roots, triangular numbers, primes, etc. 135 illustrations. 2nd revised edition. 248pp. 5⅜ x 8. T198 Paperbound **$1.00**

MATHEMATICS, MAGIC AND MYSTERY, Martin Gardner. Card tricks, feats of mental mathematics, stage mind-reading, other "magic" explained as applications of probability, sets, theory of numbers, topology, various branches of mathematics. Creative examination of laws and their applications with scores of new tricks and insights. 115 sections discuss tricks wtih cards, dice, coins; geometrical vanishing tricks, dozens of others. No sleight of hand needed; mathematics guarantees success. 115 illustrations. xii + 174pp. 5⅜ x 8. T335 Paperbound **$1.00**

RECREATIONS IN THE THEORY OF NUMBERS: THE QUEEN OF MATHEMATICS ENTERTAINS, Albert H. Beiler. The theory of numbers is often referred to as the "Queen of Mathematics." In this book Mr. Beiler has compiled the first English volume to deal exclusively with the recreational aspects of number theory, an inherently recreational branch of mathematics. The author's clear style makes for enjoyable reading as he deals with such topics as: perfect numbers, amicable numbers, Fermat's theorem, Wilson's theorem, interesting properties of digits, methods of factoring, primitive roots, Euler's function, polygonal and figurate numbers, Mersenne numbers, congruence, repeating decimals, etc. Countless puzzle problems, with full answers and explanations. For mathematicians and mathematically-inclined laymen, etc. New publication. 28 figures. 9 illustrations. 103 tables. Bibliography at chapter ends. vi + 247pp. 5⅜ x 8½. T1096 Paperbound **$1.85**

PAPER FOLDING FOR BEGINNERS, W. D. Murray and F. J. Rigney. A delightful introduction to the varied and entertaining Japanese art of origami (paper folding), with a full crystal-clear text that anticipates every difficulty; over 275 clearly labeled diagrams of all important stages in creation. You get results at each stage, since complex figures are logically developed from simpler ones. 43 different pieces are explained: place mats, drinking cups, bonbon boxes, sailboats, frogs, roosters, etc. 6 photographic plates. 279 diagrams. 95pp. 5⅝ x 8⅜. T713 Paperbound **$1.00**

1800 RIDDLES, ENIGMAS AND CONUNDRUMS, Darwin A. Hindman. Entertaining collection ranging from hilarious gags to outrageous puns to sheer nonsense—a welcome respite from sophisticated humor. Children, toastmasters, and practically anyone with a funny bone will find these zany riddles tickling and eminently repeatable. Sample: "Why does Santa Claus always go down the chimney?" "Because it soots him." Some old, some new—covering a wide variety of subjects. New publication. iii + 154pp. 5⅜ x 8½. T1059 Paperbound **$1.00**

EASY-TO-DO ENTERTAINMENTS AND DIVERSIONS WITH CARDS, STRING, COINS, PAPER AND MATCHES, R. M. Abraham. Over 300 entertaining games, tricks, puzzles, and pastimes for children and adults. Invaluable to anyone in charge of groups of youngsters, for party givers, etc. Contains sections on card tricks and games, making things by paperfolding—toys, decorations, and the like; tricks with coins, matches, and pieces of string; descriptions of games; toys that can be made from common household objects; mathematical recreations; word games; and 50 miscellaneous entertainments. Formerly "Winter Nights Entertainments." Introduction by Lord Baden Powell. 329 illustrations. v + 186pp. 5⅜ x 8. T921 Paperbound **$1.00**

DIVERSIONS AND PASTIMES WITH CARDS, STRING, PAPER AND MATCHES, R. M. Abraham. Another collection of amusements and diversion for game and puzzle fans of all ages. Many new paperfolding ideas and tricks, an extensive section on amusements with knots and splices, two chapters of easy and not-so-easy problems, coin and match tricks, and lots of other parlor pastimes from the agile mind of the late British problemist and gamester. Corrected and revised version. Illustrations. 160pp. 5⅜ x 8½. T1127 Paperbound **$1.00**

STRING FIGURES AND HOW TO MAKE THEM: A STUDY OF CAT'S-CRADLE IN MANY LANDS, Caroline Furness Jayne. In a simple and easy-to-follow manner, this book describes how to make 107 different string figures. Not only is looping and crossing string between the fingers a common youthful diversion, but it is an ancient form of amusement practiced in all parts of the globe, especially popular among primitive tribes. These games are fun for all ages and offer an excellent means for developing manual dexterity and coordination. Much insight also for the anthropological observer on games and diversions in many different cultures. Index. Bibliography. Introduction by A. C. Haddon, Cambridge University. 17 full-page plates. 950 illustrations. xxiii + 407pp. 5⅜ x 8½. T152 Paperbound **$2.00**

CRYPTANALYSIS, Helen F. Gaines. (Formerly ELEMENTARY CRYPTANALYSIS.) A standard elementary and intermediate text for serious students. It does not confine itself to old material, but contains much that is not generally known, except to experts. Concealment, Transposition, Substitution ciphers; Vigenere, Kasiski, Playfair, multafid, dozens of other techniques. Appendix with sequence charts, letter frequencies in English, 5 other languages, English word frequencies. Bibliography. 167 codes. New to this edition: solution to codes. vi + 230pp. 5⅜ x 8. T97 Paperbound **$2.00**

MAGIC SQUARES AND CUBES, W. S. Andrews. Only book-length treatment in English, a thorough non-technical description and analysis. Here are nasik, overlapping, pandiagonal, serrated squares; magic circles, cubes, spheres, rhombuses. Try your hand at 4-dimensional magical figures! Much unusual folklore and tradition included. High school algebra is sufficient. 754 diagrams and illustrations. viii + 419pp. 5⅜ x 8. T658 Paperbound **$1.85**

CALIBAN'S PROBLEM BOOK: MATHEMATICAL, INFERENTIAL, AND CRYPTOGRAPHIC PUZZLES, H. Phillips ("Caliban"), S. T. Shovelton, G. S. Marshall. 105 ingenious problems by the greatest living creator of puzzles based on logic and inference. Rigorous, modern, piquant, and reflecting their author's unusual personality, these intermediate and advanced puzzles all involve the ability to reason clearly through complex situations; some call for mathematical knowledge, ranging from algebra to number theory. Solutions. xi + 180pp. 5⅜ x 8. T736 Paperbound **$1.25**

FICTION

THE LAND THAT TIME FORGOT and THE MOON MAID, Edgar Rice Burroughs. In the opinion of many, Burroughs' best work. The first concerns a strange island where evolution is individual rather than phylogenetic. Speechless anthropoids develop into intelligent human beings within a single generation. The second projects the reader far into the future and describes the first voyage to the Moon (in the year 2025), the conquest of the Earth by the Moon, and years of violence and adventure as the enslaved Earthmen try to regain possession of their planet. "An imaginative tour de force that keeps the reader keyed up and expectant," NEW YORK TIMES. Complete, unabridged text of the original two novels (three parts in each). 5 illustrations by J. Allen St. John. vi + 552pp. 5⅜ x 8½.
T1020 Clothbound **$3.75**
T358 Paperbound **$2.00**

AT THE EARTH'S CORE, PELLUCIDAR, TANAR OF PELLUCIDAR: THREE SCIENCE FICTION NOVELS BY EDGAR RICE BURROUGHS. Complete, unabridged texts of the first three Pellucidar novels. Tales of derring-do by the famous master of science fiction. The locale for these three related stories is the inner surface of the hollow Earth where we discover the world of Pellucidar, complete with all types of bizarre, menacing creatures, strange peoples, and alluring maidens—guaranteed to delight all Burroughs fans and a wide circle of adventure lovers. Illustrated by J. Allen St. John and P. F. Berdanier. vi + 433pp. 5⅜ x 8½.
T1051 Paperbound **$2.00**

THE PIRATES OF VENUS and LOST ON VENUS: TWO VENUS NOVELS BY EDGAR RICE BURROUGHS. Two related novels, complete and unabridged. Exciting adventure on the planet Venus with Earthman Carson Napier broken-field running through one dangerous episode after another. All lovers of swashbuckling science fiction will enjoy these two stories set in a world of fascinating societies, fierce beasts, 5000-ft. trees, lush vegetation, and wide seas. Illustrations by Fortunino Matania. Total of vi + 340pp. 5⅜ x 8½. T1053 Paperbound **$1.75**

A PRINCESS OF MARS and A FIGHTING MAN OF MARS: TWO MARTIAN NOVELS BY EDGAR RICE BURROUGHS. "Princess of Mars" is the very first of the great Martian novels written by Burroughs, and it is probably the best of them all; it set the pattern for all of his later fantasy novels and contains a thrilling cast of strange peoples and creatures and the formula of Olympian heroism amidst ever-fluctuating fortunes which Burroughs carries off so successfully. "Fighting Man" returns to the same scenes and cities—many years later. A mad scientist, a degenerate dictator, and an indomitable defender of the right clash—with the fate of the Red Planet at stake! Complete, unabridged reprinting of original editions. Illustrations by F. E. Schoonover and Hugh Hutton. v + 356pp. 5⅜ x 8½.
T1140 Paperbound **$1.75**

THREE MARTIAN NOVELS, Edgar Rice Burroughs. Contains: Thuvia, Maid of Mars; The Chessmen of Mars; and The Master Mind of Mars. High adventure set in an imaginative and intricate conception of the Red Planet. Mars is peopled with an intelligent, heroic human race which lives in densely populated cities and with fierce barbarians who inhabit dead sea bottoms. Other exciting creatures abound amidst an inventive framework of Martian history and geography. Complete unabridged reprintings of the first edition. 16 illustrations by J. Allen St. John. vi + 499pp. 5⅜ x 8½. T39 Paperbound **$1.85**

THREE PROPHETIC NOVELS BY H. G. WELLS, edited by E. F. Bleiler. Complete texts of "When the Sleeper Wakes" (1st book printing in 50 years), "A Story of the Days to Come," "The Time Machine" (1st complete printing in book form). Exciting adventures in the future are as enjoyable today as 50 years ago when first printed. Predict TV, movies, intercontinental airplanes, prefabricated houses, air-conditioned cities, etc. First important author to foresee problems of mind control, technological dictatorships. "Absolute best of imaginative fiction," N. Y. Times. Introduction. 335pp. 5⅜ x 8. T605 Paperbound **$1.50**

28 SCIENCE FICTION STORIES OF H. G. WELLS. Two full unabridged novels, MEN LIKE GODS and STAR BEGOTTEN, plus 26 short stories by the master science-fiction writer of all time. Stories of space, time, invention, exploration, future adventure—an indispensable part of the library of everyone interested in science and adventure. PARTIAL CONTENTS: Men Like Gods, The Country of the Blind, In the Abyss, The Crystal Egg, The Man Who Could Work Miracles, A Story of the Days to Come, The Valley of Spiders, and 21 more! 928pp. 5⅜ x 8.
T265 Clothbound **$4.50**

THE WAR IN THE AIR, IN THE DAYS OF THE COMET, THE FOOD OF THE GODS: THREE SCIENCE FICTION NOVELS BY H. G. WELLS. Three exciting Wells offerings bearing on vital social and philosophical issues of his and our own day. Here are tales of air power, strategic bombing, East vs. West, the potential miracles of science, the potential disasters from outer space, the relationship between scientific advancement and moral progress, etc. First reprinting of "War in the Air" in almost 50 years. An excellent sampling of Wells at his storytelling best. Complete, unabridged reprintings. 16 illustrations. 645pp. 5⅜ x 8½.
T1135 Paperbound **$2.00**

CATALOGUE OF DOVER BOOKS

SEVEN SCIENCE FICTION NOVELS, H. G. Wells. Full unabridged texts of 7 science-fiction novels of the master. Ranging from biology, physics, chemistry, astronomy to sociology and other studies, Mr. Wells extrapolates whole worlds of strange and intriguing character. "One will have to go far to match this for entertainment, excitement, and sheer pleasure . . .," NEW YORK TIMES. Contents: The Time Machine, The Island of Dr. Moreau, First Men in the Moon, The Invisible Man, The War of the Worlds, The Food of the Gods, In the Days of the Comet. 1015pp. 5⅜ x 8.   T264 Clothbound **$4.50**

BEST GHOST STORIES OF J. S. LE FANU, Selected and introduced by E. F. Bleiler. LeFanu is deemed the greatest name in Victorian supernatural fiction. Here are 16 of his best horror stories, including 2 nouvelles: "Carmilla," a classic vampire tale couched in a perverse eroticism, and "The Haunted Baronet." Also: "Sir Toby's Will," "Green Tea," "Schalken the Painter," "Ultor de Lacy," "The Familiar," etc. The first American publication of about half of this material: a long-overdue opportunity to get a choice sampling of LeFanu's work. New selection (1964). 8 illustrations. 5⅜ x 8⅜.   T415 Paperbound **$1.85**

THE WONDERFUL WIZARD OF OZ, L. F. Baum. Only edition in print with all the original W. W. Denslow illustrations in full color—as much a part of "The Wizard" as Tenniel's drawings are for "Alice in Wonderland." "The Wizard" is still America's best-loved fairy tale, in which, as the author expresses it, "The wonderment and joy are retained and the heartaches and nightmares left out." Now today's young readers can enjoy every word and wonderful picture of the original book. New introduction by Martin Gardner. A Baum bibliography. 23 full-page color plates. viii + 268pp. 5⅜ x 8.   T691 Paperbound **$1.50**

GHOST AND HORROR STORIES OF AMBROSE BIERCE, Selected and introduced by E. F. Bleiler. 24 morbid, eerie tales—the cream of Bierce's fiction output. Contains such memorable pieces as "The Moonlit Road," "The Damned Thing," "An Inhabitant of Carcosa," "The Eyes of the Panther," "The Famous Gilson Bequest," "The Middle Toe of the Right Foot," and other chilling stories, plus the essay, "Visions of the Night" in which Bierce gives us a kind of rationale for his aesthetic of horror. New collection (1964). xxii + 199pp. 5⅜ x 8⅜.   T767 Paperbound **$1.00**

HUMOR

MR. DOOLEY ON IVRYTHING AND IVRYBODY, Finley Peter Dunne. Since the time of his appearance in 1893, "Mr. Dooley," the fictitious Chicago bartender, has been recognized as America's most humorous social and political commentator. Collected in this volume are 102 of the best Dooley pieces—all written around the turn of the century, the height of his popularity. Mr. Dooley's Irish brogue is employed wittily and penetratingly on subjects which are just as fresh and relevant today as they were then: corruption and hypocrisy of politicans, war preparations and chauvinism, automation, Latin American affairs, superbombs, etc. Other articles range from Rudyard Kipling to football. Selected with an introduction by Robert Hutchinson. xii + 244pp. 5⅜ x 8½.   T626 Paperbound **$1.00**

RUTHLESS RHYMES FOR HEARTLESS HOMES and MORE RUTHLESS RHYMES FOR HEARTLESS HOMES, Harry Graham ("Col. D. Streamer"). A collection of Little Willy and 48 other poetic "disasters." Graham's funniest and most disrespectful verse, accompanied by original illustrations. Nonsensical, wry humor which employs stern parents, careless nurses, uninhibited children, practical jokers, single-minded golfers, Scottish lairds, etc. in the leading roles. A precursor of the "sick joke" school of today. This volume contains, bound together for the first time, two of the most perennially popular books of humor in England and America. Index. vi + 69pp. 5⅜ x 8.   T930 Paperbound **75¢**

A WHIMSEY ANTHOLOGY, Collected by Carolyn Wells. 250 of the most amusing rhymes ever written. Acrostics, anagrams, palindromes, alphabetical jingles, tongue twisters, echo verses, alliterative verses, riddles, mnemonic rhymes, interior rhymes, over 40 limericks, etc. by Lewis Carroll, Edward Lear, Joseph Addison, W. S. Gilbert, Christina Rossetti, Chas. Lamb, James Boswell, Hood, Dickens, Swinburne, Leigh Hunt, Harry Graham, Poe, Eugene Field, and many others. xiv + 221pp. 5⅜ x 8½.   T195 Paperbound **$1.25**

MY PIOUS FRIENDS AND DRUNKEN COMPANIONS and MORE PIOUS FRIENDS AND DRUNKEN COMPANIONS, Songs and ballads of Conviviality Collected by Frank Shay. Magnificently illuminated by John Held, Jr. 132 ballads, blues, vaudeville numbers, drinking songs, cowboy songs, sea chanties, comedy songs, etc. of the Naughty Nineties and early 20th century. Over a third are reprinted with music. Many perennial favorites such as: The Band Played On, Frankie and Johnnie, The Old Grey Mare, The Face on the Bar-room Floor, etc. Many others unlocatable elsewhere: The Dog-Catcher's Child, The Cannibal Maiden, Don't Go in the Lion's Cage Tonight, Mother, etc. Complete verses and introductions to songs. Unabridged republication of first editions, 2 Indexes (song titles and first lines and choruses). Introduction by Frank Shay. 2 volumes bounds as 1. Total of xvi + 235pp. 5⅜ x 8½.   T946 Paperbound **$1.25**